C000211990

CMP

Acknowledgement is made to G.M. Seymour for the use of Figure 1 on page 206, which appears on the front cover of this book.

Structural Repair and Maintenance of
Historical Buildings II

Vol 2: Dynamics, Stabilisation and Restoration

Proceedings of the Second International Conference, held in
Seville, Spain, 14-16 May 1991.

Editors: C.A. Brebbia
         J. Dominguez
         F. Escrig

Computational Mechanics Publications
Southampton Boston

C.A. Brebbia
Wessex Institute of Technology
Computational Mechanics Institute
Ashurst Lodge
Ashurst
Southampton
S04 2AA
UK

F. Escrig
Universidad de Sevilla
Escuela Tecnica Superior de
Arquitectura
Av. Reina Mercedes 2
41012 Sevilla
Spain

J. Dominguez
Escuela Tecnica Superior de
Ingenieros Industriales
University of Seville
Av. Reina Mercedes, s/n
41012 Sevilla
Spain

British Library Cataloguing in Publication Data
Structural repair and maintenance of historical buildings II
 : proceedings of the second international conference held
in Seville, Spain.
 Vol. 2: Dynamics, stabilisation and restoration
 1. Historic buildings. Conservation
 I. Brebbia, C.A. (Carlos Alberto)
 363.69

 ISBN 1-85312-151-7

ISBN 1-85312-151-7 Computational Mechanics Publications, Southampton
ISBN 1-56252-079-2 Computational Mechanics Publications, Boston, USA

      Set
ISBN 1-85312-138-X Computational Mechanics Publications, Southampton
ISBN 1-56252-066-0 Computational Mechanics Publications, Boston, USA

Library of Congress Catalog Card Number 89-60103

This work is subject to copyright. All rights are reserved, whether the whole of part
of the material is concerned, specifically the rights of translation, reprinting, re-use of
illustrations, recitation, broadcasting, reproduction on microfilms or in other ways, and
storage in data banks.

©Computational Mechanics Publications 1991

Printed and bound by Antony Rowe Ltd, Chippenham, Wilts

The use of registered names, trademarks etc. in this publication does not imply, even
in the absence of a specific statement, that such names are exempt from the relevant
protective laws and regulations and therefore free for general use.

CONTENTS

PREFACE

The problem of the repair and maintenance of ancient buildings, bridges, aquaducts and other stone or masonry structures of historical significance, is of great interest to many organisations in different parts of the world. It is an area where there has been, and will be, considerable committment of financial resources, and where there is an ongoing interest in the accurate technical analysis of decaying structures. A considerable amount of experience exists, and it is important that this is shared between workers in the field, because there is a general lack of guidance in the form of textbooks or codes of practice.

These volumes contain the edited version of the papers presented at the Second International Conference on Structural Repairs and Maintenance of Historical Buildings, held in Seville, Spain, in May 1991. This meeting was arranged following the success of the first conference, held in Florence, Italy, in April 1989. Both conferences brought together scientists, engineers and architects active in the field, and the volumes should further stimulate interest in the theoretical, experimental and design aspects of the subject. They will also provide a useful guide to the future of the subject.

Volume one is concerned with general studies of a historical and architectural nature, that form a background to the subject; then with the properties and materials of ancient structures; and finally with various analytical and testing techniques appropriate to the assessment of structural strength.

Volume two includes a number of contributions on the effect of earthquakes and vibrations on old structures; then the problems of stabilisation, underpinning and reinforcement are discussed; the volume ends with a section on fabric restoration.

The editors wish to thank the members of the International Scientific Committee, as well as all the authors and participants for their support. The conference is also grateful to the sponsors, ie the Schools of Architecture and Engineering, and the University of Seville, the Computational Mechanics Institute of the Wessex Institute of Technology and specially to the International Centre for the Study of the Preservation and the Restoration of Cultural Property, Rome.

The editors
May 1991

SECOND INTERNATIONAL CONFERENCE
ON
STRUCTURAL STUDIES, REPAIRS AND
MAINTENANCE OF HISTORICAL BUILDINGS
STREMA/91

SCIENTIFIC COMMITTEE

C.A. Brebbia
J. Dominguez
F. Escrig
P.S. Bulson
C. Alessandri
T. Aoki
A.C. Cakmak
A. Chiarugi
J. Casadevall i Dalman

S. Hernández-Ibañez
J. Heyman
K. Hidaki
I. Hume
R. Livingston
R. Mainstone
A. Tomaszewski
M. Yorulmaz

SECTION 1: EARTHQUAKES, VIBRATIONS AND DYNAMICS

The Dynamic Response of a Church Tower to Bell-Ringing

A.R. Selby, J.M. Wilson
University of Durham, U.K.

ABSTRACT

In the English system of bell ringing the bells are swung full circle through 360^0. As a result of this, each bell imparts considerable horizontal and vertical forces onto the bell tower in proportion to the weight of the bell. The tower of St. Brandon's Church, Brancepeth, in the U.K., has been studied to investigate its response to these forces.

Measurements of bell tower movements during simultaneous ringing of bells were made using sensitive velocity transducers. The natural frequencies of tower sway in both East/West and North/South directions were deduced, together with some information about the mode shapes.

Two types of finite element model were constructed to compute the dynamic behaviour of the tower, a beam model and a fully three-dimensional model. The former was composed of a series of stepped uniform beam elements with varying section properties incorporating shear deformation and rotary inertia effects. The latter was formed from three-dimensional 20-noded brick elements to fit the tower geometry. The natural frequencies and mode shapes computed using these two models were matched with the measured values.

The transient response of the tower was computed using the beam model in a time-stepping computation, and these results compared well with measured values.

The study showed that the structural behaviour of the tower could be described by the use of a simple beam model provided that realistic equivalent stiffnesses in bending and in shear could be ascribed to the masonry walls.

INTRODUCTION

Traditionally, English churches are built of masonry and feature a bell tower which usually forms an integral part of the building. The bell tower normally houses a ring of between four and eight bells, although Cathedrals may have twelve bells, eg. Maunder[1]. The bells are supported within a bell frame in the belfry which is above the ringing chamber.

In the English system of bell ringing, see Wilson[2], the bells are rung full circle in various patterns of sequences, known as methods, to produce change ringing. Bells can also be rung in simple fixed sequences known as rounds. Additional ways of sounding bells include firing, when two or more bells are rung simultaneously at regular intervals, and tolling of a single bell.

When a bell is swung full circle from the mouth-up position it behaves as a compound pendulum undergoing non-linear oscillations.The horizontal and vertical forces produced by the swinging bell were first derived by Lewis[3] as functions of angular position and time. These forces are transmitted from the bearings through the bell frame and thence to the tower. If a bell is rung in a continual manner the forces are periodic and can be represented by Fourier series. Because of the symmetric nature of the forces, the Fourier series for the vertical force includes only the even cosine terms while the series for the horizontal force contains only the odd cosine terms, see Wilson[4]. These series represent the forces throughout a full circle oscillation of a bell. During this period the bell will sound twice, when its axis is near to vertical and the bell mouth is uppermost.Figures 1a and 1b show the typical form of the vertical and horizontal force functions, normalised with respect to the weight of the bell, as a function of time during one complete oscillation.

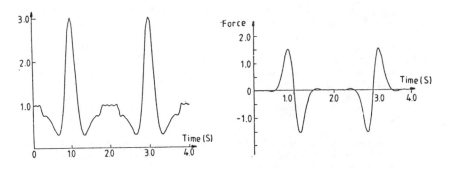

a) Normalised Verical Force   b) Normalised Horizontal Force

Figure 1 Normalised Forces During a Complete Oscillation.

The church of St. Brandon at Brancepeth, in the Northeast of England dates from the 12th Century, see Pevsner[5], and is of traditional design and construction in local sandstone. Figure 2 shows a plan of the church. It rests on boulder clay and glacial drift which overlies sandstone bedrock. The tower was probably built using the thick-wall technique[6], the walls being of sandwich construction with inner and outer skins of coursed rubble or ashlar facework retaining a

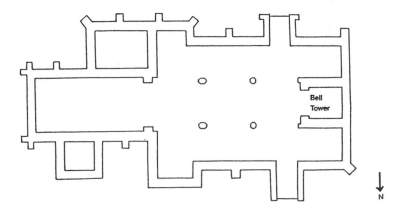

Figure 2 Plan of St. Brandon's Church.

filling of loose rubble. The skins are probably linked at intervals by tie stones. An elevation and section of the 20m .high tower are shown in Figures 3a and 3b. The tower has four levels, the belfry being uppermost. The present bell frame of steel I section is firmly joined to the tower by concrete edge beams. At all levels louvres or windows are provided in each face of the tower, although some are blocked off. Figures 3c and 3d are sections at window level in each of the upper sections of the tower. The wall thickness is 1000mm from ground level to the roof of the ringing chamber but is then stepped down to 800mm above. At the ground floor level the tower opens into the nave of the church through a large arch, Figure 2. In the west wall of the tower there is a large window and also a door at ground level. Little is known about the foundations of the tower, but it is likely that the walls are spread below the base of the tower to provide broad strip footings on the boulder clay.

The ring of bells at St. Brandon's comprises eight bells ranging in mass from the lightest, treble, bell (number 1) of some 167kg to the heaviest, tenor (number 8) of 693kg. The bells are arranged within the bell tower as shown in Figure 4, with bells 2,3,6 and 7 swinging in a N/S direction while bells 1,4,5 and 8 swing E/W. The horizontal forces on the tower when all the bells are fired are relatively small because the bells swing in opposing directions.

The first phase of the project, reported by Attewell et al[7], comprised measurements of tower sway in E/W and N/S directions at one point on the tower during tolling of each bell in turn. High sensitivity very low frequency velocity transducers (geophones) were used and signals were recorded digitally on a portable recorder, PDR1, described by Selby[8].

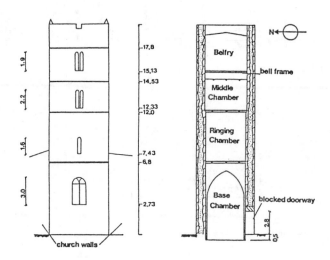

a) West Elevation   b) Vert Section

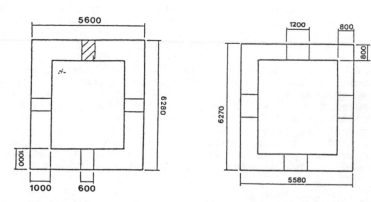

c) Section at ringing   d) Section at belfry
   chamber.   and middlechamber

Figure 3 Sections and Elevations through Tower

Recorded traces of transient velocity were compared with traces computed by a time stepping analysis for a simple vertical cantilever in response to the characteristic periodic force function described previously. Figure 5 shows traces appropriate to the tenor bell number 8. The form of the computed E/W sway response is encouraging in terms of its periodic form and of its reasonable estimate of peak particle velocities (ppvs). Similar results were obtained for tolling of the other bells. Bell number 7 caused ppvs in the N/S direction of up to 4mm/s suggesting that the tower is less stiff in that direction than in the E/W. Natural frequencies of the tower in both directions were around 2.5 Hz.

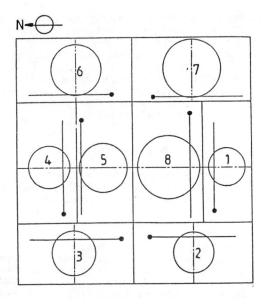

Figure 4 Arrangement of Bells in the Tower.

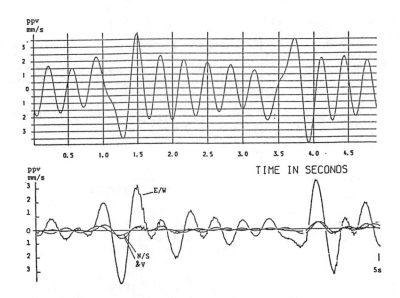

Figure 5 Computed and Measured tower E/W Response to Ringing
         Bell 8.

Several questions were raised during analysis of the first set of results with respect to the structural behaviour of the tower. How could the stiffness of the tower be estimated more accurately, working from a knowledge of dimensions and material properties? What were the dominant mode shapes of the primary tower response? Were rocking and torsional effects significant? Further investigation of these issues was next undertaken by additional measurements of the tower movements and by finite element analyses.

MEASUREMENTS OF TOWER RESPONSE TO BELL FIRING

A more detailed series of measurements was taken in the bell tower during the ringing of two bells simultaneously, or firing. The use of two bells gave much improved control over the type of forces imposed upon the tower. For example, firing bells 2 and 7 in a N/S swing imposed a greater and purer force to induce sway than could be achieved with a single bell. Firing bells 3 and 7 in opposition imposed a large torque upon the tower. (It should be noted that firing is not common practice in English change ringing.) In addition the high sensitivity low frequency geophones were positioned specifically so as to try to identify the mode shapes of the disturbances. An improved digital recorder, PDR2, was used as described by Selby and Swift[9]. The bell firing combinations used in the test series are listed in Table 1, together with the intended response mode and geophone positions.

TABLE 1 Bell Firing Combinations.

Bells	Response Mode	Geophone Positions
7&2	N/S sway	N/S levels 2&3 Vertical N wall level 3
7&3	Torsion +N/S sway	N/S in E wall level 3 E/W in S wall level 3 Vert in E wall level
8&5	E/W sway	E/W levels 1,2&3 Vert in E wall level 3
8&4	Torsion +E/W sway	N/S in E wall level 3 E/W in S wall level 3 Vert in E wall level 3

The characteristic style of response, in terms of transient velocities, is shown in Figures 6 and 7, which are relatively short traces at the defined stations. The forms of the traces are very similar in each case, suggesting a pure response in each condition.

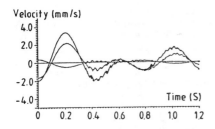

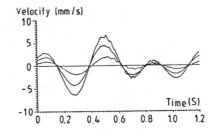

Figure 6 N/S Sway Response to
Bells 2 and 7.

Figure 7 E/W Sway Response
to Bells 5 and 8.

The clearest indication of mode shape was obtained for the
E/W sway induced by firing of bells 8 and 5. The mode shape
is superimposed upon the tower elevation in Figure 8, and
demonstrates clearly that the lower part of the tower showed
little movement, either because it was significantly
restrained by clerestory and nave or because the thicker
lower part of the tower walls were much stiffer than the
upper walls. In addition, the three recorded points lie on a
straight line, suggesting that racking shear was a major
component of the response. The small value of vertical
velocity recorded at level 3 was only 0.8mm/s; if the tower
had been responding as a cantilever in pure Euler bending
then some 3.1mm/s vertical would be expected in conjunction
with the tip sway deflection. This vertical component
probably arose from a small element of bending of the tower
which was a contributory factor to the sway.

A similar pattern emerged for tower sway in the N/S
direction in response to firing of bells 2 and 7, see Figure
9. It appears that the west end cross wall imparted some
restraint to the tower in parallel with the thickening of
the lower walls. Above this level the tower sway again
appeared to have a large component of shear deformation, as

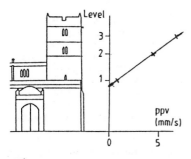

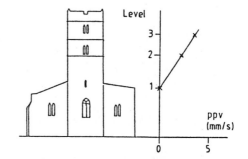

Figure 8 E/W Sway Mode

Figure 9 N/S Sway Mode.

shown by the linear response and by the small degree of vertical movement at level 3 of only 0.5mm/s (compared with an expected value of 2.2mm/s if the deformation had been due solely to bending).

No noticeable overall rocking of the tower occurred, as measurements at ground floor level gave readings of less than 0.05mm/s.

Pure torsional response of the tower was evaluated in response to firing first bells 7 and 3, and then bells 8 and 4. Bells 7 and 3 produced sway in the N/S direction of a maximum of 4.7mm/s., but only 0.4mm/s in the E/W sense so that pure torsion accounted for a mere 10% of the response. The firing of bells 8 and 4 produced insignificant response, all signals being less than 0.7mm/s. From these results it can be deduced that the tower deformation in a twisting mode was insignificant.

Finally, although the detailed analyses were conducted in terms of transient velocities, (the parameter measured directly by the geophones), the largest recorded values of displacements of E/W and N/S sway and of vertical movement at level 3, computed by integration, are tabulated in Table 2, from which rough estimates of strains in the masonry can be deduced. It is immediately apparent that these values are small, and indicate a low risk of cumulative damage to the masonry compared with weathering.

TABLE 2 Maximum Tower Displacements At Level 3

	Max. Displacements	Bells
E/W	0.60mm	8&5
N/S	0.35mm	2&7
Vert	0.07mm	8&5

STRUCTURAL MODELS

Two approaches were used in developing detailed computational structural models for the tower of St Brandon's church. The first approach was to model the structure as a three dimensional elastic continuum using solid finite elements, while the second simpler approach was to model the tower as a cantilever beam with varying sectional properties. As the tower is a form of stubby beam, the potentially important effects of shear deformation and rotary inertia were specifically included in the latter model.

For both models the following assumptions were made about the structural behaviour of the tower.
   (i) The tower is structurally independent of the rest of the church.

(ii) The tower is effectively rigidly restrained at ground level.
(iii) The material properties used for the walls are elastic, isotropic and can be related to the properties of local sandstone.

(a) The 3-D Model.
Over 100 20-noded 3-D isoparametric brick elements were used to represent the detailed geometry of the tower, including the cut-outs for windows doors and archways. The finite element mesh is shown in Figure 10. An eigenvalue solution was then undertaken using the PAFEC suite.

(b) Cantilever Beam Model
Ten beam elements incorporating normal beam behaviour plus shear deformation and rotary inertia were used to represent the tower structure. Each element was of uniform section with sectional properties as listed in the Appendix. For each element the length, second moments of area, torsional constants based on St. Venant's theory, see Timoshenko[9], and shear constants derived by Cowper's[10] method. The initial values of the shear coefficients were later modified in the light of the results of the 3-D analyses.

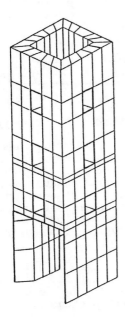

Figure 10 3-D Finite Element Model of the Tower.

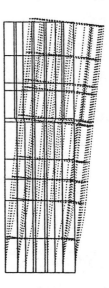

Figure 11 E/W Sway Mode Computed by 3-D Model

The two models were modified by changing stiffness
parameters to allow for the discontinuities in the wall
joints and for the sandwich construction until agreement was
achieved on both frequencies and mode shapes. This then
allowed use of the simpler beam model in the time stepping
analysis for transient response of the tower to bell forces
in a later section of the work.

Table 3 shows the first three natural frequencies in each of
the four basic mode types of E/W sway, N/S sway, torsion and
axial modes. The material properties ascribed to the
elements were an elastic modulus of 2.8GPa (compared with a
value of 17GPa for a sample of local sandstone), Poisson's
ratio of 0.2 and density of 2200kg/m^3. The mode shape for
E/W sway is shown in Figure 11.

TABLE 3 Natural Frequencies Of Tower Vibration,(in Hz.)

Mode type	N/S sway	E/W sway	Torsion	Axial
Mode No.				
1 Meas.	2.55	2.86	–	–
3-D	2.55	2.86	5.89	15.1
Beam	2.56	2.87	6.00	14.2
2 3-D	9.13	11.9	12.3	–
Beam	8.29	12.5	18.4	40.7
3 3-D	15.7	20.2	22.9	–
Beam	18.2	28.8	32.7	–

TRANSIENT TOWER RESPONSE TO DYNAMIC FORCES

A computer program, described by Wilson[3], was used to
compute the force functions on the tower due to firing of
bells 2 and 7 during the ringing cycle of 4.2 seconds. The
bells were assumed to be acting as compound pendula swinging
freely between the impulses provided by the ringers to start
and stop the motion. Input data were the mass of the bells,
their centroidal positions and their periods of small
vibration, as determined by Feldt[12]. Figure 12 shows a trace
of the periodic N/S horizontal force.

The computed force functions were then used as input data,
together with the beam model stiffness and mass parameters
to compute the time dependent response of the tower to the
firing of bells 2 and 7, using the PAFEC package.

Figure 13 shows the computed response of the tower at belfry
level, which can be compared with the short trace of
measured response in Figure 6. Figure 14 shows the
equivalent trace in the E/W direction caused by the firing
of bells 5 and 8, which may be compared with the measured
response in Figure 7.

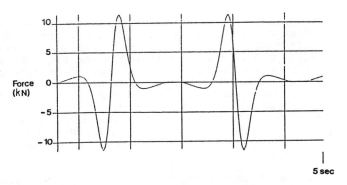

Figure 12 N/S Horizontal Force Due to Firing Bells 2 and 7

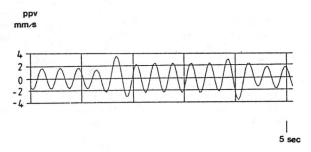

Figure 13 N/S Velocity at Belfry Level Computed Using the Beam Model

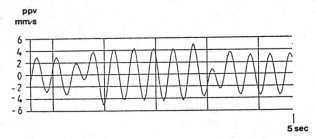

Figure 14 E/W Response at Belfry Level Computed Using Beam Model

DISCUSSION OF THE TOWER BEHAVIOUR

Two structural models were developed for the church tower. The first was a highly detailed and expensive 3-D finite element approach, while the second was or a stubby cantilever with varying section properties. Both models required assumptions of material elastic properties, which could be assigned within bands of values. By minor changes to shear stiffnesses in the beam model within the sensible range of values and to the effective elastic modulus of the sandwich walls it was found that the two models produced a closely matched set of computed natural frequencies and normal mode shapes. These computed values were found to be in broad agreement with the measured values within the sway modes, and with further minor changes in the computer models, within sensible parameter ranges, then very close matching of frequencies and mode shapes was achieved, as was demonstrated in Table 3.

Whilst achievement of a purely predictive and accurate analysis would be desirable, there are several reasons why this is not feasible. In particular, the method of construction used in the tower of ashlar masonry forming a sandwich construction, and its present condition, renders it impossible to use elastic homogeneous material properties attributable to a sandstone sample. The discontinuities in the stonework may be incorporated by a reduced elastic modulus, and the sandwich construction may be represented through transverse isotropy. A parametric study showed that the overall tower stiffness was affected only slightly by the latter. It was found that a global value of elastic modulus for the walls of one-sixth of that of plain sandstone gave appropriate results in both the 3-D and the beam models. It would be of great interest if similar data for other towers could be gathered and analysed in order to identify a range of effective modulus values for sandwich construction masonry walls of bell towers.

CONCLUSIONS

The ringing of church bells in the full circle English mode imparts large dynamic forces onto the bell tower. The response of the tower of St. Brandon's church to such forces has been studied both by measurements of dynamic response to firing of pairs of bells and by numerical modelling. The primary response modes to bell firing forces were of East/West or North/South sway. The torsional, and axial modes were insignificant, and no rocking was evident in the sway modes.

The sandwich form of masonry and rubble wall construction, which is typical of such churches, and their complex structural form makes a linear elastic structural analysis unreliable, even by advanced 3-D finite element methods.

However, by judicious choice of equivalent modulus values for the tower walls, it is possible to construct a cantilever beam model incorporating shear deformation and rotary inertia effects which can be used firstly in an eigenvalue solution to estimate natural frequencies and mode shapes of the two sway modes, and secondly in a time stepping analysis to estimate the transient sway response of the tower to bell ringing forces.

The deflections of the tower in E/W and N/S sway in response to firing of pairs of bells was found to be small, generally less than 1mm at belfry level. These deflections were thus considered to offer very low risk of direct or cumulative damage to the tower walls. Nor was risk of damage to the belfry structure considered to be a problem, provided that the bellframe bearings are maintained in good repair and the holding down connections between the frame and the edge beams remain tight.

The method of computing the forces imparted by the bells onto the frame and the tower will be of use in a situation in which a replacement frame is to be designed and installed in a traditional tower.

REFERENCES

1. Maunder, E.A.W. Masonry Buildings in Service under Dynamic Loading C&CA Res. Sem. Slough 1981

2. Wilson, W.G. The Art and Science of Change Ringing, Faber and Faber, London, 1965.

3.Lewis, E.H. Calculation of the Forces Acting upon a Church Tower, ms in Lib. of Central Council of Church Bell Ringers, Guildford,, 1914.

4. Wilson, J.M. Periodic Forces on Bell Towers Arising from Bell Ringing, Int. Rep., Dept. Eng. Univ. Durham. 1987.

5. Pevsner, N. The Buildings of England, Co Durham. 2nd ed., Penguin 1983.

6. The Towers and Belfries Comm. The Towers and Bells Handbook, Central Council of Church Bell Ringers,Guildford, 1973.

7. Attewell, P.B., Selby, A.R. and Wilson, J.M. Low Amplitude Mechanical Vibrations and Structures in The Engineering Geology of Ancient Works, Monuments and Historical Sites, IAEG, Athens pp. 1196-1200,1988.

8. Selby, A.R. Acquisition by Microcomputer of Some Ground Vibration Data During Pile Driving in Computer and Physical Modelling in Geotechnical Eng, ed Balasubramaniam et al, Balkema, 1989.

9. Selby, A.R. and Swift, J.S. Recording and Processing Ground Vibrations Caused by Pile Driving, in Proc. Int. AmsE Conf. 'Signals and Systems', Brighton AMSE Press Vol 6 pp101-113, 1989.

10. Timoshenko, S. Strength of Materials, 3rd ed, van Nostrand, London, 1955.

11. Cowper, G.R. The Shear Coefficient in Timoshenko's Beam Theory, J. of App. Mech. pp335-339. 1966.

12. Feldt, J.C. Forces in a Church due to Bell Ringing, Res. Proj. Rep. Dept. of Eng., Univ. of Durham, 1982.

APPENDIX

Properties of the beam elements

Element Number	Length (m)	Area (m^2)	I_{ew} (m^4)	I_{ns} (m^4)	Torsion Const (m^4)	Shear Coeft E/W	Shear Coeft N/S
1	2.73	15.1	60.1	68.8	50.0	0.86	0.18
2	3.00	14.9	56.0	74.3	50.0	0.86	0.18
3	1.07	16.2	61.2	74.5	143.0	0.86	0.18
4	0.63	19.8	92.1	75.2	143.0	0.86	0.18
5	1.60	17.4	83.6	68.7	50.0	0.86	0.18
6	2.97	19.8	92.1	75.2	143.0	0.86	0.18
7	0.33	16.4	80.8	66.2	127.0	0.86	0.18
8	2.20	12.6	66.1	54.8	50.0	0.86	0.18
9	0.60	16.4	80.8	66.2	127.0	0.86	0.18
10	1.90	12.6	66.1	54.8	50.0	0.86	0.18
11	2.97	16.4	80.8	66.2	127.0	0.86	0.18
					(5.0)	(0.67)	(0.67)

Evaluation of Ground Vibrations Generated by Artifical Sources

T. Hanazato

Tajimi Engineering Services, Ltd., 2-26, Nishishinjyuku 3chome, Shinjyuku-ku, Tokyo 160

ABSTRACT

The published criteria for limiting vibrations indicate that historical buildings are rather sensitive to ambient ground vibrations generated by artificial sources. This paper deals with the problems of ground vibrations due to two types of sources : traffic facilities and impulse pile driving operations.

Effective numerical methods have been introduced for the analysis of these problems. First, traffic induced ground vibrations can be analyzed by the three dimensional thin layered element method developed for that problem. Next, pile driving induced ground vibrations can be analyzed by using a substructure approach which consists of the one-dimensional wave equation method of a hammer-pile-soil system and the axisymmetric thin layered element method.

Example cases have been analyzed to demonstrate the applicability of the proposed methods. Some features specific to the traffic induced ground vibrations, as well as, the pile driving induced ones are understood from the results. Furthermore, the analytical results have been compared with the published criteria for historical buildings.

INTRODUCTION

Ground vibrations generated by artificial sources often have detrimental effects on building structures or building contents. Since historical buildings are more sensitive to the ambient ground vibrations than modern ones (Wiss,J.F.[1]), the ground vibrations may cause damages to their structures or contents when they are located in the vicinity of the sources, and this problem becomes of concern for maintenance of historical buildings.

Although it seems essential for maintenance of historical buildings to simulate the ground vibrations due to the artificial sources, there has been insufficient theoretical knowledge on this problem. This paper presents efficient numerical methods for the dynamic analyses of the ground vibrations, and demonstrates the potential applications of the proposed methods to example cases of which resulted ground vibrations may exceed the permissible level of the published criteria. In the proposed procedures, the dynamic finite element techniques using the thin layered element methods have been employed to take into account irregularities of geometries and soil conditions of near fields, as well as, to take into account wave radiation to far fields.

Incidentally, the present research deals with two types of sources : traffic facilities and impulse pile driving operations. Traffic induced ground vibrations are pseudo-steady-state ones generated by moving loads on a ground surface or in a underground tunnel. On the other hand, pile driving induced ground vibrations are transient ones generated by a distributed source along a pile which penetrates soils. The proposed methods can account these conditions specific to each type of the source.

CRITERIA FOR LIMITING VIBRATIONS

Wiss,J.F.[1] studied the construction vibration intensities related to the damage criteria which are published in some countries, and suggested that the criteria should take into account whether a building is ancient or modern. As provided in his paper, the Swiss standard for vibration, one of the most restrictive criteria in the world, categorizes all buildings in four classes according to their age and structural conditions, and prescribes the permissible intensities for objects of historical interests, being classified by types of the sources ; (1) For periodic excitation such as machines and traffic, the permissible level of peak velocity amplitude is 3mm/sec in the frequency range from 10 to 30Hz, (2) For impulse type loading such as blasting, that is 8mm/sec in the frequency from 10 to 60Hz. In this way, the vibrational sources must be the factors relating to damages, because they determine the frequency content and duration of the ground vibrations[2].

TRAFFIC INDUCED GROUND VIBRATIONS

Analytical method[3]
Description of model   A three-dimensional finite element model represents the system idealized by a finite irregular region jointed vertically to semi-infinite far fields of left and right sides, as shown in Fig.1 and Fig.2. The irregular region contains all geometric irregularities and traffic loads. The semi-infinite region represents horizontal soil layers descretized by the thin layered elements in which the exact displacement functions in the horizontal direction and an expansion in the vertical direction consistent with that used for the finite elements are defined. The proposed thin layered element can take into account the physical behavior that waves propagate and decay in the x-direction as well as in the y-direction. On the other hand, vertically radiating waves are accounted by the viscous boundary at the lower edge of the complete structure. Since the system is a three dimensional one, three components of ground vibrations can be obtained numerically. However, the system is modeled into the identical planes of elements at equal spacing on the assumption that the geometry and soil properties remain unchanged along the longitudinal direction of the structure which corresponds to the direction of the traffic loads' moving. Traffic moving loads act as vertical concentrated forces with a constant interval (L) and a constant velocity (v). A moving load is assumed to be composed of a constant static component equal to weight of a vehicle and a dynamic component. Consider that the loads move along the x-axis and one of the

loads is located at x=vt at time t(See Fig.2), the load P(t,x) can be written as;
$$P(t,x) = P_0 \, \delta(vt-x) + f(t) \, \delta(vt-x) \qquad\qquad 1)$$
$$(\ vt-L/2 < x < vt+L/2 \ )$$
, where P_0 = weight of a vehicle ; f(t) = a dynamic component of the load ;
and $\delta(\ )$ = Dirac's δ-function.
By expanding Eq.1) into the Fourier series between the interval, P(t,x) can be
expressed as the sum of harmonic motions.
$$P(t,x) = (P_0 + f(t)) \frac{1}{L} \sum_{m=-\infty}^{\infty} e^{i(\omega_m t - k_m x)} \qquad\qquad 2)$$
, where wave number $k_m = 2m\pi/L$; and $\omega_m = k_m v$.
The analytical procedure is introduced for one of the harmonic components,
$p_m(t,x)$, and conducted in frequency domain.

Finite element formulation   The finite irregular region is modeled by use of
rectangular pallarelepiped elements having three degrees of freedom per nodal
points(See Fig.3). Consider that the harmonic waves propagate in the positive x-
direction with a wave number k as a function of $e^{i(\omega t-kx)}$, the element stiffness
matrix with an infinitesimal thickness a is of the form ;
$$[L]_E = a \ (\int [\overline{B}^*]^T [H][B^*] d(area)) \qquad\qquad 3)$$
, where $[B^*]$ = an operator matrix derived by Hwang and Lysmer[4] ; [H] = a
constitutive matrix ; and $[\overline{B}^*]$ = a conjugation matrix of $[B^*]$. (See Appendix I)
The stiffness matrix for the finite region, $[K]_E$, can be formed by assembling
each element stiffness matrix appearing in Fig.3. On the other hand, the mass
matrix, $[M]_E$, can be given by the conventional procedure. The equation of motion
for the finite irregular region with an infinitesimal thickness of a is presented,
$$a[M]_E \{\ddot{u}\}_E + a[K]_E \{u\}_E = \{p\}_E \qquad\qquad 4)$$
, where $\{\ddot{u}\}_E, \{u\}_E$ = nodal acceleration and displacement vectors ; and $\{p\}_E$ = an
external force vector.
The viscous boundary condition of the lower boundary is represented by the
situation that the boundary is supported on the infinitesimal dashpots oriented
the normal and tangential to the boundary. Lysmer and Kuhlemeyer[5] proposed the
analytical method to account for the preceding condition, that is ; the addition
of the following values on the stiffness matrix's components corresponding to
the modes on the boundary.
$$c = i\omega\rho V_p A \quad \text{(for a dashpot oriented normal to the boundary)}$$
$$c = i\omega\rho V_s A \quad \text{(for a dashpot oriented tangential to the boundary)} \qquad 5)$$
, where ρ = density, V_p, V_s = velocity of P-wave and S-wave, and A = area of the
boundary relating to the dashpot concerned.

Thin layered element formulation   The semi-infinite region is modeled by means
of the horizontally thin layered elements supported on the viscous boundary. The
thin layered element, extended from the work of Hwang and Lysmer[4], has been
developed to account for the condition that waves travel horizontally in the x-
direction and in the y-direction. Since it is possible to express the
displacement in the semi-infinite region in terms of eigenfunctions
corresponding to the natural modes of wave propagation, the far field is
discretized into n horizontal layers on the viscous boundary to solve the
eigenvalue problems.Supposing that waves propagate in the y-direction with a
wave number as $e^{i(\omega t-\lambda y)}$, the element stiffness matrix as well as the element
mass matrix with an infinitesimal thickness of a and an infinitesimal length of
a are defined. The equation of free harmonic motion which corresponds to the
eigenvalue equation results in,

$$(\quad \lambda^2 [A^*] + \lambda (k[B_1^*]+[B_2^*]) + k^2[C^*] + k[D^*] + [E^*] -\omega^2[M^*])\{v\}= 0$$

6)

The matrices $[A^*]$,$[B_1^*]$,   ,$[M^*]$ are assembled by addition of layer submatrices presented in Appendix, as shown in Fig.4. For the particular case of the viscous boundary condition at the lower boundary, the additional layer of which properties are half space's ones is attached beneath the lowest layer. The submatrices of the additional layer to account for the viscous boundary condition are also presented in Appendix. The matrices in Eq.6) have order of $3(n+1) \times 3(n+1)$, therefore, the solution yields a number of real and/or complex eigenvalues, λ_s, and eigenvectors, $\{v\}_s$ equal to $6(n+1)$. The waves propagating or decaying in the positive y-direction must satisfy one of the following conditions.   i) λ_s is real and positive ; ii) λ_s is complex with a negative imaginary part. Half of the solution eigenvalues and eigenvectors of Eq.6) satisfy the above mentioned condition. The displacement of the upper and lower boundaries of the thin layered element can be written as a linear contribution of the modal shapes ;

$$\{u\} = \sum_{s=1}^{3(n+1)} \alpha_s \{v\}_s e^{-i\lambda_s y} e^{i(\omega_m t - k_m x)}$$

7)

, where α_s = a mode participation factor for the s'th mode.
The dynamic stiffness matrix of energy transmitting boundary between the finite region and semi-infinite region can be derived from the equilibration of the virtual work done by the nodal force with the one done by the stress at the interface. The relationship equation between nodal forces and nodal displacements at the interfaces is given for the desired boundary condition.

$$\{p\} = [R]\{u\}_b$$
$$[R] = -i[A^*][V][\Lambda][V]^{-1}+[B]$$

8)

, where $[V]$ = a modal matrix containing the mode shapes in its columns ; $[\Lambda]$ = a diagonal matrix with the diagonal elements of eigenvalues ; and $[A^*]$,$[B]$ = $3(n+1) \times 3(n+1)$ matrix presented in Appendix.

Analysis of complete system   The stage is now set for the analysis of the finite element region. Supposing that $\{p\}_E$ in Eq.4) defines the nodal force vector per unit length in the x-direction, $\{p\}_E$, the equation of motion for the complete system is presented,

$$[M]_E\{\ddot{u}\}_E + [K]_E\{u\} = \{P\}_E$$

9)

, where force vector p_E contains not only the external forces but also the transmitting boundary forces to take into account the effect of the wave radiation into far fields. Because of harmonic motions with circular frequency ω, time independent complex force and displacement amplitudes are introduced,

$$[K]_A\{U\}_A = \{Q\}_A$$
$$[K]_A = [K]_E - \omega^2[M]_E - [R]_R - [R]_L$$

10)

, where $\{U\}_A$ = a displacement amplitude vector ; $\{Q\}_A$ = an external force vector ; and $[R]$ = a boundary matrix provided in Eq.8) of which lower subscripts refer to the side of the semi-infinite far fields (L:Left,R:Right).

Application to example case

Example case   Fig.5 shows a typical pavement structure on a soft soil condition, analyzed in the present research. It is assumed that the road has two lanes and that vehicles with a weight of 20tons (large truck) and with an interval of 30m move in the positive x-direction at a velocity of 50km/h. The finite element meshes used in this analysis is provided in Fig.6. For the vibrating condition of a traffic load, the following cases have been analyzed.

Case A :   A load has a static component only, i.e. f(t)=0 in Eq.1).
           This condition must be realized when a pavement surface is smooth
           enough and a vehicle does not vibrate itself.
Case B :   A load has a static and a dynamic components.
           The dynamic component is assumed to be harmonic as
           $f(t) = (P_0/10) e^{i\omega_0 t}$ in Eq.1), and the circular frequency,
           ω_0, takes a value of 20π rad/sec.

Analytical results   By use of the proposed method, we can obtain time
histories of the ground vibrations. In the present research, the attenuation with
distance of the maximum velocity amplitudes for both cases is provided in Fig.7
in order to compare the results with the published criteria for limiting
vibrations. It should be noticed in Fig.7 that the dynamic component of the
traffic load gives much more significant effect on the ground vibrations than
the static ones, and that this phenomenon becomes apparent with the distance
from the source.   This result indicates that pavement surface condition, smooth
or rough, has a great influence on ground vibrations. Furthermore, it can be
recognized that the x-component expressing the amplitude in the direction of
vehicles' moving may not be neglected at the particular distance from the source.

    As presented in the chapter of the criteria for limiting vibrations, the
permissible level of peak velocity amplitude is 3mm/sec for   historical
buildings. It is found that the velocity amplitudes obtained for Case B exceed
this level within about 8m for the x-component, within about 15m for the y-
component, and within about 30m for the z-component. These results suggest that
a historical building may be damaged when it is located near a busy road of
which surface is rather rough, and that it is effective for reduction of the
ground vibrations to make the road's surface smooth enough, or to reduce the
amplitudes of the vehicles' own vibrations.

PILE DRIVING INDUCED GROUND VIBRATIONS

Analytical method
Assumption of analysis   This paper deals with ground vibrations due to
impulse pile driving operations. The proposed method consists of a non-linear
pile driving analysis of a hammer-pile-soil system and a linear analysis of
three dimensionally propagating waves in multi-layered media (See Fig.8).   The
dynamic loads which act on the interface between the soil and pile can be
calculated in time domain by the former analysis. Then, the dynamic loads are
expanded into the Fourier series, because it is necessary to conduct the latter
analysis in frequency domain. The time histories of the ground vibrations due to
the resulted dynamic loads can be obtained by the latter analysis in which the
elastic media's response can be calculated by summing up the response for each
component of the Fourier series.

Pile driving analysis   A one-dimensional wave equation model is applied to
calculate the dynamic load induced at the soil-pile interfaces.   The system is
idealized by a series of lumped masses and springs, being called Smith model (See
Fig.8). Each pile element is attached to a spring and a dashpot system, and the
soil spring is assumed to behave in an elastic-perfectly plastic manner, and the
spring stiffness is defined using the ultimate static resistance and the maximum
elastic deformation (Quake). The soil parameters used in the present research
are introduced on the basis of the achievements of Kishida et al.[6] , except for

the evaluation of shaft resistance in clayey soils, as shown in Table1. Because of the dynamic behavior, ultimate shaft resistance in clayey soils is not determined by unconfined compressive strength, but estimated from N-value.

Wave propagation analysis   An axisymmetric system consisting of radial and vertical axes is introduced to represent a pile and a wave propagating field, as shown in Fig.8.   In order to analyze the ground vibrations due to the dynamic induced loads obtained by the pile driving analysis, the finite element technique is applied with the thin layered element method developed by Waas,G.[7], Kausel,E. et al., or Tajimi et al.[9]. While the horizontally traveling waves to far fields can be taken into account by use of the thin layered element, the vertically radiating waves can be considerably taken into account by the viscous boundary at the lower edge of complete structure, as presented in the analytical method of traffic-induced ground vibrations. The thin layered element region represents the soil layers in which Rayleigh waves propagate and decay horizontally. On the other hand, the finite element region represents the pile, therefore, the diameter, the penetration depth, and the properties of the pile can be easily taken into account. Fig.9 shows the finite element including the central axis, introduced in the present research.

Application to example case
Example case   The analysis has been conducted for the case that a precast concrete pile is driven into the soil deposit which is one of the major types in urban areas in Japan. The soil deposit consists of the soft soil layer and the base layer, as shown in Fig.10. The conditions of a pile cap, a hammer, and a pile are presented in Fig.11 and Table2. In order to investigate the influence of the penetration depth on the ground vibrations, the calculation has been performed when the pile toe is near the ground surface (Df=1m), when it is at the middle depth of the soft layer (Df=5m), as well as, when it reaches the base layer (Df=10m), as shown in Fig.10. This figure also provides the discretization of the finite elements and the thin layered elements.

Analytical results   As results, this paper provides the attenuation with distance of the maximum velocity amplitudes to compare the results with the criteria.   Fig.12-1 and Fig.12-2 show the results of radial components and vertical components, respectively. It can be noticed in these figures that the penetration depth and the characteristics of the soil at the pile toe influence the feature of the attenuation curves. That is; the maximum velocity amplitudes of Df=10m have rather larger values, and they form the attenuation curve with ruggedness. As described in the chapter of the criteria, the permissible level of the peak velocity amplitude takes a value of 8mm/sec, prescribed for impulse type loadings. For the case of the radial component, the resulted amplitudes exceed the permissible level only around the source. However, for the case of the vertical component, they exceed that level within about 10m for Df=1m and for Df=5m, as well as, within about 20m for Df=10m. These results indicate that historical buildings may be damaged, when they are located near the construction sites. If a construction operation such as pile driving is conducted near a historical building, it is necessary to calculate the ground vibrations before the construction begins, and also necessary to consider a counterplan when the predicted ground vibrations exceed the permissible intensity.

CONCLUSIONS

Historical buildings are more sensitive to ground vibrations generated by artificial sources than modern ones. The permissible intensity of ground vibrations for historical buildings has been presented according to the Swiss standard.

For maintenance of historical buildings, the numerical approaches have been introduced to analyze the ambient ground vibrations due to two types of sources : traffic facilities and pile driving operations. The proposed method can not only take into account the source mechanism but also simulate propagation of waves in multi-layered media. The propagation of waves can be analyzed by the dynamic elastic finite element methods using the developed three dimensional thin layered method for traffic induced ground vibrations or using the axisymmetric thin layered element method for pile driving induced ground vibrations.

The applications of the proposed methods to example cases demonstrate that the proposed numerical methods have a great potential for evaluation of the ground vibrations. The results obtained give some features of the ground vibrations specific to each type of the source.

ACKNOWLEDGMENTS

The writer wishes to thank Dr. Keizo Ugai, Prof. of Gunma Univ., for his substantial technical contributions in the development of the dynamic analysis of the traffic-induced ground vibrations.

REFERENCES

1. Wiss,J.F.,Construction vibrations : State-of-the-art, Journal of Geotechnical Engineering Division, ASCE, Vol.107, GT2, pp167-181, 1981
2. Studer,J. and Suesstrunk,A., Swiss standard for vibrational damage to buildings, Proc. of 10th International Conference on Soil Mechanics and Foundation Engineering (Stockholm), pp307-312, 1981
3. Hanazato,T. Ugai,K., Mori,M., and Sakaguchi,R., Three dimensional analysis of traffic-induced ground vibrations, Journal of Geotechnical Engineering Division, ASCE (Accepted)
4. Hwang,R.N. and Lysmer,J.,Response of buried structures to traveling waves, Journal of Geotechnical Engineering Division, ASCE, Vol.107, GT2, pp183-200, 1981
5. Lysmer,J. and Kuhlemeyer,R.L., Finite dynamic modal for infinite media, Journal of Engineering Mechanics Division, ASCE, Vol.95, EM4, pp859-877, 1969
6. Kishida,H.,Takano,A., and Tamura,K., The impact stresses in concrete piles during driving (in Japanese), Transactions of Architectural Institute of Japan, No.241, pp19-31,1976
7. Waas,G.,Earth vibration effects and abatement for military facilities Report 3 Analysis method for footing vibrations through layered media, Technical Report S-71-14, US Army Engineer Waterways Experiment Station, 1972
8. Kausel,E.,Roesset,J.M. and Waas,G.,Dynamic analysis of footings on layered media, Journal of Engineering Mechanics Division, ASCE, Vol.101, No.EM5, pp679-693,1975

9. Tajimi,H. and Shimomura,S.,Dynamic analysis of soil-structure interaction by the thin layered element method (in Japanese), Transactions of Architectural Institute of Japan, No.243, pp41-51,1976

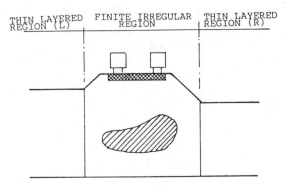

Fig.1 System idealization for traffic induced ground vibrations

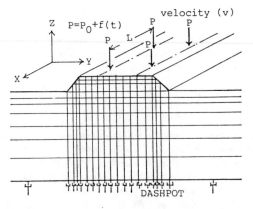

Fig.2 Representative model for traffic induced ground vibrations

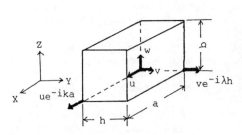

Fig.3 Rectangular pallarelepiped element assumed in analysis of traffic induced ground vibrations

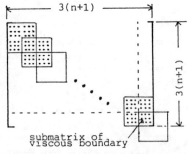

Fig.4 Matrix structure formed by assembling submatrices

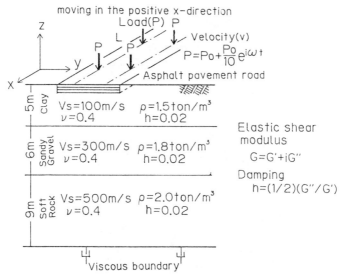

Fig.5-1 Traffic and soil conditions of example case

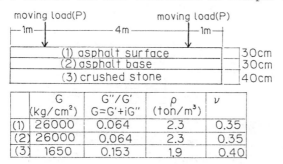

Fig.5-2 Asphalt pavement structure of example case

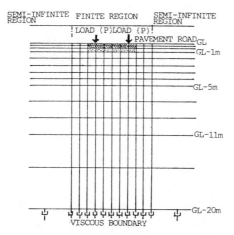

Fig.6 Finite element and thin layered element meshes for analysis of example case

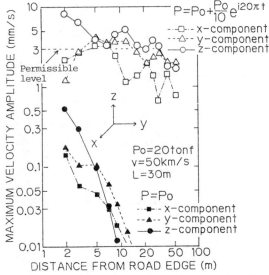

Fig.7 Attenuation with distance of maximum velocity amplitudes of traffic induced ground vibrations (Example case)

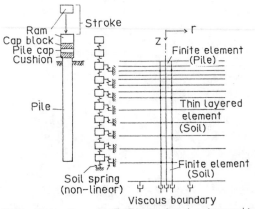

Fig.8 System idealization for impulse pile driving induced ground vibrations

Table 1 Parameters used for pile driving analysis of hammer-pile-soil system

Static ultimate resistance	Shaft	Clay	$5/8 N_c (tonf/m^2)$
		Sand	$1/5 N_s (tonf/m^2)$
	Toe		$20 N (tonf/m^2)$
Quake	Shaft		1.5 (mm)
	Toe		0.05B (B:Diameter)
Damping factor	Shaft	Clay	0.33(sec/m)
		Sand	0.16(sec/m)
	Toe	Clay	1.00(sec/m)
		Sand	0.48(sec/m)

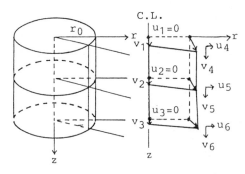

Fig.9 Axisymmetric finite element containing central axis

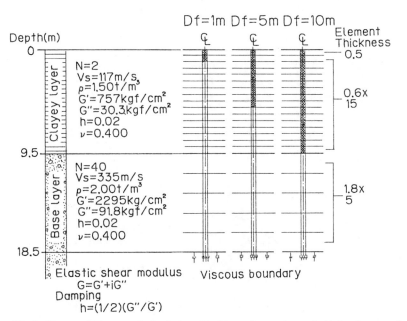

Fig.10 Soil profiles related to finite element and thin layered element meshes for wave propagation analysis of example case

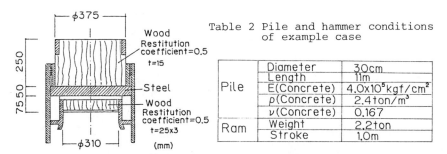

Fig.11 Pile cap used in example case

Table 2 Pile and hammer conditions of example case

Pile	Diameter	30cm
	Length	11m
	E(Concrete)	4.0×10^5 kgf/cm^2
	ρ(Concrete)	2.4ton/m^3
	ν(Concrete)	0.167
Ram	Weight	2.2ton
	Stroke	1.0m

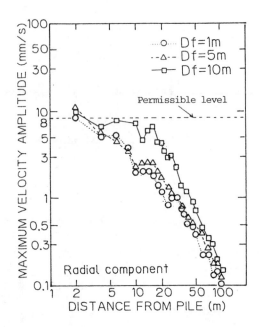

Fig.12-1 Attenuation with distance of maximum velocity amplitudes
         of pile driving induced ground vibrations
         (Example case ; radial component)

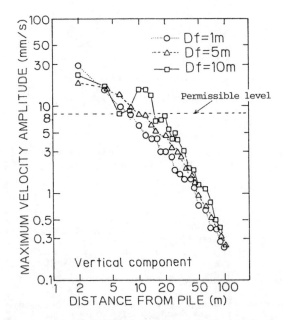

Fig.12-2 Attenuation with distance of maximum velocity amplitudes
         of pile driving induced ground vibrations
         (Example case ; vertical component)

Appendix

[H] matrix in Eq.3)

$$[H] = \frac{E}{(1+\nu)(1-2\nu)} \begin{bmatrix} 1-\nu & \nu & \nu & 0 & 0 & 0 \\ \nu & 1-\nu & \nu & 0 & 0 & 0 \\ \nu & \nu & 1-\nu & 0 & 0 & 0 \\ 0 & 0 & 0 & (1-2\nu)/2 & 0 & 0 \\ 0 & 0 & 0 & 0 & (1-2\nu)/2 & 0 \\ 0 & 0 & 0 & 0 & 0 & (1-2\nu)/2 \end{bmatrix}$$

[B*] matrix in Eq.3)

$$[B*] = \begin{bmatrix} T_{11} & 0 & 0 & T_{12} & 0 & 0 & T_{13} & 0 & 0 & T_{14} & 0 & 0 \\ 0 & T21 & 0 & 0 & T_{22} & 0 & 0 & T_{23} & 0 & 0 & T_{24} & 0 \\ 0 & 0 & T_{31} & 0 & 0 & T_{32} & 0 & 0 & T_{33} & 0 & 0 & T_{34} \\ T_{21} & T_{11} & 0 & T_{22} & T_{12} & 0 & T_{23} & T_{13} & 0 & T_{24} & T_{14} & 0 \\ 0 & T_{31} & T_{21} & 0 & T_{32} & T_{22} & 0 & T_{33} & T_{22} & 0 & T_{34} & T_{24} \\ T_{31} & 0 & T_{11} & T_{32} & 0 & T_{12} & T_{33} & 0 & T_{13} & T_{34} & 0 & T_{14} \end{bmatrix}$$

$T_{1j} = \partial h_j / \partial y$, $T_{2j} = \partial h_j / \partial z$, $T_{3j} = -ikh_j$ (j=1,2,3,4)

$h_1 = (1-\frac{z}{b})(1-\frac{y}{h})$, $h_2 = \frac{z}{b}(1-\frac{y}{h})$, $h_3 = \frac{y}{h}\frac{z}{b}$, $h_4 = \frac{y}{h}(1-\frac{z}{b})$

$[A_j^*], [B_{1j}^*]$, , $[M_j^*]$ submatrices in Eq.6) and Eq.8)

$$[A_j^*] = 1_j \begin{bmatrix} q_j & 0 & 0 & q_j/2 & 0 & 0 \\ 0 & 2m_j & 0 & 0 & m_j & 0 \\ 0 & 0 & q_j & 0 & 0 & q_j/2 \\ q_j/2 & 0 & 0 & q_j & 0 & 0 \\ 0 & m_j & 0 & 0 & 2m_j & 0 \\ 0 & 0 & q_j/2 & 0 & 0 & q_j \end{bmatrix}$$

$$[B_{1j}^*] = \frac{b_j l_j}{6} \begin{bmatrix} 0 & 1 & 0 & 0 & 1/2 & 0 \\ 1 & 0 & 0 & 1/2 & 0 & 0 \\ 0 & 0 & 0 & 0 & 0 & 0 \\ 0 & 1/2 & 0 & 0 & 1 & 0 \\ 1/2 & 0 & 0 & 1 & 0 & 0 \\ 0 & 0 & 0 & 0 & 0 & 0 \end{bmatrix}$$

$$[B_{2j}^*] = i l_j \begin{bmatrix} 0 & 0 & 0 & 0 & 0 & 0 \\ 0 & 0 & r_j & 0 & 0 & -1/4 \\ 0 & -r_j & 0 & 0 & -1/4 & 0 \\ 0 & 0 & 0 & 0 & 0 & 0 \\ 0 & 0 & 1/4 & 0 & 0 & -r_j \\ 0 & 1/4 & 0 & 0 & r_j & 0 \end{bmatrix}$$

$$[C_j^*] = 1_j \begin{bmatrix} 2m_j & 0 & 0 & m_j & 0 & 0 \\ 0 & q_j & 0 & 0 & q_j/2 & 0 \\ 0 & 0 & q_j & 0 & 0 & q_j/2 \\ m_j & 0 & 0 & 2m_j & 0 & 0 \\ 0 & q_j/2 & 0 & 0 & q_j & 0 \\ 0 & 0 & q_j/2 & 0 & 0 & q_j \end{bmatrix}$$

$$[D_j^*]=l_j \begin{bmatrix} 0 & 0 & r_j & 0 & 0 & -1/4 \\ 0 & 0 & 0 & 0 & 0 & 0 \\ -r_j & 0 & 0 & -1/4 & 0 & 0 \\ 0 & 0 & 1/4 & 0 & 0 & -r_j \\ 0 & 0 & 0 & 0 & 0 & 0 \\ 1/4 & 0 & 0 & r_j & 0 & 0 \end{bmatrix}$$

$$[E_j^*]=\frac{3l_j}{b_j^2} \begin{bmatrix} q_j & 0 & 0 & -q_j & 0 & 0 \\ 0 & q_j & 0 & 0 & -q_j & 0 \\ 0 & 0 & 2m_j & 0 & 0 & -2m_j \\ -q_j & 0 & 0 & q_j & 0 & 0 \\ 0 & -q_j & 0 & 0 & q_j & 0 \\ 0 & 0 & -2m_j & 0 & 0 & 2m_j \end{bmatrix}$$

$$[M_j^*]=\frac{\rho_j b_j}{2} \begin{bmatrix} 1 & 0 & 0 & 0 & 0 & 0 \\ 0 & 1 & 0 & 0 & 0 & 0 \\ 0 & 0 & 1 & 0 & 0 & 0 \\ 0 & 0 & 0 & 1 & 0 & 0 \\ 0 & 0 & 0 & 0 & 1 & 0 \\ 0 & 0 & 0 & 0 & 0 & 1 \end{bmatrix}$$

additional submatrices to express
viscous boundary condition in Eq.6)

$$[A_{N+1}^*]=[B_{1N+1}^*]=[B_{2N+1}^*]=[C_{N+1}^*]=$$
$$[D_{N+1}^*]=[M_{N+1}^*]=[0]$$

$$[E_{N+1}^*]= \begin{bmatrix} i\omega\rho V_s & 0 & 0 \\ 0 & i\omega\rho V_s & 0 \\ 0 & 0 & i\omega\rho V_p \end{bmatrix}$$

$[B_j]$ submatrix in Eq.8)

$$[B_j]=l_j \begin{bmatrix} 0 & -ikb_j(1-2\nu_j)/6 & 0 & 0 & -ikb_j(1-2\nu_j)/12 & 0 \\ -ikb_j\nu_j/3 & 0 & \nu_j/2 & -ikb_j\nu_j/6 & 0 & -\nu_j/2 \\ 0 & (1-2\nu_j)/4 & 0 & 0 & -(1-2\nu_j)/4 & 0 \\ 0 & -ikb_j(1-2\nu_j)/12 & 0 & 0 & -ikb_j(1-2\nu_j)/6 & 0 \\ -ikb_j\nu_j/6 & 0 & \nu_j/2 & -ikb_j\nu_j/3 & 0 & -\nu_j/2 \\ 0 & (1-2\nu_j)/4 & 0 & 0 & -(1-2\nu_j)/4 & 0 \end{bmatrix}$$

Vibration Studies on a Historic Bridge

C. Williams

Department of Civil and Structural Engineering, Polytechnic South West, Plymouth, Devon, PL1 2DE, U.K.

INTRODUCTION

The problem of vibration of structures from manmade sources has increased due to higher intensities of loading and increased axle loads of traffic, and larger construction machinery. Other forms of loading from machinery on industrial sites and blasting also can cause problems. This paper briefly reviews some of these loadings.

There has been much discussion on the levels of vibration which cause damage but there is a distinct lack of data. The problem is that every structure is different and on different soils and in a different state of repair. It is also difficult to attribute damage solely to vibration.

Historic structures are particularly vulnerable as due to their often 'massive' construction they are affected by relatively low frequency loads. Also older structures often have residual strains from previous settlement and the natural environment will have played a part in causing decay.

The paper outlines some work on vibration monitoring of what is believed to be the oldest standing concrete bridge in the U.K.

DYNAMIC LOADING

Traffic

Vibrations are produced from traffic mainly due to fluctuations of wheel contact loads caused by irregularities in the road surface. The levels of vibration are increased due to manhole covers, potholes, poor repairs, joints in concrete roads and expansion joints on bridges. Amplitudes tend to increase with speed and increased axle loads.

The effect on buildings will depend on the distance from the road and the type of ground through which the vibration is attenuated. The building components may resonate and damping will play an important role. Ellis[1] produced a study of two historic structures and found the levels present to be well below normal damage levels.

Levels of vibration recorded from traffic vary greatly. Whiffin and Leonard[2] have reported that irregularities in the road surface in the order of 20 mm in amplitude can cause peak particle velocities (PPV) in the ground of up to 5 mm/s. Steffens[3] has reviewed many papers on traffic vibrations quoting amplitudes recorded at up to 57 μm at 1m from a main road; and there have been other studies[4,5]. Frequencies have been quoted in the range 1 to 45 Hz but they usually are in the range 10 to 30 Hz.

Bridges respond to the vehicles travelling over them and the response depends on the natural frequencies of the bridge and the inherent damping[6]. Bridges are designed to be flexible and little has been reported on damage to bridges from vibration. However, bridge vibrations have adverse reactions on pedestrians and movements should be limited.

General effects from traffic which must be considered are damage, human sensitivity, soil compaction and subsequent settlement.

Piling

Pile–driving on construction sites can produce large vibrations which can still be noticeable at distances over 100 m away. A wide range of pile–driving equipment is available which produce different levels of vibration. Ground conditions differ from site to site and so the transmission of the vibration is different in each case; also the structures concerned will respond differently to the radiating vibration as they have different resonant frequencies. Driven piles produce damped free vibration of the ground where the vibration from one impact has dissipated before the next impact takes place. The vibrations produced are similar to those produced by forge or drop–stamps. The noise produced from these operations is often a nuisance to occupants of nearby buildings and legislation under the Control of Pollution Act 1974[7] is in force.

The effects from vibratory pile drivers are in general unpredictable and cases have been reported[8] where vibrations were minimal adjacent to the plant but excessive in buildings half a mile away.

Bored piles produce vibration from the base of the machine which is in contact with the soil, also when the auger hits the bottom of the shaft and from the hammering in of temporary or permanent casings. However, vibration is not usually a problem.

Ward[9] produced a graph showing a range of piling velocities with distance from source. This is reproduced in Figure 1 where the comparison with traffic and blasting vibrations can be made.

The frequency content of signals is usually in the range of 5 to 30 Hz.   This depends mainly on the ground conditions, but for vibratory driving the soil will be forced to vibrate at the set frequency of the driver.   In this case maximum velocities may be recorded when run–down of the machine occurs, and not during the normal driving, as the resonance of the soil occurs at its natural frequency[10].

Many case studies have been reported and some interesting references are to be found[3],[11-16].

Problems encountered with pile–driving are noise nuisance, vibration levels producing discomfort, structural damage, settlement and damage to underground services.

Machinery
Periodic forces are produced from reciprocating machinery which in normal running condition will produce a number of distinct frequencies; however, the start up of the machine will cover a large frequency range.   The dynamic force is produced from some out of balance or eccentric mass due to a fault in the machine design or manufacture, or wear, or from the actual product being manufactured.

The transmission of the vibrations within the structure can be significant and often anti–vibration mountings are used to limit the levels.   However, in such cases there can be significant motion of the machine itself if the machine mass is small.

Blasting and explosions
Damage to property may occur when explosives are used for mining, quarrying or civil engineering construction.

For damage reports to be meaningful, careful inspection of the structures should be made before and after each blast by a qualified engineer.

McCaughey[17] has reviewed the nature and magnitude of the effects of explosions in relation to building elements and compares the probabilities of causation of defects by explosion with other factors. He states that, following stimulation to search for defects, many cracks may be observed for the first time.   Even when other evidence may prove quite clearly to the contrary, it is not unusual for the conclusion to be reached by the observer that the crack must have been caused by the event.

The level of vibration which causes structural damage is discussed in a later section.

Human loading
Vibrational loading from human activities is not a new phenomenon – early bridges often had byelaws forbidding soldiers to march in step. As well as foot–bridges, lightweight floors and spectator arenas can have troublesome vibrations.   Although overloading and fatigue are

design considerations, it is mostly the serviceability in terms of human tolerance to the vibration that causes problems.

Vertical forces exerted by a person walking have been calculated[18] at 180 N (25 per cent of the static weight of the pedestrian). This is the basis of the forcing function of footbridges as defined in BS5400[19].

Group activities pose a greater problem when several people move together in unison when marching or dancing.

VIBRATION LEVELS CAUSING STRUCTURAL DAMAGE

The level of vibration to cause structural damage is very difficult to predict and many researchers have reported different values at which damage occurs. The nature and duration of the dynamic loading, position and measurement, the properties of the building materials, type of construction and state of repair are all factors to be considered when comparing data. The indirect consequences of vibration due to dynamically induced settlement must also be considered as well as human response.

DIN Standard 4150 Part 3[20] includes guideline values which, if complied with, prevent damage in terms of a reduction in the stability of a structure or component, or in the load–bearing capacity of floors, or crack formation in the wall plaster or enlargement of cracks already present. Table 1 shows the guideline values at the foundation and in the plane of the floor of the uppermost full storey for various types of building. DIN 4150 states that if these values are observed damage is unlikely to occur. It also states that in the case of short term vibration of floors values up to 20 mm/s are acceptable at the centre of the floor.

A British Standards Committee is investigating the vibration effects on buildings. However, there is a distinct lack of comprehensive data at which damage occurs. This is particularly so for historic buildings and bridges.

Vibration on bridges is expected as they are known to be more flexible than buildings. However, older bridge structures may suffer distress from increased traffic and the higher loads that are now present. A case study is given later.

Blasting operations and building damage have always been the subject of some discussion. Some early work by Northwood and Crawford[21] found that threshold levels of damage were about 75 mm/s for houses tested. The structural condition of the house must be considered.

Konon and Schuring[22] reported that during the period 1950 to 1980 the U.S. Bureau of mines adopted a 50 mm/s ground particle velocity as the level below which there should be no structural damage. This was said to be not a safe limit and particularly so for historic and older structures.

Crocket[11] reported some general conclusions from work on over 40 ancient buildings.   He found that the buildings invariably leaned over more towards the road carrying the traffic than away from it. Also their foundation settlement were seen to be exactly proportional to the estimated number of traffic and soil vibration cycles, to their maximum amplitude, the number of major vehicles passing, and to the number of centuries they have been passing.

Contractors blasting rock in construction often have the level of vibration that may be induced in nearby houses limited to a value of 25 mm/s.

Watts[23] reported on the effects of traffic induced vibration on four very different heritage buildings.   It was concluded that although measurable levels of groundborne vibration were present in all buildings, reaching perceptible levels in some, the observed damage was likely to have been caused by other site factors rather than the exposure to traffic vibration.

In a survey of traffic–induced vibrations, Whiffin and Leonard[2] proposed that, in the absence of more directly applicable data, the peak particle velocity of 5 mm/s be adopted for the maximum level of vibration in houses to minimise 'architectural' damage by traffic.

Thus it can be seen from these brief reviews that there is a wide range of threshold values quoted and much research work is required in this field.

The current U.K. situation concerning damage to buildings from ground–bourne vibration is set out in a Building Research Station Digest[24].   It sets out guidelines from some international standards and details of information to be reported from tests.

AXMOUTH BRIDGE – TRAFFIC AND PILING VIBRATIONS

Axmouth Bridge (Figure 2) is believed to be the oldest standing concrete bridge in the U.K. being built about 1877 by Philip Brannon[25].   The bridge carries two lanes of traffic in and out of Seaton in South East Devon.   Major works were carried out on the bridge in 1956 after a large transverse crack had developed in the main arch[26].   The weight of the traffic was relieved from this arch by carrying a timber deck on ten steel girders.   In 1976 the bridge was designated on Ancient Monument (number 955).   In the late seventies a survey showed the bridge to be in a poor state and in need of major repair.   At this stage a weight restriction of 7½t was imposed.

The bridge has three round headed arches of approximate lengths of 9.1, 15.2 and 9.1 m and rises of 1.7, 2.3 and 1.7 m respectively. The overall width is 7.3 m and 6.4 m between parapets.

The construction was of mass concrete but with 'void formers' and has simulated joints as if built of masonry. The concrete appears to have been made with as–dug beach gravel varying from about 3 mm to 120 mm aggregate but with no fines.

A series of vibration monitoring studies was carried out in 1988–89 in order to:

1.   assess the level of vibration produced by vehicles on the bridge;

2.   assess the performance after repair work;

3.   assess the levels of vibration from piling work for a replacement bridge close by.

A system of three Willmore seismometers were used to monitor vibration levels in three orthogonal directions. These were linked by FM landline systems to data recording and analysis equipment located off the bridge.

Test 1   Eight locations on the bridge were monitored and the vibration due to the passage of a 7½–ton lorry over the bridge were recorded. During the tests all other traffic was prevented from passing over the bridge.

The results showed the bridge to be performing in a strange manner with the maximum peak particle velocity (PPV) of 2.8 mm/s recorded above the west pier.   A normal bridge would show large vertical movements on the spans with some transverse and longitudinal movements at a lesser level. However, Axmouth Bridge showed large transverse and longitudinal vibrations at the west pier; it had also subsided some 600 mm at this point. It was decided that this pier was 'floating' and repair work was necessary to stabilise it.

Test 2   Micro–piling work was carried out to stabilise the west pier and abutment and a repeat of Test 1 then carried out.

It was difficult to make direct comparisons of vibration data with Test 1 as the road surface profile had changed due to the micro–piling work.   However, the bridge did appear to perform as one would expect, i.e. with large vertical vibrations at the middle of the main span. The maximum PPV at the west pier had also reduced from 2.8 to 1.8 mm/s.

Test 3   Three different pile driving rigs were used to drive steel sheet piles next to the bridge. This was in order to assess the levels to be expected when the main piling for the new bridge started, and also to select the rig which produced the least vibration on the bridge. The seismometers were located at the west abutment and the nearest pile (No. 8) was 3m from this location. Table 2 shows the results of the PPV recorded from the test sequence.

CONCLUSIONS

The prediction of levels of vibration which cause damage is very difficult and many researchers have provided a variety of figures. It is particularly important that historic structures are protected and where possible the source of vibration removed.

The study on Axmouth Bridge showed that repair work was urgently needed. Also the expected levels due to piling were predicted. The piling for the new bridge did not cause distress in the old bridge.

ACKNOWLEDGEMENTS

Devon County Engineers Department

REFERENCES

1.   ELLIS, P.   'The effects of traffic-induced vibration on historic buildings'.   Proceedings of the Institute of Acoustics.   Vol. 7 Part 2 (1985).

2.   WHIFFIN, A.C. and LEONARD, D.R.   'A Survey of Traffic-induced Vibrations'.   TRRL Report of I.R. 418 (1971).

3.   STEFFENS, R.J.   'Structural Vibration and Damage'.   BRE Report (1974).

4.   HOUSE, M.E.   'Traffic induced vibration on historic buildings'. *The Highway Engineer*, pp 6–13 (February 1973).

5.   BEAN, R. and PAGE J.   'Traffic induced ground vibration in the vicinity of road tunnels'.   Transport and Road Research Laboratory, Supplementary Report 218UC (1976).

6.   EYRE, R. and SMITH, I.J.   'Wind and traffic induced dynamic behaviour of some steel box girder bridges'.   Paper 5, TRRL Supplementary Report 275 (1977).

7.   HMSO, Control of Pollution Act 1974.

8.   WELTMAN, A.J. (ed).   'Noise and vibration from piling operations'.   CIRIA Report PG9 (October 1980).

9.   WARD. H.S.   'Dynamic Disturbances'. *Civil Engineering* (August 1975) London.

10.   O'NEIL, D.B.   'Vibration and dynamic settlement from pile driving'.   Proceedings of Piling Conference ICE (September 1970).

11.   CROCKETT, J.H.A.   'Some practical aspects of vibration in civil engineering'.   Proceedings of Symposium on Vibration in Civil Engineering (London 1965) Butterworth 1966.

12.   CROCKET, J.H.A.   'Piling vibrations and structural fatigue'. Proceedings of Conference on Recent Developments in the Design and Construction of Piles, ICE, London (1979).

13.   LANGLEY, M.S. and ELLIS, P.C.   'Noise and vibration during piling'.   Proceedings of Conference on Recent Developments in the Design and Construction of Piles, ICE, London (1979).

14. MARTIN, D.J.   'Ground vibrations from impact pile driving during road construction', TRRL.   Supplementary Report 544 (1980).

15. MALLARD, D.J. and BASTOW, P.   'Some observations on the vibrations caused by pile driving'.   Conference on Recent Developments in the Design and Construction of Piles, ICE, London (1979).

16. ADAMS, J.L. and HANNA, T.A.   'Ground movements due to pile driving'.   Proceedings of ICE on Piling, ICE, London (1970).

17. McCAUGHEY, J.D.   'Damage from explosions – real or imaginary', *The Structural Engineer*, Vol. 62A, No. 5 pp. 151–157 (May 1984).

18. BLANCHARD, J., DAVIES, B.L. and SMITH, J.W.   'Design criteria and analysis for dynamic loading of footbridges'. Proceedings, Symposium on Dynamic Behaviour of Bridges, Supplementary Report 275, Transport and Road Research Laboratory, Berkshire, England, pp 90–106 (May 1977).

19. BS5400: 'Steel, Concrete and Composite Bridges'.   British Standards Institution.

20. DIN 4150, Part 3:   'Structural vibration in buildings: Effects on structures' (1986).

21. NORTHWOOD, T.D. and CRAWFORD, R.   'Blasting and building damage'.   Canadian Building Digest, No. 63 (March 1965).

22. KONON, W. and SCHURING R.   'Vibration criteria for historic buildings.   Journal of Construction Engineering and Management American Society of Civil Engineering, Vol. 111, No. 3, (Sept. 1985).

23. WATTS, G.R.   'The effects of traffic induced vibration on heritage buildings – further case studies.   Transport Road Research Laboratory.   Report No. 207, 1989.

24. Damage to structures from ground–borne vibration. Building Research Station Digest 353, Building Research Establishment, Watford, U.K., July 1990.

25. WAINE, N.D.   'A concrete ancient monument'.   Proceedings of the Conference on The Life of Structures and the Role of Physical Testing Brighton (April 1989).

26. Private Communication with Mr. M. R. Hawkins, County Engineer, Devon County Council.

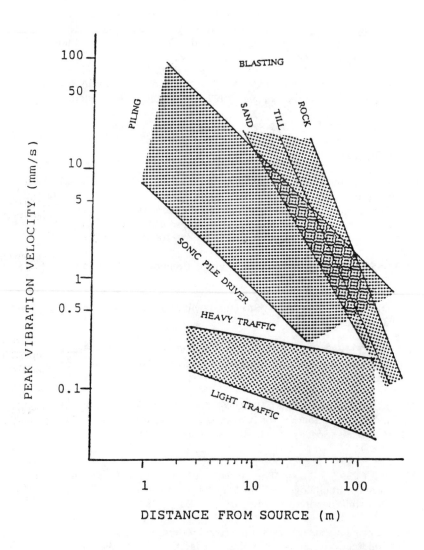

FIGURE 1   COMPARISON OF SOME SOURCES
           OF GROUND VIBRATION (WARD)

FIGURE 2   AXMOUTH BRIDGE, BUILT IN 1877

Table 1

DIN Standard 4150[20]

Guideline values of vibration velocity, v_i, for evaluating the effects of short-term vibration

| | Vibration velocity, v_i in mm/s | | | Plan of floor of uppermost full storey |
| | Foundation At a frequency of | | | |
	less than 10 Hz	10 to 50 Hz	50 to 100* Hz	Frequency mixture
Building used for commercial purposes, industrial buildings and buildings of similar design.	20	20 to 40	40 to 50	40
Dwellings and buildings of similar design and/or use.	5	5 to 15	15 to 20	15
Structures that, because of their particular sensitivity to vibration, do not correspond to those listed above and are of great intrinsic value (eg, buildings that are under a preservation order)	3	3 to 8	8 to 10	8

*For frequencies above 100 Hz, at least the values specified in this column shall be applied.

Table 2

Maximum peak particle velocities recorded at west pier on Axmouth Bridge due to piling

Pile No.	Maximum peak particle velocity (PPV) (mm/s)								Approximate level (m)
	1	2	3	4	5	6	7	8	AOD
BSP 600N double-acting air hammer		0.5	0.6	0.8	1.0	1.1	1.2	1.6	+4 to -27
	0.8	0.9							-7 to -7.5
Vibrating hammer MS-15H					1.6	1.3	1.3	1.2	-2.7 to -7.5
BSP hydraulic hammer HH3	2.1		3.5						-2.7 to -7.0

The air hammer generally produced the lower vibration on the bridge while the hydraulic hammer produced the largest PPV values and induced longer vibrations than were recorded from the $7\frac{1}{2}$-ton lorry test.

Seismic Retrofit of Historic Structures in California

S.E. Thomasen, C.L. Searls

Wiss, Janney, Elstner Associates,Inc., Emeryville, California, U.S.A.

ABSTRACT

The development of regulations for seismic design of new buildings and for the retrofit and strengthening of existing buildings in California dates from the 1920's. The objective of these early building codes was primarily to reduce loss of life and injury during an earthquake, while accepting property damage up to and including total building loss.

A better understanding of earthquake behavior and the realization that the economic loss from a seismic event could be devastating has, over the years, led to increased requirements for seismic resistance of buildings. These higher standards have greatly mitigated the earthquake hazards in new buildings but the standards have not been retroactively applied to the existing building stock. The seismic strengthening of historic buildings and monuments is now being done using a variety of techniques.

INTRODUCTION

Protection of historic structures and their contents from damaging earthquakes is a special engineering challenge. For new buildings, the generally accepted goal of seismic design for major earthquakes is the protection of life while allowing structural and non-structural damage to the building. For seismic retrofit of an important historic structure, it would be desirable not only to provide for life safety, but to protect the building and its contents from damage. It is furthermore desirable that the strengthening is done with respect for both the original historic fabric and the original structural concept. To achieve these goals for historic structures often entails making choices between life safety and reducing property damage on one hand and preservation of the architecture without visually intrusive interventions on the other. For this reason the criteria for seismic retrofit of historic structures in California is sometimes less stringent than the requirements for new structures.

Most historic structures in California are not in conformance with current building regulations in regard to life safety and earthquake resistance. Many of these structures are being demolished because of the mistaken belief that there is no alternative to the costly and destructive seismic strengthening. But seismic upgrading of a historic structure is feasible and it is being done in California.

HISTORIC STRUCTURES IN CALIFORNIA

Historic buildings and monuments are unique structures in California where little remains of construction done before 1850. Man is responsible for some of the destruction but many early Spanish and Mexican buildings were destroyed by earthquakes. With the exception of the Spanish missions and presidios and a few wood and adobe structures from the Mexican period, most historic structures in California date from the period 1850 to 1930. These structures include bridges and lighthouses, turn of the century factories, churches, residences and hotels, and many of the commercial buildings that form the core of the older cities. These structures are of a wide variety of structural types and materials including:

o   Light wood frame buildings from one to four stories in height.
o   Timber framed structures including bridges, churches and public facilities.
o   Steel and concrete framed buildings from three to 30 or more stories in height with infill walls of unreinforced masonry. These often monumental structures are the older public, commercial, and residential buildings forming the historic center of larger cities.
o   Unreinforced masonry bearing wall buildings often with wood floor framing. These buildings of one to six stories in height are generally seen to represent the greatest seismic hazard.

SEISMIC BUILDING CODES AND STANDARDS IN CALIFORNIA

Despite the devastating damage during the 1906 San Francisco earthquake, the special nature of seismic forces was not recognized in California building codes for a long time. Seismic safety in new structures was typically provided for in a manner similar to wind design.   The 1927 Uniform Building Code was the first to include special seismic requirements based on building mass and soil type. These requirements were, after the 1932 Long Beach quake, made mandatory for all school construction, but it was not until the 1940's that seismic requirements were extended to all types of building construction.

Seismic design requirements in California have continued to become more detailed in response to earthquake experiences both in the United States and abroad.   Engineers today are generally of the opinion that the design values for new construction are realistic and attention is now directed to older building stock.

The Uniform Building Code (UBC) [1] is mandatory for all new construction and for additions and major remodels to existing buildings. The regulations for listed historic buildings are found in State of California Historical Building Code [2], while the Uniform Code for Building Conservation (UCBC) [3] is intended for use in older buildings. Seismic retrofit of existing structures is presently not mandatory unless the structures are altered or the occupancy changed. However, California is developing a program for identifying and mitigating seismic hazards in all existing structures. As the first phase, the program includes the more than 60,000 structures of unreinforced masonry construction. The program will require that the owners of these structures, within the next few years obtain a seismic evaluation and, if necessary, strengthen the structure to mitigate earthquake hazards. Many of the large and monumental historic structures in California are of unreinforced masonry construction and they will be affected by this program.

Uniform Building Code (UBC)

The regulations in the UBC are mandatory for the design and construction of all new structures in California. It is the intention that structures designed in conformance with these regulations should [4]:

    a. Resist a minor level of earthquake ground motion without damage;

    b. Resist a moderate level of earthquake ground motion without structural damage, but with some non-structural damage;

    c. Resist a major level of earthquake ground motion having an intensity equal to the strongest either experienced or forecast for the building site, without collapse, but possibly with some structural as well as non-structural damage.

It is expected that structural damage, even in a major earthquake, will be limited to a repairable level. The level of damage depends upon a number of factors, including the building configuration, type of lateral force resisting system, materials selected for the structure, and care taken in construction.

Uniform Code for Building Conservation (UCBC)

Additions to an existing building are required to conform to the UBC. A newly developed code, the UCBC, is suggested for use in remodels and alterations of existing buildings. This code recognizes that the retrofit required to bring existing structures into compliance with the UBC is sometimes not feasible and the code, as an alternate, sets minimum standards with the aim of reducing life safety risk.

State of California Historic Building Code

Regulations for rehabilitation and retrofit of historical structures in California were first enacted in 1976. These regulations apply to all structures on existing or future national, state and local registers, official inventories such as the National Register of Historic Places, State Historical Landmarks and City and County registers and landmarks. The intent of the code is to provide means for the preservation of California's architectural heritage by recognizing the unique construction problems inherent in upgrading historical buildings. Concurrently, the code intends to provide reasonable safety from fire and seismic hazards for the occupants of such buildings. It is specifically stated that it is not the intent to protect the property if by doing so the historical integrity of the structure is adversely affected.

While the historical building code applies to all registered historic structures, other equally important structures, which, for some reason are not registered, are excluded and any rehabilitation or retrofit of these structures must comply with the governing local code (often the UBC). Registered historic structures where the occupancy is critical to the safety and welfare of the public, such as schools, hospitals, police and fire stations and large assembly areas, must always comply with the higher standards of the UBC.

The State Historical Building Code differs from other codes in that the regulations are performance-oriented and archaic materials are permitted. The Code contains alternative structural regulations that are applied by an architect or engineer experienced in earthquake resistant design. A survey is first made of the existing conditions and the expected maximum seismic force on the structure, as determined by the engineer, is compared with the earthquake resistant capacity. The evaluation may be based upon the ultimate capacities of the structure, giving due consideration to ductility and reserve strength of lateral force resisting materials and systems. Broad judgement may be exercised regarding the strength and performance of materials not generally recognized by prevailing code requirements. Past performance of the structure or similar structures may also be used in the evaluation.

SEISMIC RETROFIT CRITERIA

Earthquakes expose a structure to dynamic forces which must be considered in the seismic retrofit design. The structure must provide a continuous transfer of these forces to the foundation. A well designed retrofit of a historic structure should improve the strength, the ductility and the redundancy of the structure in regard to resisting the seismic forces. Earthquakes are effective in exposing any weakness in the design concept or detailing. Therefore, any vulnerable links in the lateral load resisting system must be addressed in the seismic retrofit.

The presently accepted seismic design criteria in California expects a new structure to respond in the inelastic range in order to satisfy energy dissipation demands. This is accomplished by permitting large deformations which might damage both structural and non-structural elements such as exterior walls, ceilings and partitions. The problem for the seismic retrofit of historic structures is to find the balance of interventions that reduces the risk for injury or property damage to an acceptable level without unduly destroying the historic fabric. This requires ingenious solutions from the design professionals and it often entails making choices between life safety and property damage mitigation at one hand and preservation on the other. It requires allowing large deformations during the earthquake in order to reduce force levels, but it also requires reducing the deformations in order to limit damage to the structure and its contents.

SEISMIC RETROFIT TECHNIQUES

The two methods presently used for seismic retrofit of historic structures in California are conventional structural strengthening and energy dissipation systems.

Conventional Structural Strengthening

Conventional structural strengthening is intended to increase the lateral load resisting capacity by improving the strength, ductility and redundancy of the existing structural system.   The lateral load resistance capacity of the structure can be increased by strengthening the existing elements or by adding additional elements such as shear walls, floor diaphragms or diagonal bracing.

A ductile structure is able to tolerate repeated deformations during the duration of the seismic shaking without losing its load carrying capacity even when structural materials are damaged.   In historic structures, the existing materials are often brittle rather than ductile.   An example of improvement to the ductility of the seismic resisting system is the encapsulating of a brittle material, such as hollow clay tile walls within reinforced plaster coatings, which allows the walls to maintain their stability during an earthquake even when the tile crushes.

Redundancy is the existence of a back-up structural system which prevents collapse after the primary seismic resisting system has been damaged.   In a seismic retrofit of a historic structure, redundancy is sometimes provided by installing a back-up system in the form of a vertical steel frame which is independent of, but connected to, the primary load bearing system.

The effect on the entire structure of strengthening existing or adding new elements must be considered.   For example when new concrete shear walls are introduced in a masonry building, the added stiffness will shorten the natural period of vibration of the structure, and this often increases the seismic forces.   The introduction of new elements can also create additional torsional effects or it can overstress existing structural elements.

Energy Dissipation Systems

A number of recently developed imaginative approaches to improved seismic performance and damage control by energy dissipation can be applied to historic structures.   They are based on the principle that the shaking of the soil causes motions in the structure and motion is a form of energy.   If, by some means, the structure could be isolated from the soil shaking or if installation of supplemental damping devices could dissipate the energy, then the seismic demand on the structure itself would be reduced and the deformations controlled.

Base isolation systems use special bearings with sandwiched layers of steel and rubber to uncouple the structure from the horizontal components of the earthquake ground motion, while at the same time supporting the vertical weight.   The bearings, in effect, lengthen the structure's period of vibration sufficiently to reduce the level of transmitted energy and the bearings dissipate some of this energy, so that the relative displacement between the structure and the ground can be controlled.   The structure will still have to be strengthened by conventional means for the lower level of forces transmitted through the bearings.   During an earthquake, large displacements will occur across the flexible bearings, which are often installed above the footings and below column bases.   Providing for these large displacements in architectural, mechanical and electrical systems can be both difficult and expensive.   For this reason, base isolation has up to now only been applied to a few historic structures in the United States.   It has, however, been used for retrofit of bridges and industrial structures in California and it is currently being considered for protection of museum installations.

Other energy dissipation systems use mechanical devices to provide damping of the earthquake induced shaking. This supplemental damping can, for some structures, be an effective means of controlling the structural response, thus reducing the risk of severe damage. Most damping devices rely on friction between viscoelastic materials or on yielding of steel to provide the required level of energy dissipation. The energy dissipation system used for historic retrofit in California is the eccentrically braced frame, where the diagonals in a vertical steel frame are slightly offset and the horizontal members are designed to yield.

STATUS OF SEISMIC RETROFIT OF HISTORIC STRUCTURES IN CALIFORNIA

Many historic buildings in California are well built and have inherently good earthquake resistance. But most of these buildings are not in conformance with current building regulations in regard to life safety and earthquake resistance, and their retrofit and seismic strengthening often involves the destruction of historic fabric or the disruption of the building's visual appearance. And often historic structures are demolished in the mistaken belief that there is no alternative to the costly and destructive replacement of the primary structural system.

Seismic retrofit of a historic structure requires understanding of its behavior during a seismic event, it requires respect for the historic fabric, and it requires money. But it is achievable and it is being done in California. Typical methods of seismically upgrading structures are:

o   Wood frame buildings, 2-3 stories high, with a basement. Typically, the basement walls and the first floor diaphragm are strengthened by bracing or with plywood shear panels, the exterior wood siding is renailed to improve the shear capacity and control deformations, the walls are secured to the foundations, and towers and chimneys are braced.
o   Masonry and wood frame structures, 1-4 stories high, with a soft first story. This is a common building type along city streets where the first floor is used for retail stores and the front elevation has been left open. These buildings are strengthened by incorporating a steel frame into the front elevation in order to improve the strength of the front wall at the ground floor level and make its stiffness compatible with the rest of the structure.
o   Unreinforced masonry bearing wall structures. This is considered the most hazardous type of structure during an earthquake. Different seismic retrofits have been used, such as installing backup systems in form of an exposed steel frames inside the structure, or by strengthening the walls by removing part of the masonry wall thickness and replacing it with reinforced concrete. In some seismic retrofits the existing masonry has been internally reinforced by coring the walls from the roof to the foundation and placing reinforcing steel in the grout filled voids.

Short of a complete seismic retrofit much work is also done on historic structures in California to mitigate hazards and improve their performance during an earthquake. Facade ornaments such as finials, urns and roof parapets are reanchored and braced. Floor diaphragms are strengthened by plywood or concrete toppings or by underfloor bracing, and floors and roofs are securely anchored to the exterior walls to prevent walls falling outwards. Tall masonry walls, as often found in churches and monumental structures, are secured against buckling by bracing or other means. Mechanical and electrical systems are upgraded to avoid rupture of piping, and boilers, pumps and other equipment is secured from sliding off their support.

Much work is also being done to limit damage to the contents of historic structures. Many of these structures contain original artifacts and some are used as museums. Elevated objects are being secured to their pedestals and the pedestals bolted to the floor. Objects on shelves are prevented from sliding, cabinets and bookcases are restrained from toppling, and pounding damage to paintings is mitigated by installing thick elastic pads at each corner.

CONCLUSION

It must be recognized that some seismic risk must always be accepted since earthquakes are random events and for every big earthquake in the past there may be a bigger one in the future. The objective of seismic retrofit of historic structures in California is to reduce the risk of injury or property damage to an acceptable level without unduly destroying the historic fabric we are trying to preserve.

REFERENCES

1. "Uniform Building Code, 1988 Edition", International Conference of Building Officials, Whittier, California.
2. "State Historical Building Code", Title 24.   State   Building Standards, State of California.
3. "Uniform Building Code for Building Conservation", International Conference of Building Officials, Whittier, California.
4. "Recommended Lateral Force Requirements and Commentary", Seismology Committee, Structural Engineers Association of California.

The Earthquake Resistance of Apollo Epikourios Columns

C.L. Papantonopoulos

Committee for the Preservation of the Temple of Apollo Epikourios, Athens, Greece

SYNOPSIS

In the present work an investigation procedure for the evaluation of seismik risk of the Epikourios Apollo 37 doric columns still standing is presented. The scope of the paper is a) to study the vulnerability of columns as part of general studies being performed for preservation purposes and b) to develop consistent safety criteria for the repair and strengthening against seismic actions. In order to improve the seismic stability two major measures can be taken: return of the leaning columns into the vertical position and strengthening of broken foundation members (βατηρες).

INTRODUCTION

The temple of Apollo Epikourios stands as one of the most remarkable and best preserved monuments of classical architecture (last quarter of the 5th century B.C.). It stands on one of the natural plateaux of Mt. Kotylion at an altitude 1130m above sea level, 14 km from the village of Andritsaina in SW Peloponnesos. The monument is a Doric temple, it measures 38.24X14.48m at the level of the stylobate (Fig. 1). The main building material is a light grey, hard but very anisotropic, sedimentary limestone. Because the stylobates have settled, the columns have tilted away from the vertical position, in some cases by more than 20cm at the top of the column. Also all the foundation members still in place suffer from considerable fractures. The building material has deteriorated extensively which has reduced the static efficiency of most of the blocks and the structure as a whole.

The constructors of these freely supported, articulated buildings have taken into serious consideration the possibility of strong horizontal earthquake forces. Today, in order to protect and properly preserve the monument, it is necessary to study in depth their structural function and mainly their seismic responce. In this paper, behaviour of freestanding columns under seismic excitation is studied.

SEISMIC HAZARD

Seismic hazard in a certain site is defined as the expected value of a parameter of the seismic motion (ground acceleration, velocity etc) at this site with certain probability of exceedence during certain period of time. Seismic risk (effects of earthquakes) is considered as the convolution of seismic hazard and the vulnerability of the structure. The site of the temple according to the zonation of Greece is found in seismic zone II, where the maximum ground acceleration (γ) as a function of the main return period is expressed by the equation

$$\log\gamma = 0.277\log T + 1.579$$

For a probability of exceedence 10% in the next 50, 100, 200 years (mean return period 475, 950, 1900 years) the ground accelerations are equal to 0.21g, 0.26g, 0.31g and the ground velocities 23cm/sec, 30cm/sec, 40cm/sec respectively. For a probability of exceedence 63% in the next 50, 100, 200 years the ground accelerations are equal to 0.14g, 0.17g, 0.21g and the ground velocities 10cm/sec, 13cm/sec, 17cm/sec respectively.

ANALYSIS

Equation of motion
A rigid block subjected to horizontal and vertical ground accelerations on a rigid base is shown in rotated position in Fig. 2. It is assumed that the contact surface between the block and the base is sufficiently rough so that sliding cannot occur. Depending on the ground acceleration, the block may move rigidly with the ground or be set into rocking. The equations of motion when the block is pivoted about the centres of rotations are:

$$Io\theta+W(1+a_y/g)R\sin(\theta c-\theta)=-WR\cos(\theta c-\theta)a_x/g$$
$$Io\theta+W(1+a_y/g)R\sin(\theta c+\theta)=-WR\cos(\theta c+\theta)a_x/g$$

For rocking response, the rigid body is characterized

by its weight W and its mass moment of inertia about O (O´) Io. The location of mass center is defined by the distance R and the angle θc. Here θc is the critical (maximum) angle to which the block can be tilted without toppling over under gravity. For the case of a typical monument column the respective values (Fig. 3,4) are:

$D_1=1.11m$, $D_2=0.90m$, $H=5.95m$, $R=2.93m$, $Io=51.57m^6$

It can be shown (eg. Housner [1]) that the period of free vibration is governed by the equation:

$$T = (4/p)\cosh^{-1}\{1/(1-\theta o/\theta c)\}$$

where p is considered as the system frequency given by

$$p^2= WR/Io \text{ (typical column } p=1.62)$$

The period of free vibration is strongly and non-linearly depedent on the amplitude ratio $\theta o/\theta c$ (Fig. 5); increases from zero to infinity as the amplitude ratio increases from zero to one.

Coefficient of restitution
The ratio of kinetic energy after and before impact is:

$$r= (1/2Io\dot\theta_2)/(1/2Io\dot\theta_1)= (\dot\theta_2/\dot\theta_1)^2$$

or

$$r= [1-WR^2(1-\cos2\theta c)/gIo]^2$$

where $\dot\theta_1,\dot\theta_2$ the angular velocities before and after impact. The coefficient of restitution is defined as:

$$e= \dot\theta_2/\dot\theta_1 \qquad (r=1-e^2)$$

For the typical column r=0.893 (10.7% energy loss) and e=0.945. The variation of coefficient of restitution for the typical column with the location of the reaction force (eg. Giannini [2]) is shown in Fig. 6.

It is possible to represent the rocking block as a single degree of freedom oscillator (eg. Priestley [3]) with an equivalent viscous damping

$$\lambda=1/\pi vln(\varphi o/\varphi v)$$

where $\varphi v=\theta v/\theta c$ the amplitude following the v-th impact ($\varphi_0 = \theta_0/\theta_c$ initial value). From Fig. 7 for the typical column we conervatively adopt $\lambda = 5\%$.

Overturning Criteria

A constant acceleration (α) lasting for a time (t) may or may not overturn the column, depending upon the magnitude of (α) and the duration (t) (Fig. 8). Similarly the conditions under which a half-cycle sine-pulse will overturn the column are governed by:

$$\alpha/g\theta_c = \{1 + (\omega/p)^2\}^{1/2}$$

where $\omega = 2\pi/T$. In Fig. 9 we can distinguish 3 regions, as function of the amplitude and of the frequency of the sine wave ground motion: I=no motion, II=stable, III=unstable. It can be observed that the typical column is unsafe at low frequencies, lower than the predominant ones in the Fourier spectrum of earthquake accelerograms.

Housner [1] presented an approximate analysis, based on energy concepts, of overturning of blocks by earthquake ground motion. The pseudo-velocity spectrum value Sv -with 50% probability of overturning- is given by the equation

$$Sv = \theta_c(gR)^{1/2}/ (MR^2/I_0)^{1/2}$$

For the temple column we obtain Sv=114cm/sec. This value is extremely high, the corresponding value of Kalamata earthquake for a damping value 5% was only 60cm/sec. The velocity amplitude , which is the lower limit of the maximum ground velocity to overturn a rigid block is given (eg. Ishiyama [4]) by the equation

$$\upsilon_0 = 0.4[2g/R(i^2+R^2)(1-\cos\theta_c)/\cos^2\theta_c]^{1/2}$$

where i is the radius of gyration of the body. For the typical column υ_0=63cm/sec. This value is also very high in comparison with the expected values from the seismic hazard investigation. The displacement criterion (d_o), which is the lower limit of the maximum ground displacement to overturn the column:

$$d_o = \upsilon_0^2/\alpha_o$$

where α_o the lower limit of the maximum acceleration to overturn the body. For the typical column d_o=20.0cm, when the maximum displacement for the Kalamata earthquake was only 7.2cm.

The response spectrum approximation

If it is assumed that the peak response to seismic excitation depends only on the equivalent elastic characteristics (T,λ) at peak response, then a trial-and-error response spectrum approach may be used to determine the peak rotation (eg. Priestley [3]). An estimation of maximum rotation (θ_1) is initially conjectured, the corresponding period (T_1) is read off Fig. 5, a new rotation (θ_2) is found from the tripartite response spectrum for the equivalent elastic system (T_1,λ), a new period (T_2) is read off Fig. 5 and so on. Using this technique a maximum rotation $\theta=3$ degrees (corresponding period $T=2.2sec$) is found for the Kalamata earthquake $(\lambda=5\%)$.

Whether overturning through rocking can be brought about by an earthquake will depend upon how, and for how long, inertia forces happen to be applied on the column. It is evident from the response spectrum approach that the predominant periods of an earthquake are much shorter than the rocking periods of column (eg. Ambraseys [5]).

Response sensitivity

The rocking response of the column is very sensitive to minor changes in the system parameters (coefficient of restitution, size) and the details of ground motion. A small additional input of energy at the right time could be sufficient to overturn the column. Overturning of the column by a ground motion of particular intensity does not imply that the column will necessarily overturn under the action of more intense ground motion. Vertical ground motion also affects the rocking response but not in a systematic way.

In contrast to the deterministic way, systematic trends are observed when the response is studied from a probabilistic point of view with the ground motion modelled as a random process. Plotting the results of Yim et al [6] in a peak normalized acceleration versus ˊnatural frequencyˊ (p) space (eg. Allen et al [7]) we obtain for the typical column 10%, 50% and 90% overturning probabilities for acceleration values 0.34g, 0.45g, 0.60g respectively.

Parametric studies

In order to evaluate the results of the preceding analysis a time domain step-by-step integration scheme was adopted to three suitable earthquake time histories (Fig. 10). The equations of motion were integrated numerically using the Runge-Kutta method with a time step equal to $\Delta t=0.001sec$. The

appropriate computer program was implemented by J.
Psycharis. The results are summarized in Fig. 11.

The maximum rotation for the Kalamata earthquake is
about 3.5 degrees that is close enough to the
approximated value (3 degrees) calculated from the
response spectrum approach. The peak ground
accelerations to overturn the column were estimated
equals to 0.70g, 0.80g and 1.50g for the Kalamata, El
Centro and Peru earthquakes respectively. It is clear
that the ground acceleration could not be the unique
criterion for the assesment of seismic risk. Other
parameters such as frequency content, duration etc.
are also very important for the estimation of the
column collapse.

Further studies now in progress have shown the major
role of other parameters such as initial inclination
or foundation conditions. For instance, for an
initial inclination equal to 0.03 rad the column is
unstable for a ground acceleration greater than 0.5g
(Kalamata earthquake).

CONCLUSION

The present analysis is only approximate and it can
be used as a rough estimate of the column
vulnerability. The analysis should be used in such a
way so as to give a deeper rather qualitative insight
in the behaviour of the structure. Although the
rocking response is a poorly conditioned phenomenon
some general conclusions can be drawn.

Both calculations and field evidence suggest that
columns in fact are more stable against earthquakes
than might have been expected. These particuliar
structures -at least in their initial condition- are
not very sensitive to seismic action.

The importance of monuments such as Apollo Epikourios
should not lead us to great values of safety
coefficient, since it would cause enhancements and
even tranformation of the initial structural system.
Such interventions are unacceptable according to the
rules of good practice in restoration. On the other
hand any assesment of present safety should start
with an examination of all that the structure itself
can show us about its resistance capacity. The
measures to be taken were prescribed by the ancient
constructors.

In order to enable the monument to withstand
earthquakes two major measures can be taken, return

of the leaning columns into the initial vertical position and strengthening of broken foundation members (βατηρες). In our opinion these interventions will restore the initial geometric configuration and also improve the earthquake resistance through the rocking behaviour, which constitutes the traditional energy absorption mechanism.

AKNOWLEDGEMENT

The author would like to thank Dr. J. Psycharis for the computer analyses.

BIBLIOGRAPHY

1. Housner, G.V. The behavior of inverted pendulum structures during earthquakes, Bull. Seism. Soc. Am., Vol.53,pp. 404-417,1963

2. Giannini, R. Considerationi sulla modellazione numerica di sistemi di blocchi rigidi sovrapposti Studi e Ricerche sulla Sicurenza Sismica dei Monumenti, Colonna Antonina, Rap.4, 1986

3. Priestley, M.J.N. Evison, R.J. and Carr, A.J. Seismic response of structures free to rock on their foundations, Bulletin of the New Zealand Nation. Soc. for Earthquake Engineering, Vol.11, No 3,pp. 141-150, 1978

4. Ishiyama, Y. Motion of rigid bodies and criteria for overturning by earthquake excitations, Earthquake Eng. Struct. Dyn., Vol.10,pp. 635-650, 1982

5. Ambraseys, N. On the protection of monuments and sites in seismic areas, Procceedings 2nd int. meeting for rest. of Akropolis monum., pp.207-228 Athens, 1985

6. Yim, C.S. Chopra, A.K. and Penzien, J. Rocking response of rigid blocks to earthquakes Earthquake eng. struct. dyn., Vol.8, pp.565-587, 1980.

7. Allen, R.H Oppenheim, I.J. Parker, A.R. and Bielak J. On the dynamic response of rigid body assemblies, Earthquake eng. struct. dyn.,Vol.14, pp.861-876, 1986

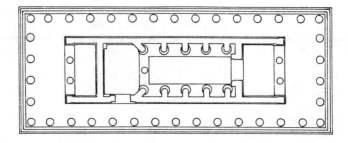

Fig.1 Temple of Apollo Epikourios

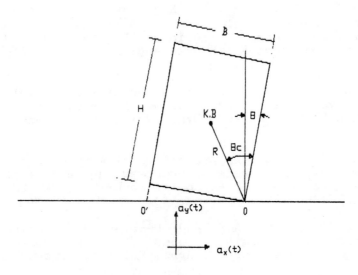

Fig.2 Rocking block

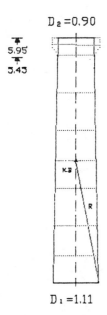

Fig.3 Typical column

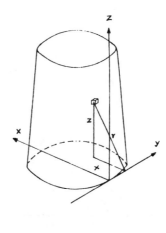

Fig.4 Moment of inertia round a
       tangent of the column base

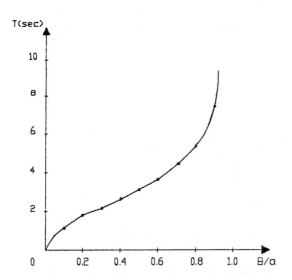

Fig.5 Free vibration period of rocking column

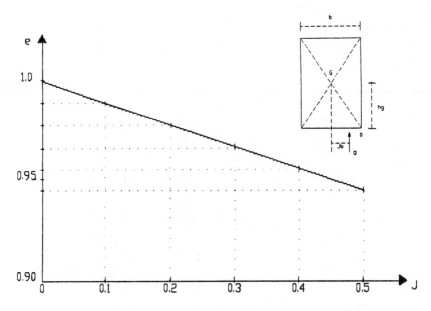

Fig.6 Relationship between coefficient of restitution
and location of reaction force

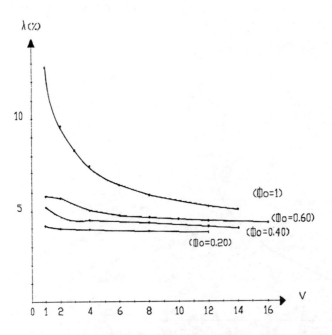

Fig.7 Equivalent viscous damping subsequent to v-impact

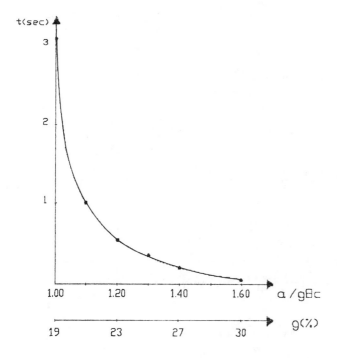

Fig.8 Constant acceleration of duration t required for overturning

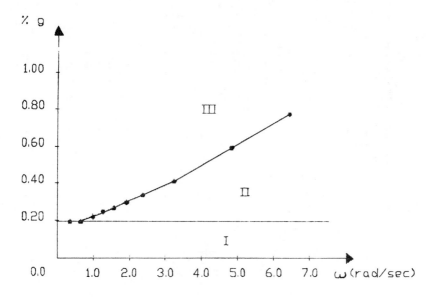

Fig.9 Sinusoidal acceleration pulse required for overturning

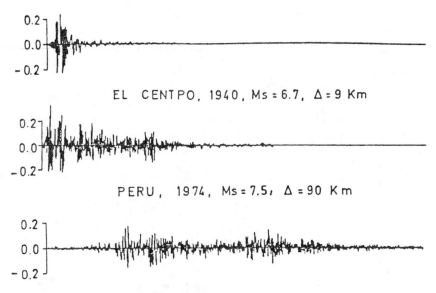

Fig.10 Ground accelerations

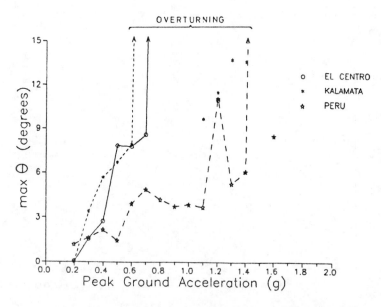

Fig.11 Relationship between maximum rotation and peak
ground acceleration

Seismic History at Monumental Sites by AI Working Environment

L. Faravelli, P.G. Gherardini(*)

Institute of Energetic, University of Perugia, I06100 Perugia, Italy

(*) CNR, Istituto M. Picone, I00161 Roma, Italy

ABSTRACT

A graphical interface is used to represent, on a computer screen, the map of the region around the site where the historical building under investigation is situated. The building is identified by the position of the mouse pointer. For each selected position, the historical sequence of seismic events around the site is automatically retrieved from the seismic catalogue.

INTRODUCTION

When a historical building has to be repaired or its maintenance scheme has to be developed, some preliminary non-structural analyses are generally necessary. The goals to be achieved are: (i) the identification of the sources of damage which engaged the building and (ii) the identification of the sequence of the damage which was actually recorded (Casciati-Faravelli, [5]).

The methodology for the collection and the classification of the damage which occurred during the building life is still in a preliminary stage in view of the creation of a data bank for automatic consultation.

When the sources of damage are seismic events, they are, generally, already organized in a database. In Italy, for instance, there is a catalogue with information that goes back to the 11th century (CNR, [7]).

The two analyses present common aspects. The main one is that the expertise of the analyst can strongly reduce the analysis' time. Expertise, in fact, means:

- to know the suitable archives where the information is potentially stored;
- to know the way of accessing these archives;
- to have at one's disposal the procedures by which the information can be summarized and put in a format suitable for a successive computer analysis;
- to have an exact understanding of the reliability of the single different sources of the available data.

Also, the steps from the availability of a data bank to the act of retrieving from it the information of interest, are common for the two kinds of analysis; one has:
(i) to identify the sample's properties which can be of some interest in view of the successive analyses on the building;
(ii) to locate the building in the coordinate system of the data bank;
(iii) to establish the format to be given to the knowledge for the particular building under investigation.

Attention is focused in this paper on the identification of past seismic events as potential sources of damage for a building. The approach is implemented into an appropriate expert systems prototype. In particular, it will be framed into the Artificial Intelligence (AI) working environment NEXPERT (Nexpert Object, [9]). For this purpose, after a description of the Italian seismic catalogue, a review of some aspects of the Nexpert world is given. Then the resulting prototype is discussed and a brief consultation is illustrated.

THE ITALIAN SEISMIC CATALOGUE

The availability of old Italian historical documents made it possible to organize a seismic catalogue of more than 40000 events which covers the period ranging between the years 1000 and 1980. Most of them (approximately 30000 events) occurred during the last century. Nevertheless, the first 10000 events, referred to the period from years 1000 to 1883, are an exceptional collection of data with sources appropriately checked and quite reliable.

Figure 1 lists the main items collected in the catalogue for a single seismic event. 'Number' denotes the order number into the catalogue. The year is generally associated with month, day, hour, minute and second of the event. Especially the last three values, however, are unknown for non-recent earthquakes: they are marked '-9' in the corresponding block of the catalogue. 'Map' should contain the reference to the geographical map of the Italian Military Geographic Institute where the epicentral site is included. The epicentral site is characterized by a name (VARZI in Figure 1) and its geographical latitude (d = degree, m = minute) and longitude (d and m). Finally, one also finds the hypocentre depth and the intensity of the seismic event. The intensity is given by its value in the Mercalli Scale multiplied by a factor ten. Additional information on the available bibliographic references and on the corresponding magnitudo of the event is also included in the catalogue. These parameters, however, are not shown in Figure 1.

The seismic catalogue is, generally, used in order to develop the so-called macro- and micro-zonation. For this purpose it is necessary:
1) to select the site of interest;
2) to retrieve from the catalogue the seismic events which may have been effective at the site;
3) to introduce an attenuation law modelling the motion propagation from the source to the site. Alternatively one can consult the maps where the contour lines of equal seismic intensity have been drawn for the different seismic events;
4) to calculate for each seismic event listed in 2), the corresponding intensity at the site by the procedure selected in 3);
5) to perform a statistical analysis of the resulting sample;
6) to use statistical inference for prediction of the seismic activity at the site;
7) to select, eventually, the seismic intensity suitable for the design of a building located at that site.

Generally, steps 1) to 7) are not a structural engineer's task but are the activity of experts. The criterion for the classification of the single site can be changed on the basis of different socio-economical considerations (and, hence, the entire analysis repeated), but the final result for the structural engineer always will be a design value of the seismic intensity.

A different situation arises when the restoration of historical buildings is considered (Casciati-Faravelli, [2], [3], [4]). In this case the catalogue of seismic events becomes important for the structural engineer. In fact its preliminary consultation provides:
i) the sequence of the seismic excitations which engaged the building. In order to be operative, this information has to be used in connection with the maps modelling the motion propagation and the database of damage and repairs consequent on each event;
ii) the location of the seismic sources around the site. This becomes very useful when sophisticated seismic models of a seismological nature (Carli-Faravelli, [1]) are adopted as input for the dynamical analysis of the building;
iii) an idea of the actual seismic intensity at the site without the socio-economic 'filters' the expert introduces when operating a macro zonation.

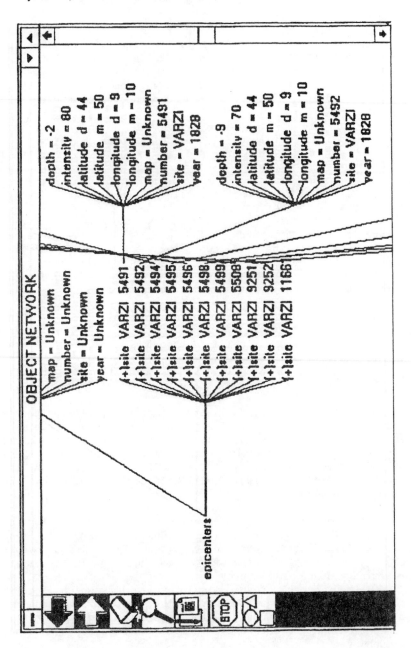

Figure 1. Class, properties and objects, for Nexpert implementation. The result of a data base search (over the period 1000-1883) by epicenter name (VARZI in the example) is illustrated.

The idea of this paper is to put the expertise required by this consultation into an expert system prototype. For this purpose an AI development environment has been considered to meet the need of consulting large data base and of working over geographical maps. The final result is to obtain a prototype of "friendly use" which admits successive developments for a complete understanding of the state of health of any single historical building.

THE AI WORKING ENVIRONMENT

Implementing an automated catalogue of seismic events, in fact, is only the first step towards the construction of complex knowledge based systems to be used both in historical investigations and in the modelling of seismic data. The ultimate goal is a system able to retrieve information from past records, linking all the relevant facts, and to use such information in specific monitoring and simulation tasks, which involve mathematical models, probabilistic analyses (Gherardini, [8]), graphical interfaces, user interaction, and so on. From the software engineering site then, it is clear that one has to look for an open development environment, as opposed to a specific tool, however sophisticated.

Commercially available AI tools (see Casciati-Faravelli, 1991 among others) vary greatly in scope, price and portability across different hardware configurations: however one such tool seemed to stand up among the competitors, and this was the Nexpert Object system (Nexpert Object, [9]). Here are a few technical reasons for picking up this particular system:
- open architecture: Nexpert comes with an Application Programs Interface which allows a complete integration with other, however different, software tools, in particular databases and hypertext tools;
- powerful representation of the data structure, including explicit support of object oriented views and inheritance;
- knowledge representation through rules which can be examined with different, and user modifiable, inheritance strategies;
- availability on the commonest hardware platforms, including portable 286/386 PCs.

All these reasons led the Italian Seismic Mitigation Group (GNDT) to adopt Nexpert for its activity (Casciati-Yachaya-Faravelli, 1990). A brief review of some aspects of the Nexpert world, is given in this Section.

Data representation
The elementary unit of knowledge description in Nexpert is an 'object', which can stand on its own or be linked to other

objects to define a 'class'. Both objects and classes can be given 'properties', i.e. attributes whose value qualify the particular item. Objects can have sub-objects, and complex hierarchies can be built, to fully exploit natural dependencies among the data and structural inheritance of values.

Each property, also called 'slot', can be functionally described through 'metaslots'. These are given to define two kinds of behaviour:
- Order of Sources, specifying the list of sources to look at, in order to assign a value to the property; in particular the value can be set through function calls or real time external devices, thus providing a link towards different code fragments or input sources;
- If Change, defining actions which will occur immediately upon modification of the property's value (demon). Any operation supported by the system can be specified in this metaslot, including exchanging data with external sources or modifying the knowledge processing strategy.

Objects can be created and linked to each other dynamically, and the designer is able to keep a firm control on the properties, metaslots and/or values' inheritability.

Reasoning representation
Nexpert rules have the general format:
IF ... (Left Hand Side) THEN hypothesis AND DO ... (Right Hand Side) with the following conventions:
- all the conditions in the LHS are connected with the and operator: the or operator is implemented writing two or more rules sharing the same hypothesis name;
- hypothesis is a boolean object which can be given a true/false state;
- the do actions are only executed when all the LHS conditions are met; they include any sequence of operations required as a consequence of the hypothesis being verified: assigning values to properties, creation/deletion of objects, execution of external routines, retrieving or writing data base records, showing report or pictures files, changing the inference strategy, and many others.

Any hypothesis can be named as a boolean variable in the LHS of rules, making it possible backward reasoning. On the other hand, actions following the firing of any rule can set new values for data which are used in the LHS of other rules, so as to trig forward reasoning. Finally, rejected hypotheses can be checked again as a consequence of actions executed upon firing of rules: a sort of reasoning revision is then achieved.

Once started (e.g. by setting the value for one or more unknown variables, or by suggesting the hypothesis to check

first) the Nexpert knowledge processor automatically defines
an Agenda, i.e. a set of tasks and their execution order,
according to an event-driven architecture: a rule becomes
relevant as a consequence of something happening which is
linked to its LHS conditions.

IMPLEMENTING THE SEISMIC CATALOGUE CONSULTATION

The implementation of the expert system prototype required the
organization of several pieces of knowledge recorded in the
seismic catalogue as 'object properties'. This was done by
defining the class "epicenters", having a set of properties
(depth, intensity,...), whose objects are the single
epicentral sites see Fig. 1.

The site under investigation had to be identified in the
appropriate map. Its geographical coordinates had to be
specified in order to retrieve from the catalogue all the
epicenters whose distance from the site is lower than a given
reference value d_O. This is a classical problem in the
graphical representation of sites, but had to be solved in
order to satisfy the following requirements:

   i) the graphical facilities of Nexpert must be used;

   ii) the operator consulting the expert-system prototype
is supposed to be devoid of any specific background in
topographical theory.

   In this framework the following procedure was
implemented:

   1) The geographical maps were bitmapped (i.e. assumed by
rastering) through a simple scanner;

   2) Zoom in the classical sense is not available but
clicking over a map (Figure 2), with the mouse right button
permits one to select a map (Figure 3) of higher-scale which
includes the site marked by the pointer; two clicks make it
possible to go back to the previous lower-scale map.

   3) For each map, the geographical coordinates of three
marked points are given in an associated file.

   4) Each map is pre-processed as follows: a specific
software (which captures the mouse) associates to each clicked
point the pixel coordinates; clicking over different sites
produces a data base. A preliminary clicking over the three
points given in 3) permits one to convert pixel coordinate to
geographical coordinates.

   The map is now ready for the consultation. For this
purpose the user just clicks the site of interest. If this is
close to points in the data base created in 4), the
coordinates of the closest points are automatically selected.
The prototype provides the epicenters inside a circle with
assigned radius d_O from the previous coordinates. An option
makes possible to select just the events with intensity
greater than a fixed lower bound I_O.

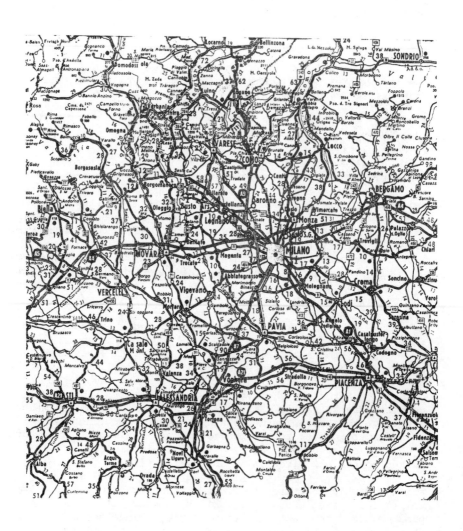

Figure 2. The region around Pavia in a map 1:1.000.000 as appears on the screen. The circle denotes Varzi area, the one used for the consultation of Figure 1.

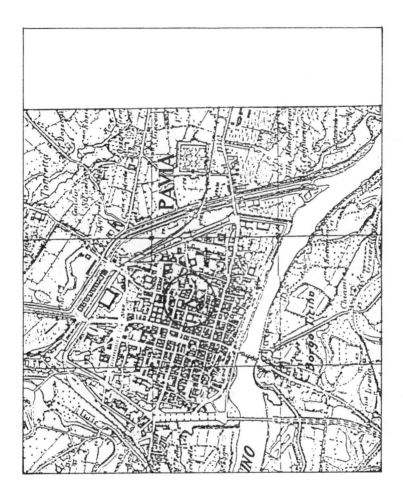

Figure 3. The region around Pavia as appears on the screen in
a map 1:25.000. The mouse denotes the position under selection.

When the user clicks too far from the points of the original data base, he will be questionned by the expert-system on his intention to add this new point to that database.

AN EXAMPLE OF CONSULTATION

Through the consultation the user went to the map of Western-North Italy of Figure 2 and from this to the map of Pavia (Figure 3). Here, the mouse is put upon the town area below the river (Borgo Ticino). By clicking one activates the scanning of the seismic catalogue. This gives the user, among other things, the results of Table I for a reference distance d_0 of 10 km and for events in the period 1000-1883.

The same results for d_0 = 50 km are given in Table II, where they are presented grouping the events at the site.

Table I. Seismic events within 10 km from Borgo Ticino

Number	Year	Intensity	Name	Distance (km)
5422	1826	60	PAVIA	1.31
5423	1826	40	PAVIA	1.31
5424	1826	30	PAVIA	1.31
5425	1826	30	PAVIA	1.31
5426	1826	30	PAVIA	1.31

Table II. Seismic events within 50 km from Borgo Ticino

Number	Year	Intensity	Name	Dist. (km)
111	1249	70	LOMBARDIA	37.83
128	1276	80	MILANO OVEST	37.22
264	1369	80	PECETTO	47.13
266	1369	70	MILANO EST	37.83
405	1452	70	NOVI LIGURE	48.70
457	1473	90	MILANESE	17.15
2487	1780	60	CASTELNUOVO	25.94
2488	1780	60	SERRAVALLE	25.94
5370,1	1824	50,50	CABELLA	46.52
5422,3,4,5,6	1826	60,40,30,30,30	PAVIA	1.31
5491,2,4,5,6,8,9	1828	80,70,35,40,50,40,45	VARZI	37.22
5508	1828	30	VARZI	37.22
7101	1845	50	VILLAVERNIA	44.76
9251	1867	40	VARZI	37.22
11661	1882	30	VARZI	41.10

CONCLUSIONS

In this paper the process of identifying the historical sequence of the potential seismic sources of damage which engaged the single monumental building is organized in an expert system.

The modelling for propagating such events from the source to the site of the building and for collecting the list of damages which were recorded as a consequence will be included in a second stage, as result of ongoing research. For this purpose the methodology developed in this paper will be preserved, but different knowledge bases will be introduced.

ACKNOWLEDGEMENTS

This research has been supported by funds of the National Group of Seismic Mitigation (GNDT) of the Italian Council of Research (CNR). The research program is coordinated by professor A. Corsanego responsible of the national research group on Vulnerability.

REFERENCES

1. Carli, F., Faravelli, L., (1991). "Modelling Non Stationary Ground Motion." Accepted for pubblication in European Journal of Earthquake Engineering

2. Casciati, F., Faravelli, L., (1989a). "Seismic Vulnerability Via Knowledge Based Expert Systems." In Brebbia C.A.(ed.), Structural Repair, and Maintenance of Historical Buildings, Computational Mechanics Publ., Southampton, 299-307.

3. Casciati, F., Faravelli, L., (1989b). "Uncertainty Treatment in a Vulnerability-Assistant Expert System." Prog. IABSE Colloquium, Expert Systems in Civil Engineering, Bergamo, 97-106.

4. Casciati, F., Faravelli, L., (1990), "Expert Systems and Seismic Vulnerability." Proc 9th ECEE, Moscow, Vol.1, 23-32.

5. Casciati, F., Faravelli, L., (1991). "Fragility Analysis of Complex Structural Systems." Research Studies Press Ltd.

6. Casciati, F.,Yachaya, D., Faravelli, L., (1990). "NEXPERT for Seismic Mitigation Studies." Proc. NEXPERT User Group Meeting, Munich

7. CNR, (1980), Sismap List, Geodynamics Project, Italian National Research Council

8   GHERARDINI,P.,(1990). "Implementazion Object-oriented di
un modello di calcolo per reti causali". Atti della XXXV
Riunione   Scientifica   della   Societa'   Italiana   di
Statistica, Padova, pp. 393-400.

9.   NEXPERT Object, (1987). Neuron Data Inc., Palo Alto.

Seismic Analysis of an Ancient Church and a Proposal of Strengthening Repairs

F. Vestroni, R. Giannini, F. Grillo

Dipartimento di Ingegneria delle Strutture, delle Acque e del Terreno Università dell'Aquila, Italy

ABSTRACT

The safety analysis of an ancient church located in seismic area has been developed in view of designing a strengthening repair. The seismic hazard of the site is first determined, making use of historical data and a Poissonian model of seismic activity. Then the structural behaviour has been analysed through two models: a linear 3D finite element model and a nonlinear generalized single degree-of-freedom model representative of a most probable failure mechanism of the structure. On the combined information drawn by the two models is based the proposal of the strengthening design, whose main goal is to obtain an acceptable level of global and local resistance, without strong modifications of the original structure.

INTRODUCTION

In the analysis of safety of monumental buildings no general rules have been established up to day; indeed the attention must be focused on the peculiarity of the monument, which in general is a single case, mainly as concerns typology, materials and integrity conditions [1].

In this respect the methodologies developed for obtaining the vulnerability of civil buildings do not hold good, just since they are notably related to statistical considerations and are valid within specific typologies. Notwistanding it is difficult to imagine a general procedure for the analysis of whatever monument, the several cases studied and realized in the recent times in Italy have produced some more clear ideas about the design of monuments strengthening. In particular need is strongly felt of an in-depth study of the different aspects of safety analysis of monuments; a correct selection of a seismic protection level must be pursued in view of limiting those repairing works which modify the original characteristics of the structure. In this context it is collocated the present paper devoted to the evaluation of safety of the ancient church "S. Maria in Valle Porclaneta" in the central Italy and to the elaboration of a proposal for strengthening repair. It follows and develops a previous work [2].

The first part of the work concerns the seismic hazard analysis of the region where the church is located. Making use of historical data collected in the Italian Seismic Catalogue, different seismogenetic areas have been determined. With the aid of attenuation law, the seismic activity of the area under consideration is obtained and therefore the probability of occurrence of an earthquake of given intensity.

The study of the structural behaviour of the church follows; since it is very complicated, two different models have been used to obtain those information useful to the above-mentioned goals. The first one is a linear 3D finite element model which permits a detailed stress analysis of the structure. The second model is a generalized nonlinear singledegree-of-freedom system representative of a most probable collapse mechanism of the structure. It has been used to develope a risk analysis of the system. The combined use of the two models allows for a selection of a suitable maximum design earthquake intensity. Accordingly, the strengthening repair proposed are sufficiently soft and in some cases reversible, mainly devoted to improve the global behaviour of the structure and the local resistance of weak elements and vulnerable connections.

DESCRIPTION AND HISTORY OF THE MONUMENT

The Church of Santa Maria in Valle Porclaneta was erected between eight or ninth century at a location near an important road crossing; around a century later a modest convent was added to it. The church conserves, to this day, its original design of three aisles, separated by round arches. The aisles, the highest in the center, are covered with a roof held up by notable stiffening truss. The construction has its principal axis parallel to the slope and the foundations are at different levels. A small crypt was taken from just below the presbytery. This is closed from semicircular apse corresponding to the central aisle. From the monastic building there still remains only the nartex with a large arch and a part of the construction rearranged many times during the time, added to the facade, as well as a room adjacent to the right aisle (fig. 1).

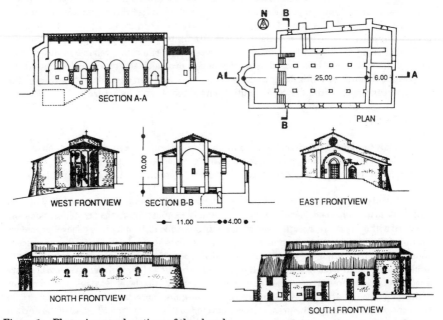

Figure 1 - Plan, views and sections of the church.

Probably in 1200, a violent earthquake of an intensity comparable to an XI° on the Mercalli Scale determined the collapse of the whole apsidal section; the actual aspect of its external face declares signs of the reconstruction. Since the mid thirteenth century the church entered into a phase of relentless decline. The information of the church, already very scarse, is altogether missing at least until the beginning 900's, except of two activities during '700: the reinforcement of the north wall and the construction of the three spurs, still existent, as a support of the downward wall. In 1904 and 1915, because of the Rosciolo and Avezzano earthquakes, the church suffered localized damages mainly in the apsidal zone and in the body added to the right aisle. In recent time (from 1931 until 1967) the church had been subjected to various static restorations concentrated on the northern wall and on the terminal of the southern wall; beams were built on the summit of the mansory, some arches were completely remade and some pillars were reinforced.

The foundations are built of irregularly arranged stones with small amounts of mortar. Their sizes vary from zone to zone: in some places as large as its above wall, at others a little larger. The depth varies from 20/30 cm to 2,0 meters. They are set at different levels, due to the fact that the church is on a slight decline with a slope of less than 20%. The masonry of both external and internal walls are made of two external faces with an internal filling. The faces are formed of irregular shaped stones mostly rounded except at the apsidal zones that are made of squared stones . The columns delimiting the central aisle are made up of an external face, constituted of blocks of regularly shaped stones, that encloses at its interior a nucleus built of small irregular stones. The roof structure is a frame of wooden trusses; above them, a board is fixed on which the final layer of the roofing is placed.

PROBABILISTIC SEISMIC HAZARD

The assessment of seismic hazard, based on pioneering work of Cornell [3], is a now a standard procedure, even though the model approximation and the incompleteness of data needs many subjective assumptions. The procedure may be subdivided into the following steps:
- reconnaissance of potential sources areas, based on the knowledge of sites neotectonic structure and distribution of historical events;
- computation of seismic activity of sources regions by statistical regression of historical data;
- seismic hazard assessment of site on the basis of activity of source regions and suitable attenuation laws.

The definition of region with homogeneous seismic activity has been carried out following the subdivision proposed by Giannini et al. [4] and plotted in figure 2. In the second step the seismic activity of each region was described by means of the truncated Gutemberg-Richter law:

$$N(i) = N_0 F_I^*(i) \tag{1}$$

where $N(i)$ is the annual number of earthquakes exceeding the intensity i, N_0 is the total number of events in one year and $F_I^*(i)$ is the complementary distribution function of intensity. This last depends on some parameters which along with N_0, have been computed with the maximum likelihood method from historical data.

The final step of determination of site seismic hazard requires the use of an attenuation function. Here an anisotropic law, developed by Ortolani and Giannini [5] was employed. The coefficient of this law have been computed by fitting the macroseismical data recorded in each region. For an event occurred in the point s of the region j, the probability that the site intensity exceeds i is:

$$P(i|s,j) = P [i_s - \Delta I > i |s,j] \tag{2}$$

where ΔI is the attenuation from source to site. The probability of occurrence of an event of intensity in the site greater then i, given an event in the region j, is then:

$$P(i|j) = \int_{Aj} P(i|s,j) \, dF(s) = \frac{1}{A_j} \int_{Aj} P(i|s,j) \, dA \tag{3}$$

The total annual expected number of earthquakes N(i) of intensity greater then i will be obtained multiplying (3) by N_{0j} and adding over the whole number of seismic regions. The resulted relationship of intensity versus the inverse of return period is reported in figure 3. The analysis has been carried out in terms of macroseismical intensity since the available data are expressed in this scale. Neverthless in the structural analysis it is more convenient to express the intensity as peak ground acceleration; the conversion has carried out by the available empirical formula: $\log A = (I/3 - 0.5) \ cm/sec^2$.

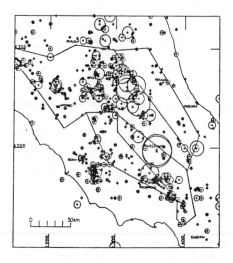

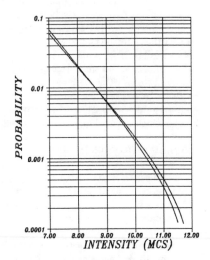

Figure 2 - Sources of all past earthquakes in the region of interest.

Figure 3 - Intensity of expected earthquakes versus occurrence probability.

STRUCTURAL ANALYSIS

The design of strengthening of a monument is quite difficult to dealt with because it must satisfy two contrasting requirements, in contrast to a certain extent. On the one hand the structure must be resistant enough to withstand the expected earthquakes, on the other hand the strengthening works cannot strongly modify the original structure. In this respect the structural analysis must be devoted to ascertain the actual resistance of building, taking into account that local lacks of strength have not to be considered very important because they can be removed with soft works.

A model which correctly takes into account the detailed aspects of nonlinear dynamic behaviour of the monument is practically out of hand; indeed the monument has a spatial distributed structure which, even if discretized, requires a high number of variables, the material is quite complicated, strongly anisotropic and no-tension, and the insufficient knowledge of the integrity makes the analytical description more uncertain. In view of the foregoing, two models of different complexity have been referred to, a linear 3D finite element model and a nonlinear singledegree-of-freedom oscillator, whose combined use can furnish useful information to design strengthening repairs.

The first model is used to develop a detailed stress analysis of structure, outlining the weak elements; in particular it is possible to determine that value of spectral earthquake intensity which can be supported by the structure with only slight works. The second model is used to study the nonlinear response of a substructure which is likely to be the most probable failure mechanism. This simple, but realistic, model permits to develop a sophisticated risk analysis of the system and to evaluate the safety of the structurewith the level of resistance adopted.

Linear 3D finite element model

A view of the model is represented in figure 4. It is a standard f.e. model with about one thousand of nodes, nine hundred plate-shell elements and one hundred beam elements.

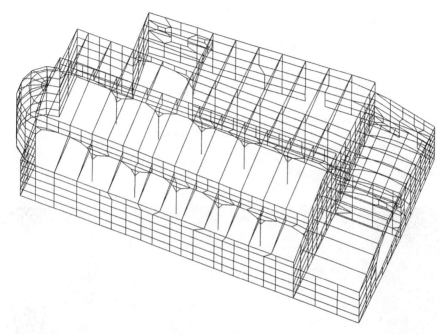

Figure 4 - Mesh of the finite element model of the church.

First stresses due to dead loads are computed taking into account the way of loading application. Successively seismic analysis is developed by means of modal superposition technique; the stresses obtained for an assigned intensity are combined with the results of static analysis and the crack limit condition is verified through the Coulomb criterium.

The dynamic behaviour of the church is enlighted by the results of free oscillations. The modes are quite uncoupled with prevaling component in one direction (fig. 5); moreover, the first two modes are very important and almost sufficient to describe seismic response. From the analysis of mode shapes it can be seen that the roof structure does not result rigid in - plane; therefore in the longitudinal direction the main part of inertia forces are carried by longitudinal walls with tangential stresses, while in the transversal direction inertia forces produce high bending stresses in the central zones of longitudinal walls, far from the rigid in - plane transversal walls.

The church results more vulnerable for a transversal earthquake; so, this condition has been analysed in more detail. The element stresses have been computed for a spectrum with different increasing intensities. The dynamic stresses are combined with the static ones and the limit crack condition is verified. Up to a value of spectral intensity equal to 0.2 g the element which do not verify the limit condition are few and concentrated in some well defined parts of

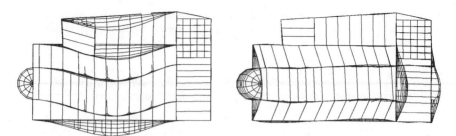

Figure 5 - Shapes of the first two modes.

the structure. It occur at the base of the central zone of the longitudinal walls, in the zones where they are connected with transversal walls and in some other elements near the arches (fig. 6).

This level of intensity appears a convenient reference value for the strengthening repair, which can be limited to a series of local resistance improvements. The tridimensional elastic model has been very useful to obtain an evenly distributed safety factor with respect to craking condition. Above this intensity value many other elements will crack and this kind of analysis cannot give useful information.

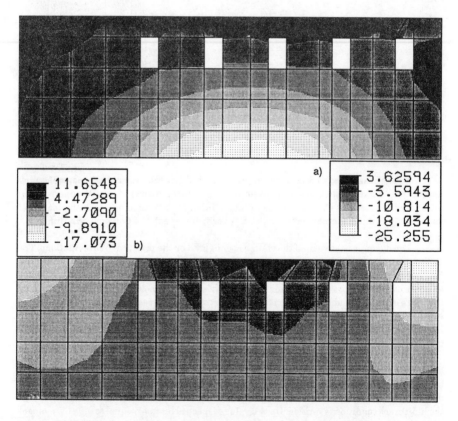

Figure 6 - Bending forces (kN,m) around horizontal (a) and vertical axes (b).

Nonlinear generalized model

With the aim of investigating the safety of the structure under earthquakes of higher intensity, reference is made to the singledegree-of-freedom oscillator, obtained as a generalized model of the central transversal part of the church (fig. 7), whose deformed configuration is represented by only one variable. The loops of restoring force under cyclic loading is illustrated in figure 8, where two main aspects are taken into account: a) as the rigid block system, during the unloading the curve passes through the origin and b) the system, different from the pure blok system, exhibits a certain degree of hysteresis which models the dissipation of opening and closing of craks. The parameters defining the model are: the initial elastic stiffness k_0, the post-elastic stiffness k_1 and the maximum resistant force F_m. As already outlined these last parameters are obtained from the analysis of rigid body system, meanwhile k_0 is obtained from the elastic analysis of the structure. The relationship described in figure 8 is used in the equation of motion as restoring force; damping force is also introduced by means of linear viscous coefficient v.

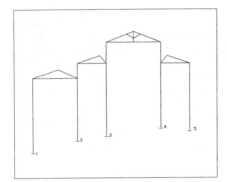
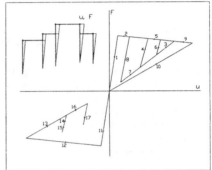

Figure 7 - Scheme of the central part of the church.   Figure 8 - Restoring force model.

Reliability analysis Under seismic loading the theoretical collapse is attained when the displacement reaches the value where the curve of restoring force intersects the horizontal axis. In practice, due to decay of base section under cyclic loadings and equilibrium considerations, a value u_l is assigned as limit value. Therefore the collapse condition can be written:

$$g(x \mid A) = u(k_e, k_1, F_m, v \mid A) - u_l = 0 \tag{4}$$

where $x = (k_0, k_1, F_m, v, u_m)^T$ is the vector of random variables. The function $u(.)$ gives the maximum displacement attained by the oscillator under the earthquake with peak acceleration A; it is not a proper function but is obtained by numerical integration of equation of motion.

Every random variable has been assumed to have log-normal distribution with mean value already adopted in the previous deterministic analysis and standard deviation selected subjectively on the basis of uncertainty in the knowledge of these quantities (Table 1).

The importance of the four parameters k_e, k_1, F_m, v which govern the dynamic response of the system is enlightened in the figure 9 where the section of the collapse surface with the planes x_i, A are reported. The different curves can be compared since the variation of the variables is measured by standard deviation σ. The trend of k_1, v, F_m, and u_l is quite regular; the maximum intensity monotonically decreases with k_1 and increases with the other ones. The relation of k_e versus A is less regular, its variation influences the collapse only when it is strongly decreased. Although the assumed c.o.v.'s in Table 1 must be borne in mind, maximum resistante force and limit displacement are the parameters more important, mainly the last.

Fragility curve of the system is obtained from the probability of collapse for an assigned intensity A, evaluated as the probability of exit from the safety domain:

$$P_F(A) = P_r[g(x|A) > 0] \tag{5}$$

Since g(.) is not explicit function, $P_F(A)$ is determined by means of simulation method, in particular directional simulation is used. In this method the probability to reach the boundary of the safety domain is calculated along a certain number of directions. To improve the efficiency of the procedure, the importance sampling technique has been followed that leads to a major use of those directions where the distance of the collapse surface from origin is minor [6-8].

The fragility curve depends on the accelerogram selected for the numerical investigation. Indeed it is well-known that the response is strongly affected by the frequency content of earthquake, and in special way for the systems with strength decay. To account for this aspect of the problem, without considering the shape of earthquake as random variable, an approximate procedure has been followed. An earthquake is considered which matches a different spectrum with higher decreasing branch for T > 0.6 sec; it decreases with $T^{2/3}$ while the spectrum of the original accelerogram decreases with $T^{1/3}$. The difference between the responses to these two accelerograms is considered as the standard deviation of a new random variable c, with mean value equal to unity, which directly multipies the function g(.) considered as mean value of response. In the figure 10 the fragility curves are reported for two values of limit displacement and with (b) or without (a) considering the randonmess of the earthquake. The influence of u_ℓ is strong as it would be expected, while it is also very strong the effect of earthquake randomness.

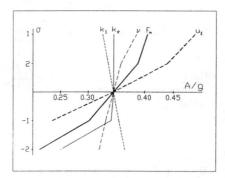
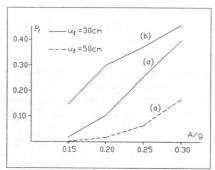

Figure 9 - Section of plans x_i, A with collapse surface.

Figure 10 - Fragility curves without (a) and with (b) randomness of earthquake.

Table 1   Mean values and coefficients of variation of random variables.

	k_0	k_1	F_m	u_1	v
mean	2560	68.9	52.79	30	0.03
c.o.v.	0.40	0.20	0.30	0.50	0.20

Taking into account the distribution of seismic intensity and the fragility curve of the structure it is possible to evaluate the probability of occurrence of collapse through a convolution procedure. This leads to the result of a probability of about $0.60 \cdot 10^{-2}$ a year, which is a value comparable with those usually obtained for non historical buildings.

PROPOSAL OF THE STRENGTHENING

The designed strengthening of the church tends to bring each structural element to a similar level of resistance. Such objective is pursued with the following works:
- of general type, that have the purpose of improvement the mechanical characteristic of masonry, the geometric and mechanical chartacteristics of foundations, the joints of the walls, the connection of the arches,the spurs with the walls on which they are abutted
- of specific type, to improve the structural frame, an increase of resistance of the vertical central parts of the external wall, an improvement of the connections between the roof structure and the walls and connections of the foundations between them.

The forecasted works must be carried out with suitable techniques based on the general principles of restorations. The chosen techniques take into consideration whereas possible, criteria of reversibility of the works, durability of the materials to be substituted or added and philologist coherence of the designed proposal. In these works modern and old technologies are used. In the first case materials are chosen taking account for their properties of integrating with the existing materials. In the second case lapidary material of the same nature and quality as the existing ones with constructive techniques similar to those used in the past and in the partial reconstruction of the church.

The designed works concern foundations, structures in elevation and roof structures. The proposalhas taken into consideration the result from the investigations on the static conditions of the church carried-out with distructive and non-distructive tests (Ceradini and Grillo, [9]).

Static and geometrical characteristics of foundations are improved by means of consolidation, enlarging the dimensions wherever are too small. The foundations of the walls and pillars are connected by means of a grid of beams. All of this, to obtain   continuous foundations at an equal level. Finally steel bars are inserted, with a slight tension, in the perimeter of the foundations in order to obtain its enclosure (fig. 11).

Structures in elevation are strengthened by eliminating the present internal cavities and by realizing a more effective bondage between the two external perimeters and its internal filling. The central parts of the longitudinal wall are reinforced by putting steel bars into masonry and in the connections of the walls. The voids within the filling of the pillars are eliminated and the external layers are better connected with the internal ones (fig. 12).

The foreseen works on the roofing consist of an effective connection between the vertical masonry and the roof structure with stiff reinforced concrete beams along the perimeter (fig. 13). More details can be found in Ceradini and Grillo [10].

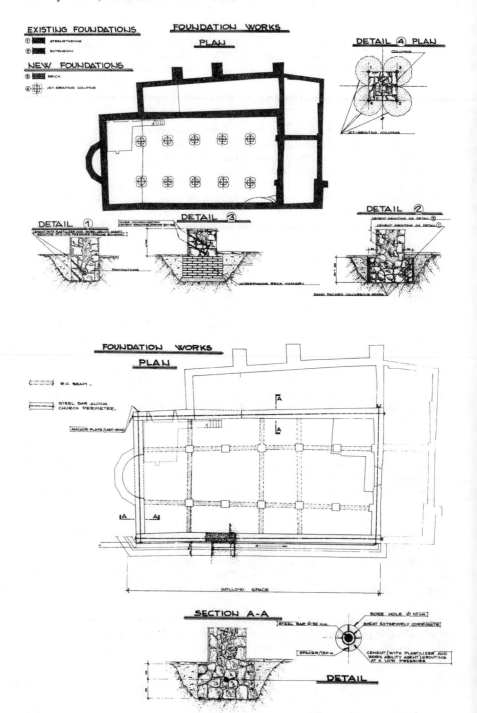

Figure 11 - Foundation works.

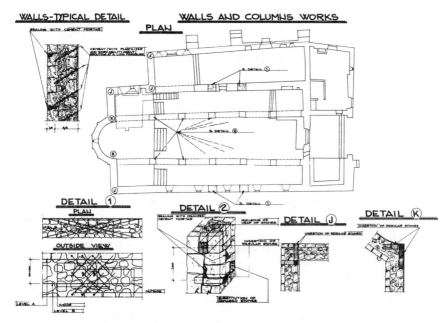

Figure 12 - Consolidation of walls and columns.

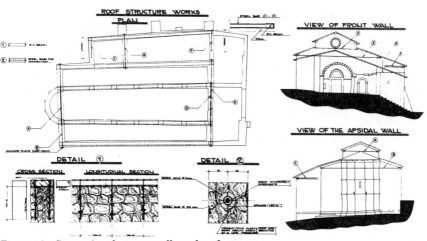

Figure 13 - Connections between walls and roof structure.

ACKNOWLEDGEMENTS

This work is partially supported by the funds of CNR (Italian Research Council) under CT 89.01987.54..

REFERENCES

1. Heyman, J., The Care of Masonry Buildings. The Engineer's Contribution, Proceedings of Structural Repair and Maintenance of Historical Buildings (Editor C.A. Brebbia), pp. 3-12, Comp. Mechs. Publishing, 1989.
2. Giannini, R., Ortolani, F., Pinto, P.E. and Vestroni, F., Evaluation of Seismic Risk of Monumental Buildings. The Case of a Church in Abruzzo (in Italian), Proceedings of Italian Conf. on Earth. Eng., Vol. 2, pp. 900-912, Milano, 1989.
3. Cornell, C.A., Engineering Seismic Risk Analysis, Bull. Seism. Soc. Am., Vol. 58, pp. 1583-1606, 1968.
4. Giannini, R., Giuffrè, A., Nuti, C., Ortolani, F. and Pinto, P.E., Evaluation of Seismic Risk: Methods and Case Study on the Town of Subiaco (in Italian), Proc. 2nd Italian Cont. on Earth. Eng., Rapallo, 1984.
5. Ortolani, F., and Giannini, R., A Proposal of Attenuation Laws of Seismic Events in Rome (in Italian), Dipartimento di Ing. Strutturale e Geotec., Studi e Ricerche 1/88, Università di Roma "La Sapienza".
6. Ditlevsen, O., Hasofer, A.M., Bjerarger, P. and Olesan, R., Directional Simulation in Gaussian Process, DGAMM Raport No. 359, Technical University of Denmark, Lingby, September 1987.
7. Ditlevsen, O. and Bjerarger, P. Plastic Reliability Analysis by Directional Simulation, DGAMM Report No. 353, Techn. University of Denmark, June 1987.
8. Ciampoli, M. Giannini, R., Nuti, C., and Pinto, P.E., Seismic Reliability of Non-Linear Structures with Stochastic Parameters by Directional Simulation, ICOSSAR-89, S. Francisco, 1989.
9. Ceradini, A. and Grillo, F., Destructive and Non-destructive Tests on the Church of Santa Maria in Valle Porclaneta and S. Maria di Collemaggio (in Italian), Proceedings Int. Conf. on Non Destructive Tests, Perugia, 1988.
10. Ceradini, A., and Grillo, F., Design of Strengthening Repairs of S. Maria in Valle Porclaneta (in Italian), Sovrintendenza BAAAS in Abruzzo, 1990.

Review of Structural Damage to Existing Buildings, and Seismic Rehabilitation Lessons from the 1989 Loma Prieta (San Francisco) Earthquake

M. Bruneau

Civil Engineering Department, 161 Louis Pasteur, University of Ottawa, Ottawa, Ontario, Canada, K1N 6N5

INTRODUCTION

On October 17, 1989, at 17:04 Pacific standard time, a magnitude 7.1 earthquake occurred along the San Andreas fault near mount Loma Prieta in the Santa Cruz mountains and was strongly felt in the San Francisco-Oakland-San Jose Bay Area. The occurrence of severe damage to many engineered structures 80 km away from the epicentre of this earthquake (having only $^1/_{60}$ of the energy of the San Francisco 1906 magnitude 8.3 historical event) is a major cause of concern.

Shortly after the occurrence of the main shock, the author undertook a 6-day intensive structural damage reconnaissance visit to review the nature of structural failures that occurred and assess the significance of this damage in a Canadian perspective; earthquakes of magnitude 7.0 are expected to occur near many urban centres in eastern and western Canada, and a large number of existing historical and heritage structures in these regions, never designed to withstand such high level of lateral forces, are exposed to this risk.

This paper is intended to provide a brief description of the seismic characteristics of this event, a report on the various types of building damage and major modes of structural engineering failures that occurred, and recommendations on how the collected data can be used to improve earthquake preparedness. Emphasis is placed on the behaviour of building structures whose construction characteristics can be found through North-America, and most importantly on historical and heritage structures. Preliminary findings on the reasons for structural failures are based on observational analysis. Examples of typical building failures or satisfactory performance are presented. The performance of bridges and single-family dwellings has been reported elsewhere by the author [Bruneau 1990] and by others [EERI 1990].

SEISMIC CHARACTERISTICS OF THE LOMA PRIETA EARTHQUAKE

A large number of strong motion instruments have recorded the last event. The Office of Strong Motion Studies of the California Division of Mines and Geology [CSMIP 1989] reports that over 90 of their seismograph stations have recorded the earthquake.

Detailed analyses of this seismological data are available elsewhere [EERI 1990, Housner 1990]. The attenuation of peak ground accelerations (PGA) with distance is illustrated by Figure 1. While a maximum PGA of 0.65g has been recorded by the Corralitos station, at 15 km from the epicentre, the PGA has rapidly decreased to 0.11g as early as 40 km away from the epicentre in some instances. PGA on rock in San Francisco were of the order of 0.10 g., considerably less than required to even initiate damage in properly designed new construction in California. The duration of strong motion averaged approximately 10 seconds.

OVERVIEW OF BUILDING DAMAGE

Marina District, San Francisco

A large number of residential dwellings in the Marina district collapsed during the earthquake. Very soft soils of reclaimed land underlie the most severely damaged structures. While this has likely produced an amplification of the otherwise moderate ground motion, and a large number of instances of localized soil liquefaction, the collapses should have been predictable by simple observation of the typical structural systems used.

As seen in Figure 2 of a typical residential building which nearly collapsed, the first story of this structure is mainly open to be used for parking purposes. A softer story is therefore created, i.e. a story where a relatively small number of partitions is available to resist the seismic excitation, when compared with the upper stories which are subdivided by a large number of wall partitions. Consequently, all the energy (i.e. structural damage) will be constrained to take place in the first story. It is noteworthy that most modern structural engineering codes are not rigorously designed to prevent this undesirable behaviour. Further, in most damaged buildings, not only were there few structural elements on the first story effective in resisting lateral forces, but those remaining elements were often walls of latticed wood construction, not believed very good in transferring the seismically induced shear forces. Soft stories have been recognized to be a

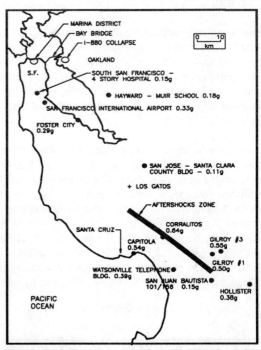

Figure 1 Maximum peak-horizontal-ground-accelerations recorded at various seismograph stations (adapted from CSMIP 1989)

problem in engineered structures since the Richter Magnitude 6.6 San Fernando Valley earthquake (Bertero 1979); this is the first time it has been observed on residential structures to such a large scale.

Few buildings had bracing on their first level. The photo in Figure 5 was taken from one such rare building; the diagonal bracing element is seen to have buckled. This building was adjacent to others that had totally collapsed and unquestionably owes its survival to the presence of these nominal lateral-loads-resisting structural elements.

Damage to Buildings

Not surprisingly, unreinforced masonry (URM) buildings were the most severely hit during this earthquake. Damage to masonry structures was observed in Oakland and San Francisco, and most dramatically in Santa Cruz, Watsonville, Hollister, and Los Gatos.

Figure 2 Surface evidence of detrimental soil behaviour (Marina District)

Most well-known types of un-reinforced masonry building failures were observed, including severe diagonal cracking in columns between windows, loss of masonry walls improperly tied to the rest of the building, roof joists or beam slipping off their supporting wall, fallen parapets, cornices, exterior cladding/glazing or veneers, or decorative elements, and, of course, failure of the building as a whole due to insufficient lateral load resistance. Pounding of adjacent buildings was also apparent in many instances. A few steel and reinforced concrete buildings suffered limited structural damage; Case-studies are briefly presented elsewhere [Mitchell et. al. 1990, EERI, 1990].

This paper is mostly concerned in reviewing the performance of older buildings of the type and construc-

Figure 3 Nearly collapsed soft-story building in Marina District: (a) General view of structure; (b) Close-up view of first story sway.

tion deemed to be of historical or heritage interest. Some typical building failures are illustrated following. The performance of some particular heritage buildings will be reviewed in a subsequent section.

In the epicentral region, buildings in Santa Cruz were amongst the hardest hit, most notably those at the Pacific Garden street open-air mall. One of these most severely damaged building is shown in Figure 6. In this case, the URM side walls of the taller adjacent building failed outward and the impact of that falling masonry is accountable for a major portion of the visible damage. However, considerable damage also occurred along this building, away from the impacted side, in the form of fallen parapet, damaged bearing structural elements, and internal damage.

Figure 4   Examples of collapsed soft-story buildings: (a) loss of one story; (b) loss of two stories (second one from impact with ground level) (Marina District)

Several other such URM buildings, where numerous modes of failures combined to make repairs prohibitively expensive (Figure 7) must be considered as total losses.

However, the most frequently encountered form of structural damage resulting from this earthquake was that of out-of-plane failure of URM wall. These were mostly a consequence of inadequate connections between floors and roofs to the exterior walls.

The Golden State Bank building in downtown San Francisco (Figure 8) exhibited such undesirable behaviour. In other cases, such as shown in Figure 9 (Santa Cruz Pacific Garden Mall), this out-of-plane failure was precipitated by pounding damage from an adjacent building.

This pounding between adjacent buildings was evidenced in many other occasions. The dramatic ultimate consequences of pounding have been well demonstrated dur-

Figure 5   Buckled braced in first story of damaged (but non-collapsed) building of the Marina District.

ing the Mexico earthquake of 1985. Had the duration of the strong motion during the Loma Prieta earthquake been longer, more serious structural distress due to this inter-building impacting would have been noticed, and possible some collapses. Damage from pounding can be seen in Figure 10 where a non-ductile reinforced concrete building hit an adjacent URM shorter building. The diagonal shear cracking of typical deep R/C beam spanning between windows is also visible on this figure (unrelated to pounding).

Figure 6 Total destruction of a building at the Pacific Garden Mall, Santa Cruz.

In Watsonville, the wide-spread non-structural and structural damage put the business district of main street out-of-business. In many cases, only non-structural damage was visible from the outside. As this may be the expression of internal structural damage, many buildings were closed awaiting detailed investigations. One such example of unusual non-structural damage was the severe cracking of the facade wall of FORD's department store (Figures 10 and 11).

It must be recognized that even modest levels of damage can lead to significant repair costs. Although hair-line cracks in URM structures can be epoxied, cracking of the severity shown in Figure 13 would require reconstruction of the wall, a very expensive operation whose market value may in fact be inflated by the shortage of labour available to urgently perform the needed repairs immediately follow-ing the earthquake. In addition, a restoration of the structure only to its pre-earthquake condition would obviously not be acceptable in this case, and a complete seismic retrofit would certainly be required by building officials. Even for a modest URM building, expenses typically in the many thousands of dollars would make repairs pro-

Figure 7 Typical severely damaged URM building in Watsonville.

Figure 8 Out-of-plane failure of URM wall in downtown San-Francisco.

hibitive. The building would then be demolished.

In other cases, building failure was the result of slippage of roofs from their bearing masonry walls. The lack of positive anchorage between a roof and its supporting wall will make the two respond independently to the seismic excitation; the roof will cave in as soon as the wall fails to provide adequate support (Figure 14).

While some retrofitted structures have been reported to behave well during this earthquake by others [Mitchell et. al. 1990], the author would like to emphasize the importance of adopting a global perspective in seismic rehabilitation activities. It is a well established earthquake engineering rule that damage will occur in the weakest link of a structure. Special care should be taken to reveal those links during rehabilitation activities. The URM building in Figure 15, located in San Francisco, had already been subjected to rehabilitation activities in the past, as evidenced by the presence of steel-plates/tie-anchors along the height of the corner pier. While this may have positively contributed to prevent separation of the floors from their wall supports during an earthquake, it obviously did little to prevent out-of-plane failure of the wall in the unrestrained other direction. While it may be argued that the scope-of-work for which the engineer was hired restricted the rehabilitation work to another non-seismically related problem, this still raises legitimate questions on the merit of partial retrofitting activities in seismic-regions, and on the profession's liability to the general public. It is noteworthy that the falling masonry killed two persons in this case.

Figure 9   Out-of-plane failure of unreinforced masonry wall (Pacific Garden Mall, Santa Cruz).

Figure 10   Typical shear failure of deep beam and evidence of pounding with adjacent building (downtown San Francisco).

Figure 11   Damaged facade of Ford's store (Watsonville).

Damage to heritage and historical buildings

It is paradoxical that many North American towns and cities invest large sums to renovate and make attractive their main street in order to enhance and preserve their heritage flavour (and simultaneously attract tourism) while not addressing the seismic adequacy of these downtown districts, predominantly of URM construction. In Santa Cruz, the Pacific Garden Mall, was such a district. This open-air shopping complex of more than 30 buildings was a total loss, with all structures sufficiently damaged to be declared hazardous and demolished. The loss of The Cooper House, a turn of the century heritage building that had become a landmark to Santa Cruz, is such an example. The Palomar Inn also in Santa Cruz and the 100 Front Street Building (1893) in Watsonville are other such examples.

Figure 12 Damaged facade of Ford's store in Watsonville (close-up view).

The 100 Front Street Building is worthy of a particular attention. This landmark of Watsonville, dated 1893, has survived the Loma Prieta earthquake with little apparent external damage, with the exception of the failure of a very heavy URM parapet (Figures 16 and 17). This is admirable considering the proximity of Watsonville to the epicentre of this earthquake, and the fact that this structure was never designed to resist earthquakes. The fallen parapet also testifies to the absence of past seismic retrofitting activities. More importantly, the mere presence of this building also attest to its survival of the 1906 San Francisco earthquake, during which the San Andreas fault is reported to have ruptured as far south as San Juan Bastista (a few miles east of Watsonville). This frequently observed capacity of some old heritage and historical buildings to survive earthquakes is important, especially for the seismic rehabilitation activities in Eastern North America. Research activities are currently underway at the University of Ottawa to identify the features of such old buildings which are responsible for their surprising performance.

The Cooper House (Figure 18) is another such URM building. Although it suffered internal damage, and the loss of a gable, the remaining exterior masonry was virtually uncracked. This landmark building, when declared unsafe and levelled, was an emotional loss to the inhabitants of Santa Cruz.

Another severely damaged landmark is the Watsonville church (Figure 19 and 20). Churches, largely

Figure 13 Typical in-plane shear failure of URM wall (Santa Cruz).

due to their architectural configuration and slender elements of URM, are notoriously damage-prone during earthquakes. In this case, the out-of-plane failure of a gable occurred, and the church spires are severely cracked. Had the earthquake been slightly longer, the spire may have totally collapsed. This pattern of damage is typical, and similar reports of damage during past North American earthquakes can be found in the literature [e.g. Hogdson, 1927].

Figure 14 Typical failure due to slip of roof joists off their wall supports (Santa Cruz).

The Palomar Inn (Pacific Garden Mall) is a seven-story hotel, in Santa Cruz. Its architectural features suggest that it may have been constructed sometimes in the early 1920's, and thus was likely never designed to resist earthquakes (Figure 21). Due to Santa Cruz proximity to the epicentre, this structure must have been subjected to an PGA of roughly 0.5g. The building did not collapse, nor were any of its occupant killed. The structure is made of non-ductile reinforced concrete. Exterior damage consisted mostly of shear failure of the deep columns between window (Figure 22). Nonetheless, taking into account the additional interior structural and non-structural damage, the decision to demolish this building was taken.

The performance of this building raises interesting questions regarding the goals to be achieved by seismically rehabilitating existing historical and heritage buildings. It is recognized and accepted that seismic resistant design guidelines are intended only to prevent total collapse of buildings during major earthquakes and allow the safe egress of occupants. Building damage is thus anticipated and accepted during major earthquakes, as explicitly recognized by most buildings codes, including the National Building Code of Canada. Consequently, the retrofit heritage or historical structures simply to make them comply with current code seismic design requirements may be insufficient. In fact, de-facto compliance was achieved by the Palomar Inn, without any seismic rehabilitation, and yet this heritage structure was found unsalvageable. The same could be said of The Cooper House in spite of the potential life-threatening hazard created by the gable failure. Alternate seismic rehabilitation philosophies are thus needed should the preservation of heritage be the objective. It is noteworthy that the effectiveness of seismic strengthening, had it been performed on this buildings, cannot be

Figure 15 Wall failure of inadequately strengthened URM building (San-Francisco).

gauged at this time; by the same token more severe earthquakes than for the Loma Prieta one are also anticipated in California.

LESSONS LEARNED

Generally speaking, no new seismic rehabilitation lessons were learned from this earthquake. These lessons were first learned following earthquakes in other parts of the world; they may only be more likely to be remembered now that they hit home. While the above review of building damage is valuable to the structural engineer, the most import-ant seismic rehabilitation lessons to be learned from this earthquake, in the author's view, are ones of policy, planning, and hazard awareness. This is explained following, in a Canadian perspective.

Figure 16   Parapet failure of 100 Front Street Building (Wat-sonville).

Most of the observed damage from the October 17, 1989, earthquake is directly pertinent to Canadian seismic-resistant design and earthquake prepared-ness, as many Eastern and Western Canadian are within or near geological regions deemed capable of generating Richter Magnitude 7.0 or greater earthquakes (Basham et. al. 1982).

The damage to older bridges and buildings far from the epicentre, thus at low peak ground accelerations, is of a direct pertinence as many existing structures in Canada have never been designed to resist earthquakes. The deficient seismic strength or ductility of many older existing structures is a particularly acute problem in Canada as the first effective seismic requirements were implemented in the NBCC in 1953, and adopted by local by–laws only as late as 1967 in some cases. In many instances, these older structures are of unreinforced masonry, the North American type of construction most vulnerable to earthquakes. Paradoxically, many of those buildings house key infrastructure or governmental activities, and others would need to be operational in post-disaster situations.

The problem is particularly severe in Eastern Canada where the gen-erally lower level of seismic activ-ity instills a lack a earthquake awareness. Consequently, recom-mendations to review the seismic resistance of existing structures meets considerable resistance, even for key post-disaster critical struc-tures. Owners typically fear that engineers would perform seismic-resistance adequacy evalu-ations based on conservative ana-lytical assumptions, mostly disre-

Figure 17   Large URM units from the fallen parapet of the previous Figure.

garding the potentially favourable contribution of structural or non-structural elements whose effects cannot be quantified. For example, century-old buildings can sometimes be found to have no or little "theoretical" resistance to wind when analyzed according to accepted modern structural engineering practice and procedures, whereas the loading history of such structures actually demonstrates otherwise.

Figure 18 Failure of URM gable of The Cooper House (Santa Cruz).

Although the Loma Prieta earthquake has again demonstrated the vulnerability of older structures to even moderate seismic excitations, concerned owners must also reconcile the potential need for expensive structural retrofitting with the levels of seismic risk and consequences of inaction. Clearly, for the mitigation of the seismic hazards to proceed effectively in Canadian regions of low to moderate seismicity, the adequacy evaluation of existing structures must be closely inter-related to the reliability and performance level expected of the targeted facilities by owners, as well as the various probabilities of earthquake occurrence. In that perspective, the prime engineering goal would be to synthesize a realistic, neither unduly conservative nor permissive, statement of the seismic resistance capacity and ductility of the structural as well as architectural components of the buildings. Conducting all steps of the seismic adequacy evaluation using conservative engineering analysis and design assumptions will make this goal unattainable. Similarly, over-estimating the actual capacity of each structural or non-structural element to resist damaging cycles of seismic excitation could lead to a false and dangerous sense of security. The challenge lies in establishing a realistic analytical model of the system and providing the most accurate and reliable assessment of its actual capacity balancing the views obtained from the buildings' recorded performance history and the results from state-of-the-art analysis techniques.

The tools to allow owners to unambiguously specify their earthquake-survivability requirements at various reliability levels, and assisted by the technical recommendations of engineers, must be developed through further research. Such research is currently being conducted at the University of Ottawa.

In parallel, a methodology for the seismic adequacy review of Canadian existing structures, based on the aforementioned premises, should also be developed and presented in a format that can lead to its

Figure 19 Out-of-plane failure of church URM gable (Watsonville).

adoption and implementation by regulating bodies. Guidelines to assist owners of large inventory of structures in prioritizing their conduct of large scale seismic adequacy reviews should be integrated to such a methodology. In addition to structural engineering considerations, geotechnical factors must be included in such a priority list. Micro-zonation maps, delimitating zones where soils are expected to have various levels of detrimental influence during earthquakes, such as those developed for Quebec City (Chagnon and Doré 1987), would greatly assist in that respect.

CONCLUSIONS

The Loma Prieta earthquake of 1989 has provided an opportunity to re-learn some seismic rehabilitation lessons. The performance of URM structures and older buildings was in many instances inadequate. On the other hand, some buildings never designed to resist earthquakes responded surprisingly well in meeting the design philosophy embedded in modern building codes, sometimes in spite of damage not economically repairable. This emphasizes the need to rethink the earthquake design philosophy underlying seismic retrofitting activities intended to preserve existing historical and heritage buildings.

Figure 20   Severe diagonal cracks in church spire (Watsonville).

ACKNOWLEDGEMENTS

The author wishes to thank Professors Vitelmo Bertero and Stephen A. Mahin, of the University of California, Berkeley (UCB) for their on site-assistance, other UCB faculty for sharing ideas and findings on the major failures, as well as to numerous CALTRANS engineers, city building officials and fire and police chiefs too numerous to name here. The author is also most grateful to Morrison Hershfield Limited and the University of Ottawa for jointly funding this reconnaissance visit.

REFERENCES

1.   Basham, P. W., Weichert, D. H., Anglin, F. M., Berry, M. J., New Probabilistic Strong Seismic Ground Motion Maps of Canada: A Compilation of Earthquake Source Zones, Methods and Results, Earth Physics Branch Open File Number 82-33, Energy Mines and Resources Canada, Ottawa, Canada, December 1982.

Figure 21   Overall view of Palomar Inn (Santa Cruz).

2. Bertero, V. V. Seismic Per-
    formance of Reinforced Con-
    crete Structures, Anol. Acad.
    Ci. Ex. Fis. Nat. Buenos
    Aires, Tomo 31, 1979.

3. Bruneau, M., Preliminary
    Report of Structural Damage
    from the Loma Prieta (San
    Francisco) Earthquake of 1989
    and Pertinence to Canadian
    Structural Engineering Prac-
    tice, Canadian Journal of Civil
    Engineering, Vol.17, No.2,
    1990, pp. 198-208.

Figure 22   Typical exterior damage to the Palomar Inn (Santa Cruz).

4. CSMIP staff, Quick Report on CSMIP Strong Motion Records from the October
    17, 1989, Earthquake in the Santa Cruz Mountains, Office of Strong Motion
    Studies, Division of Mines and Geology, Department of Conservation, State of
    California, October 19, 1989.

5. EERI, Loma Prieta Earthquake Reconnaissance Report, Earthquake Spectra,
    Supplement to Volume 6, May 1990.

6. Chagnon, J.Y., Doré, G., Le Microzonage Séismique de la Région de Québec:
    Essai Méthodologique, Cahier du C.R.A.D., Vol.11, No.1, Université Laval, 1987

7. Hodgson, E.A., The Saint-Lawrence earthquake of March 1, 1925, Publications
    of the Dominion Observatory, Ottawa, Vol. VII, No. 10, Dept. of Mines and
    Technical Survey, Canada, 1950, pp.365-436.

8. Housner, G.W., Competing Against Time, Report to Governor George Deukmejian
    from the Governor's Board of Inquiry on the 1989 Loma Prieta Earthquake, State
    of California, Office of Planning and Research, California, USA, May 1990.

9. Mitchell, D., Tinawi, R., Redwood, G.R., Damage to Buildings due to the 1989
    Loma Prieta Earthquake - A Canadian Code Perspective, Canadian Journal of
    Civil Engineering, Vol.17, No.5, 1990, pp.813-834.

10. USGS, Probabilities of Large Earthquakes Occurring in California on the San
    Andreas Fault, U.S. Geological Survey Open-File Report 88-398, 1988.

The Use of Friction Dampers in the Seismic Design and Retrofit of Buildings

S. Cherry, A. Filiatrault

Department of Civil Engineering, University of British Columbia, Vancouver, Canada and L'École Polytechnique, Montreal, Canada

ABSTRACT

In the last decade, many energy dissipating systems have been proposed to raise the seismic design and retrofit of structures beyond the conventional ductility design approach. Among these new systems, friction damping has shown some great potential. In a friction damped system, friction damping devices are inserted in a structure and slip at a predetermined optimum slip load during severe seismic excitations, before any yielding of the structural members has occurred. Slipping of the devices allows the structure to dissipate the input seismic energy mechanically by friction rather than by inelastic deformation of the structural elements.

This paper presents an overview of the recent research conducted in the area of friction damping at the University of British Columbia. Analytical and shake table test results are first summarized to illustrate the superior earthquake performance of friction damped structures compared to the performance of conventional building systems. The development of a design slip load spectrum for the rapid evaluation of the optimum slip load distribution is then presented. The availability of this design slip load spectrum simplifies the design procedure for framed structures equipped with friction devices and should lead to a greater acceptance by the engineering profession of friction damping as an innovative and viable earthquake resistant design method. The dampers can be used in new construction or can be inserted in existing buildings for retrofit purposes.

INTRODUCTION

Earthquake excitation transmits a finite quantity of energy to a structure. The amount of seismic energy transmitted greatly depends on the ratio of the fundamental period of the structure to the predominant period of the ground motion. The damage experienced by a structure as a result of an earthquake is directly related to the amount of hysteretic energy absorbed by yielding of the various elements of the structure as it deforms.

It has long been recognized that it is not economical to design typical structures to remain free of damage during a major earthquake. The seismic philosophy of most modern building codes involves the concept of ductility balance: a structure must be designed to ensure that the ductility demands developed in its members as a result of the energy which it absorbs during a severe earthquake are balanced by the ductility capacities of the members to safely absorb this energy while undergoing large inelastic deformations. In this context, many building codes adopt the following criteria:

• *Minor earthquakes* at the building site shall not cause *any structural or non-structural damage.*

• *Moderate earthquakes* shall be the basis for the design. The building shall be proportioned to resist moderate ground motions, which can be expected during the lifetime of the building, *without significant damage* to the basic structure.

• *Severe earthquakes* may cause *significant structural damage*; however, *collapse* of the structure and *loss of human life must be avoided.*

This philosophy of earthquake protection of buildings concentrates essentially on preventing collapse of the main structure during a major seismic event. While this approach may be adequate for many types of structures, safer approaches are desirable, and certainly the mere avoidance of structural collapse is not sufficient for buildings whose functions are crucial in the immediate aftermath of a severe earthquake (hospitals, police stations, communication buildings, etc.). In recent years, many researchers have directed their attention to the development of new aseismic structural systems which are intended to limit the dynamic forces that are developed in the structural members. This paper presents the results of some research on a new system that incorporates friction damping devices to limit seismic response.

DESCRIPTION OF FRICTION DAMPING SYSTEM

General Description

Recently, a novel structural system for the aseismic design of steel framed buildings has been proposed by two Canadian researchers [1]. The system basically consists of an inexpensive mechanism containing friction brake lining pads introduced at the intersection of frame cross-braces. Figure 1 shows the location of the friction devices in a typical steel frame. The general arrangement of an actual friction device is presented in Fig. 2.

The device is designed not to slip under normal service loads and moderate earthquakes. During severe seismic excitations, the device slips at a predetermined load, before any yielding of the main members has occurred. Slipping of a device dissipates the seismic energy and also changes the natural frequency of the structure and allows the structure to alter its dynamic characteristics during a severe earthquake. The friction devices can be used in any configuration of the bracing system needed to meet the architectural requirements. Some possible bracing arrangements are shown in Fig. 3.

<u>Hysteretic Behaviour</u>
If the diagonal braces of an ordinary braced frame structure were designed not to buckle in compression, a simple slotted friction joint could be inserted in each diagonal member. In this case each slip joint would act independently of the other. However, it is frequently not economical to design the braces in compression and, more often, since the braces are quite slender, they are designed to be effective in tension only. In such cases, a simple friction joint would slip in tension but would not slip back during reversal of the tension load, or in the compression (buckled) regime. The energy absorption therefore would be relatively poor, since the brace would not slip again until it was stretched beyond the previous elongated length, as illustrated in Fig. 4. The use of the friction damping mechanism described earlier improves the energy absorption capability of the diagonal cross- braces.

Consider the hysteretic behaviour of a simple friction damped structure under seismic load as shown in Fig. 5. Let
V=lateral load at the girder level representing the seismic load,
Δ_1= relative displacement of node C with respect to node A (defined positive in figure),
Δ_2= relative displacement of node B with respect to node D (defined positive in figure),
P_1= load in brace 1 (positive in tension),
P_2= load in brace 2 (positive in tension).

Figure 5 illustrates five stages during a typical load cycle. The load-deformation curves of both braces and the associated deformed shape of the frame are shown for each stage. The following points should be noted during the cycle.

(1) In the very early stages of loading both braces are active and behave elastically in tension and compression.
(2) At very low load the compression brace buckles while the tension brace continues to stretch elastically.

(3)   The device is set to slip before yielding in the tension brace.   When slippage occurs, the four links of the special mechanism are activated and deform into a rhomboid shape; this deformation pattern tends to eliminate the buckled shape of the compression brace.   Thus, at the end of the slippage, P_2 is still the buckling load but now the compression brace is assumed to be straight.

(4)   When the load is reversed this straightened brace can immediately absorb energy in tension.

(5)   After the completion of one cycle, the resulting areas of the hysteresis loops are identical for both braces.   In this way, the energy dissipation is comparable with that of a simple friction joint when used with braces that are designed not to buckle in compression.   In other words, the energy dissipated in each cycle is essentially doubled through the use of the friction devices in combination with slender diagonal braces.

ANALYTICAL INVESTIGATION

Optimum Slip Load Distribution

The energy dissipation in a Friction Damped Braced Frame (FDBF) is equal to the product of slip load by the total slip travel summed over all devices.   For very high slip loads the energy dissipation in friction will be zero, as there will be no slippage.   In this situation the structure will behave exactly as a conventional Braced Moment Resisting Frame (BMRF).   If the slip loads are very low, large slip travels will occur but the amount of energy dissipation again will be negligible.   In this case the structure will behave exactly as an unbraced Moment Resisting Frame (MRF).   Between these extremes, there is an intermediate slip load distribution which results in optimum energy dissipation.   This intermediate distribution is defined as the "Optimum Slip Load Distribution".   The efficient design of the FDBF involves the determination of the optimum slip load distribution to minimize structural response.

The optimum slip load distribution can be evaluated by a series of time-step dynamic analyses using general purpose computer programs such as DRAIN-2D [2].   In this approach, the friction devices are modelled as an assemblage of axial and bending elements with pseudo yielding characteristics [3].

Typical results obtained from a DRAIN-2D analysis for the optimum slip load study of the 3-storey model frame structure used in the experimental studies described below are presented in Fig. 6.   The curves are envelopes of lateral deflections for slip loads ranging from 0 to 10 kN (representing the elastic region of the cross-braces) when the structure is subjected to the Parkfield 1966 N65E earthquake scaled to 0.52g peak ground acceleration.   Similar curves were obtained for response envelopes of beam and column moments and shears.   Results for zero slip load represent the response of an unbraced structure.   The figure clearly shows the effectiveness of the friction devices in improving the seismic response of the frame.   As the slip load is increased, the deflections decrease steadily up to a slip load of 6 kN.   For a slip load between 6 kN and 10 kN, there is very little variation in the response.

The application of a general purpose non-linear computing program for defining the optimum slip load distribution is tedious, requires extensive main frame computer time, and is not readily practical for most design offices.   To avoid this shortcoming, Filiatrault and Cherry [4] have developed a special and efficient computer program for the analysis and design of friction damped braced frames.   The hysteretic properties of the friction devices are derived theoretically and included in this Friction Damped Braced Frame Analysis Program (FDBFAP), which is adaptable to a microcomputer environment.   The optimum slip load distribution is determined by minimizing a relative performance index (RPI) derived from energy concepts.   This new numerical approach is much more economical to use than DRAIN-2D and is of great value for the practical design of friction damped braced frames.

The results of a uniform slip load optimization by FDBFAP for a typical low-rise steel industrial building that is to be retrofitted with the friction damping system (without modifying the main structure) for the Taft 1952 S69E earthquake, scaled to 0.36g, is shown in Fig. 7.   The optimum slip load for each device is 45 kN.   Fig 7 also shows that the variation in the relative performance index for slip loads in the vicinity of the optimum value is small.   This suggests that the seismic response of this structure is not particularly sensitive to variations in the optimum slip load, which may occur due to environmental and construction factors, such as temperature change and adjustment variability.

Figure 8 presents the energy time-histories calculated by FDBFAP for this same industrial structure with the slip load tuned to the Newmark-Blume-Kapur artificial earthquake [5], scaled to a peak acceleration of 0.5g (slip load of 134 kN for each device).   The friction devices are very efficient in dissipating the seismic energy input.   At the end of the earthquake record, 86% of the input energy has been dissipated by friction.

Comparison of Response Behaviour of Conventional and Friction Damped Structures

The superior earthquake performance of friction damped structures can be demonstrated analytically by comparing the seismic behaviour of conventional frame systems with those equipped with optimally tuned friction devices. Three examples are offered to illustrate the benefits of friction damping.

The distribution of structural damage in the various members of a 10-storey conventional BMRF and a FDBF at the end of the 1940 El Centro NS earthquake was determined from the computer program DRAIN-2D, and is indicated qualitively in Fig. 9. The damage is represented by the damage ratio (DR), which is defined here as the ratio of the number of yielded members to the total number of members. It can be seen that the FDBF response reduction system performs very well when excited by the El Centro event. All members of the FDBF remain elastic, while some damage occurs in the beams, columns and braces of the BMRF. Envelopes of the shear forces developed in the columns of this structure are presented in Fig 10; the FDBF is very effective in reducing the base shear.

As a second example, Fig. 11 shows the damage induced in the various members of the low-rise industrial structure referred to above. Substantial yielding occurs in the members of the original braced moment resisting frame; all members of the retrofitted friction damped structure remain elastic. The time history of the top-floor lateral deflection of each building system is presented in Fig.12. The superior performance of the structure equipped with friction devices is evident. The original braced structure experiences a peak deflection of 71 mm and 11 cycles of vibration have amplitudes larger than 50 mm (structure height/200). The peak deflection of the retrofitted friction damped structure is 60 mm and only one vibration cycle has an amplitude larger than 50 mm.

The final example presents response values obtained from an analysis of the 3-storey model frame structures used in the experimental studies described below. Typical envelopes of the response parameters for the different model frames under white noise excitation, scaled to a peak ground acceleration of 0.50 g, are presented in Fig. 13. The deflection at the top of the FDBF is only 12% of the equivalent deflection in the MRF and 25% of the deflection in the BMRF. The maximum moment at the base of the FDBF is only 20% and 43% of the corresponding values in the MRF and the BMRF respectively. The results clearly indicate the superior performance of the FDBF compared to conventional aseismic building systems.

EXPERIMENTAL INVESTIGATION

A number of qualification tests have been performed in the laboratory to verify the theoretical studies related to FDBF. These include cyclic tests on isolated friction devices and earthquake simulator tests on braced frame structures incorporating friction damping devices.   These experiments are summarized below.

Cyclic Tests of Friction Devices
To be effective the friction devices must present very stable, non-deteriorating hysteresis loops.   Cyclic load tests on prototypes of the friction devices were carried out in a standard testing machine [6].   One end of a diagonal link of the friction device was bolted to a rigid testing bench while the opposite end was attached to a vertical hydraulic actuator.

The results of these tests clearly indicate that a rectangular load-deformation curve can only be obtained if the fabrication tolerances of the friction devices are minimized.   This was achieved by inserting steel bushings in the 4 corner holes of the mechanism.   As a result, the fabrication tolerance was reduced from 2 mm to 0.25 mm.

A typical hysteresis loop developed with these modified devices is shown in Fig. 14.   The hysteresis loop is very nearly a perfect rectangle and exhibits negligible fade even after 50 cycles.

Seismic Tests on Shake Table
A 1/3 scale model of a 3 storey FDBF was used in a series of shake table tests [6].   The overall dimensions of the model frame were 2.05x1.40 m in plan and 3.53 m in height.   Two identical frames were fabricated for the experimental study.   The beam-column connections were designed such that the FDBF could be transformed easily into a MRF or a BMRF as needed.

The test frames were mounted on a shaking table and subjected to various earthquake accelerograms with different intensities expressed in terms of peak acceleration.   A variety of sensors were used to measure displacement, acceleration, friction pad slippage and strain at critical locations in the frame.

The MRF and BMRF did not perform well during the tests corresponding to a major earthquake.   Very large strains occurred in the base column, and in the first and second floor beams of the MRF.   Although the main structural members of the BMRF remained elastic, many cross-braces yielded in tension.   The elongation of the braces was very large and they buckled significantly in the compression regime; this indicates that heavy non-structural damage likely would have occurred in a real building (cracks in walls, broken glass, etc.). However, the FDBF performed very well; no damage occurred in any member and the accelerations, deflections and beam moments were far less than the values measured in the two other types of construction.

Typical response characteristics illustrating the relative behaviour for the model frames of the three structural configuations are presented in Figs. 15 to 18. The envelopes of the measured peak accelerations for a Newmark-Blume-Kapur artificial earthquake [5] scaled to 0.3 g are shown in Fig. 15 and the measured horizontal accelerations due to an extremely severe earthquake--Taft 1952 S69E component scaled to a peak accelerations of 0.9 g--are presented in Fig. 16. The influence of the new damping system in reducing response is clearly apparent. The maximum acceleration amplifications experienced by the three frames under the former earthquake are 1.98, 5.08 and 6.63 for the FDBF, BMRF and MRF respectively, while the corresponding figures for the latter excitation are 1.58, 2.49 and 2.97.

Figures 17 and 18 compare typical measured and calculated responses of the model frames when subjected to a horizontal motion equal to the vertical component of the Taft 1952 earthquake, scaled to a peak acceleration of 0.60 g. (The experimental responses of the BMRF are not shown since many cross-braces had yielded in tension in a previous series of tests and a new set of braces was not available for this series.) Figure 17 shows the envelope of lateral deflections. It can be seen that the measured deflection at the top of the FDBF is only 31% of the equivalent deflection in the MRF. The envelopes of beam bending moments are shown in Fig. 18. Notice that the first floor beam of the MRF reaches its plastic moment under this earthquake, whereas the equivalent moment in the FDBF is only 31% of the plastic moment. Good agreement is observed between the measured and predicted values of the BMRF and the FDBF. The overestimate of the actual damage in the beams of the MRF by the analytical prediction can be attributed to the unrealistically low values of supplementary viscous damping used in the analysis; the use of larger viscous damping values, that would be more appropriate for this structure given the large amplitude vibrations actually experienced by the model during this earthquake, would reduce the difference between the predicted and measured values for the MRF.

SIMPLIFIED DESIGN PROCEDURE FOR FRICTION DAMPED STRUCTURES

It has been demonstrated that the optimum slip load distribution plays an important role in the design of friction damped structures. A method of rapidly evaluating this key parameter must be available if this innovative design concept is to gain acceptance by the engineering profession. A simple procedure for evaluating the optimum slip load has been developed by Filiatrault and Cherry [7]. Their complete study involved: the development of a specialized computer program for analyzing FDBF, that invokes a slip load optimization procedure; the application of an existing synthetic computer model to generate the earthquake accelerograms used in the study; an analysis to determine the dimensionless parameters controlling the optimum slip load; and a sensitivity study to determine the most important parameters identified by the dimensional analysis. These investigations culminated in a full parametric study of the important factors influencing the response of friction damped structures. The results of the parametric study were examined by a multi-regression analysis based on the least square method. This led to the construction of a design slip load spectrum as shown in Fig. 19.

It can be seen that the design slip load spectrum takes into account the properties of the structure (T_u and m) and of the ground motion (T_g and a_g): V_o is the total optimum slip shear for the structure, m is the total mass of the structure, a_g is the peak ground acceleration anticipated at the building site, T_g is the Kanai-Tajimi [8, 9] predominant period of the ground motion as determined by the method of spectral moments [10], and T_u is the fundamental period of the unbraced structure alone. This spectrum is completely described by specifying the ordinate α, corresponding to $T_g/T_u = 1$, and the ordinate β, corresponding to $T_g/T_u = 15$. The ordinates α and β can be evaluated from [7]:

$$\alpha = (-1.24NS - 0.31) \, T_b/T_u + 1.04NS + 0.43 \qquad (1)$$

$$\beta = (-1.07NS - 0.10) \, T_b/T_u + 1.01NS + 0.45 \qquad (2)$$

where NS is the number of storeys and T_b is the natural period of the fully braced structure (before any slippage occurs).

The optimum slip shear at each storey V_s is given by

$$V_s = V_o/NS = 2\sum_i P_i \cos\phi_i \qquad (3)$$

where P_i is the optimum slip load of the ith friction device in the storey and ϕ_i is the angle of inclination of the cross braces from the horizontal. The optimum slip load for each friction device can be obtained from Eq.(3).

Fig. 7 compares the optimum slip load obtained from the design slip load spectrum with the value obtained from FDBFAP for the seismic retrofit study of the low-rise 3-storey steel industrial building referred to previously. It can be seen that the proposed design procedure adequately predicts the optimum slip load of the structure.

The availability of this design slip load spectrum provides structural engineers with a simple and straightforward procedure for the rational seismic design of friction damped structures.

CONCLUSION

The proposed friction damping system is an exciting development which may offer new opportunities in earthquake resistant design. The use of such devices in a building protects its main structural elements (beams and columns) from yielding during a major earthquake. In view of the encouraging analytical and experimental results obtained to date, it would be desirable to undertake further research studies. In particular, studies should be conducted to verify if the devices creep and are still in working condition after many years of service; maintenance methods may have to be developed to ensure the long-term reliability of the friction devices.

REFERENCES

1.   Pall, A.S., and Marsh, C., "Response of Friction Damped Braced Frames", ASCE, Journal of the Structural Division (ST6), p.1313-1323, 1982.

2.   Kannan, A.E., and Powell, G.M., "DRAIN-2D, a General Purpose Computer Program for Dynamic Analysis of Inelastic Plane Structures", Report EERC 73-6, Earthquake Engineering Research Center, University of California, Berkeley, C.A., 1973.

3. Filiatrault, A., and Cherry, S., "Comparative Performance of Friction Damped Systems and Base Isolation Systems for Earthquake Retrofit and Aseismic Design", Earthquake Engineering and Structural Dynamics, (16:3), p. 389-416, 1988.

4. Filiatrault, A., and Cherry, S., "Efficient Numerical Modelling for the Design of Friction Damped Braced Steel Plane Frames", Canadian Journal of Civil Engineering, Vol. 16, p. 211-218, 1989.

5. Newmark, N.M., Blume, J.A., and Kapur, K.K., "Seismic Design Spectra for Nuclear Power Plants", ASCE, Journal of the Power Division, Vol. 99, p. 287-303, 1973.

6. Filiatrault, A., and Cherry, S., "Performance Evaluation of Friction Damped Braced Steel Frames Under Simulated Earthquake Loads", Earthquake Spectra, (3:1), p. 57-78, 1987.

7. Filiatrault, A., and Cherry, S., "Seismic Design Spectra for Friction Damped Structures", ASCE, Journal of the Structural Division, (ST5), p. 1334-1355, 1990.

8. Kanai, K., "Semi-Empirical Formula for the Seismic Characteristics of the Ground", Bulletin of the Earthquake Research Institute (35), University of Tokyo, Tokyo, Japan, 1957.

9. Tajimi, H., "A Statistical Method of Determining the Maximum Response of Buildings During Earthquakes", Proceedings of the Second World Conference on Earthquake Engineering, Tokyo and Kyoto, Japan, Vol. 2, p. 781-797, 1960.

10. Lai, S.P., "Statistical Characterization of Strong Motions Using Power Spectral Density Functions", Bulletin of the Seismological Society of America, (72:1), p. 259-274, 1982.

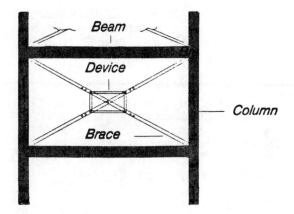

Fig.1 Typical Location of Friction Device

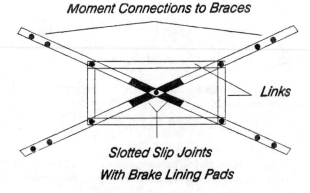

Fig.2 Detail of Friction Device

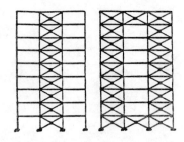

Fig.3 Possible Bracing Arrangements for Friction Device

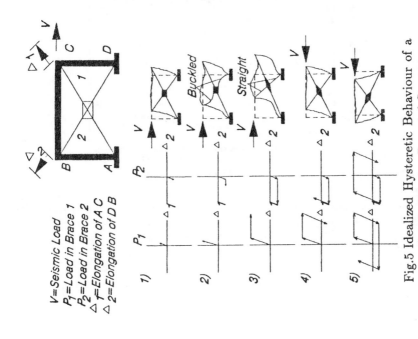

V=Seismic Load
P_1=Load in Brace 1
P_2=Load in Brace 2
$\triangle_1$=Elongation of A C
$\triangle_2$=Elongation of D B

Fig.5 Idealized Hysteretic Behaviour of a Simple Friction Damped Structure

Fig.4 Idealized Hysteretic Behaviour of a Friction Joint with tension bracing

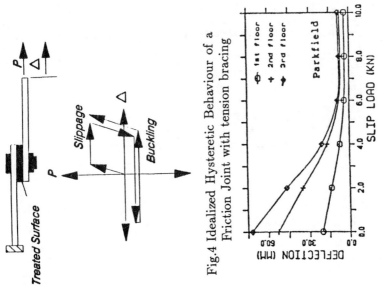

Fig.6 Optimum Slip Load Study for Experimental Frame, Parkfield Earthquake, 0.52g

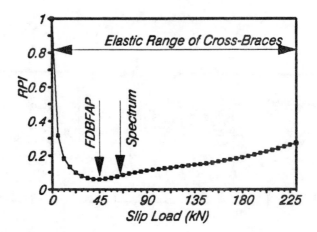

Fig.7 Uniform Slip Load Optimization for a Low-Rise Steel Building, Taft Earthquake, 0.36g

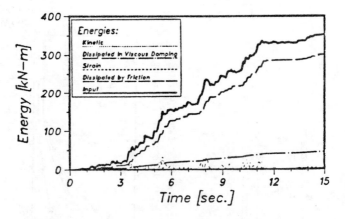

Fig.8 Energy Time-Histories for Friction Damped Low-Rise Steel Building, N-B-K Artificial Earthquake, 0.50g

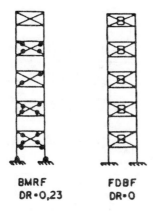

Fig.9 Structural Damage for 10-Storey Frame,
El Centro Earthquake, 0.34g

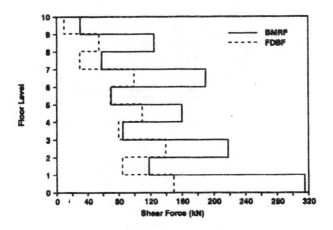

Fig.10 Envelopes of Shear Forces in Columns,
El Centro Earthquake, 0.34g

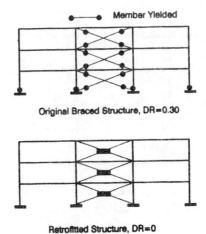

Fig.11 Structural Damage for Low-Rise Steel Building,
        Taft Earthquake, 0.36g

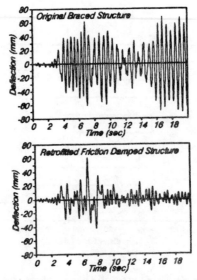

Fig.12 Time-Histories of Top Floor Lateral Deflection for
        Low-Rise Steel Building, Taft Earthquake, 0.36g

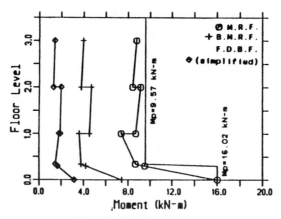

Fig.13 Response Envelopes for Experimental Frame,
White Noise Excitation, 0.50g

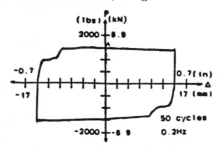

Fig.14 Hysteresis Loop From Friction Device

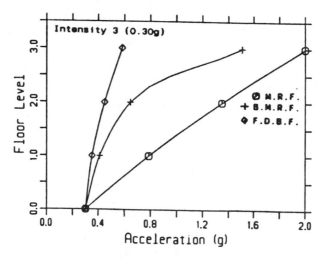

Fig.15 Measured Peak Accelerations for Experimental Frame,
N-B-K Artificial Earthquake, 0.30g

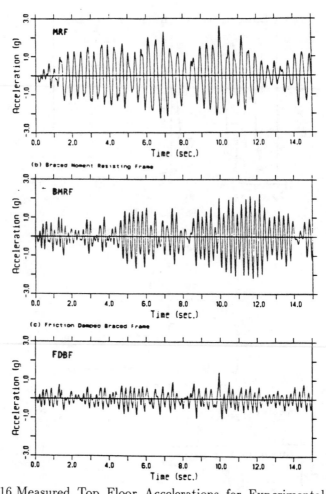

Fig.16 Measured Top Floor Accelerations for Experimental Frame,
Taft Earthquake, 0.90g

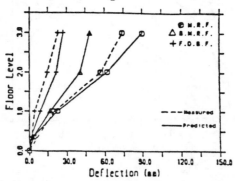

Fig.17 Envelopes of Lateral Deflections for Experimental Frame,
Taft Earthquake, 0.60g

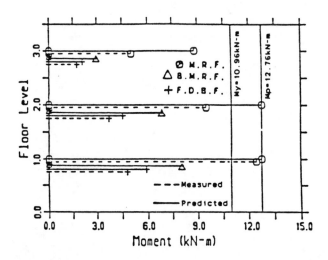

Fig.18 Envelopes of Beam Bending Moments for Experimental Frame,
Taft Earthquake, 0.60g

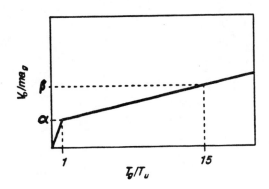

Fig.19 Construction of Design Slip Load Spectrum

The Use of Impulsive Actions for the Structural Identification of Slender Monumental Buildings

C. Blasi(*), M. Carfagni(**), S. Carfagni(*)
(*) Department of Civil Engineering
(**) Department of Mechanics and Industrial
Technologies, Florence University, Italy

SUMMARY

This paper presents a procedure of dynamic identification for slender monuments, such as towers and bell-towers, based on the use of impulsive dynamic actions, applied by means of a pendulum provided with a piezoelectric force transducer for measuring strength, and on the interpretation of data by means of a numeric model.

It also gives the results of the studies made with this procedure on the fourteenth century bell-tower of the Church of the Badia in Florence.

1. INTRODUCTION

Widespread use is now made of methods of dynamic identification for defining the mechanical characteristics of buildings in concrete and in steel.

However, the application of these procedures to masonry buildings and in particular to monumental buildings, in order to establish among other things the degree of deterioration, still presents considerable uncertainties and difficulties even at the experimental level.

Of all monumental buildings, those characterised by slenderness such as columns, towers and bell-towers, appear to be those for which it is possible to obtain the best results with these methods.

Some research has already been carried out in past years by the Department of Civil Engineering in Florence on the procedures of dynamic identification applied to ancient columns and colonnades [1].

More recently, concern over the collapse of the civic tower of Pavia has prompted a campaign of experimental tests and research for the specific use of dynamic identification procedures for towers and bell-towers in masonry.

One of the fundamental problems at the experimental level concerns the excitation of the structures and the quantification of the excitation for the purpose of determining the frequency response functions.

In the tests carried out on the tower of Palazzo Vecchio [2], for example, an oscillator with excentrically rotating masses was used , which was carried with difficulty to the top of the tower in separate pieces; however, the best results for the definition of the first model forms were obtained by recording the oscillations caused by the wind.

The use of an oscillator with excentrically rotating masses is sometimes ineffectual because of the low frequencies, generally lower than 1 Hz, that are characteristic of these structures.

It may moreover be difficult to install an oscillator that is sufficiently powerful at the top of the towers or bell-towers, to which narrow stairs often provide the only access.

Recently tests of dynamic identification have been carried out on the fourteenth century bell-tower of the Badia in Florence and, after a few negative results obtained by different methods of excitation, a system based on the application of impulsive forces was used, by means of the impact produced by a pendulum. The results were extremely positive.

Subsequently the experimental methodologies used will be explained as well as the system of numeric modelling adapted for the interpretation of the data recorded.

2. THE BELL-TOWER OF THE BADIA IN FLORENCE

The fourteenth century bell-tower of the church of the Badia is one of the most slender constructions in Florence; it is in fact 64.7 metres high and has a diameter of approximately 7 metres at its base.

The lower part, up to a height of approximately 11 metres, has a circular section and is all that remains of the ancient bell-tower of the eleventh century; the upper part which was built in around the year 1300, is in the form of a hexagonal section, with increasingly high mullioned windows on all sides, which together with the 16.5 metres high steeple confers a special lightness and slenderness on the bell-tower.

The walls consist of blocks of "strong" sandstone.

The bell-tower is structurally independent even though it is joined to the walls of the church and the walls are affected by a series of vertical lesions, which appear at the height of the bells, cross the wide windows and almost reach the base of the bell-tower.

3. EXPERIMENTAL METHODOLOGY

The purpose of the experiment was to evaluate the content of the structure in frequency of vibrations and hence its fundamental dynamic parameters through the spectral analysis of the result.

To accomplish this piezo-electric transducer were placed at various levels (fig.1): more precisely, these were accelerometers brought to the most appropriate electric level by the respective amplifiers of measurements.

The signals were sent to an analysor of spectrum with the task of digitalising the signal, of transforming it into the domination of the frequency and of giving a visual indication of the calculated function.

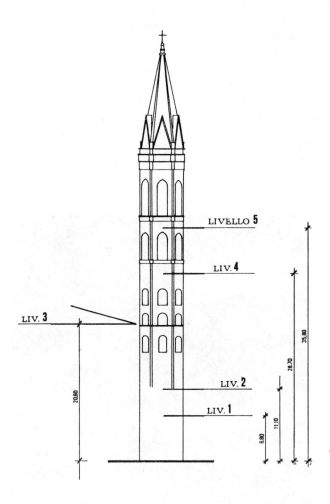

fig.1 Levels of measurements

While a traditional method of measurement was used, the excitation method used constitutes an innovation for experiments of this type, applied to structures such as those being examined.

Since in order to make a reliable evaluation of the modal parameters it is necessary to construct the frequency response functions, that is to say to measure the force as well as the results at the various levels, an excitation method with calibrated impulses was adopted.

In fact when the force is of the impulsive type it has an almost continous spectrum in frequency, and this allows us to identify with certainty the values of the first modal frequencies of the structure.

The pendulum that enabled us to carry out this type of experiment, consists of a steel bar on which sufficient weights were placed to reach the required weight (approximately 200 Kg).

This was hung with a double steel cable from the supporting structure of the bells and made to strike against a plate, suitably anchored to the wall, on which the site for the piezoelectric force transducer had been prepared.

To avoid the impact of the pendulum on the plate being one of steel on steel, in other words to avoid generating a spectrum of intensity relevant to high frequencies, a spherical calotte made of rubber was interposed, which allowed the concentration of the spectrum of excitation below a certain value, given the low value of the frequencies characteristic of similar structures.

fig.2 The pendulum in operation

The piezoelectric force transducer enabled us to measure the strength produced by each strike, while at the same time the accelerometers recorded the oscillations produced at the various heights.

The relationships between the results of the structure at various heights and the agent force, in frequency, carried out automatically by the analysor provided the frequency force transducer.

Six measurements at different levels were sufficient to allow an evaluation of the first three modal frequencies and the corresponding forms of the structure.

In order to make a comparison with the levels of vibration relating to real recurrent dynamic situations for the structure, a survey was also made of the vibration induced by the action of the bells and the traffic.

4. EXPERIMENTAL RESULTS

The spectra of the signals recorded for each level studied are given here, as well as the signals relating to the vibrations induced at the highest measuring point after the impact of the pendulum, after the movement of the bells and the traffic.

An examination of these last three diagrams reveals the minimal influence of the traffic on the building.

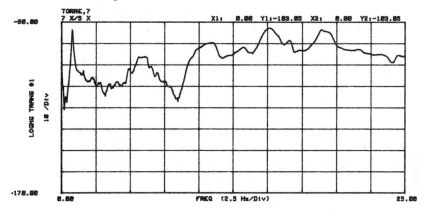

fig.3   Spectrum of the signal at Level 7

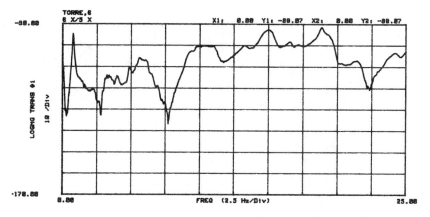

fig.4 Spectrum of the signal Level 6

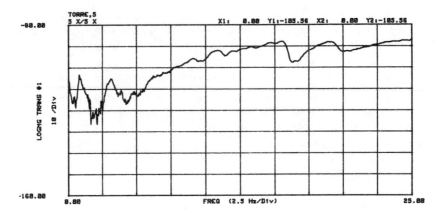

fig.5 Spectrum of the signal Level 5

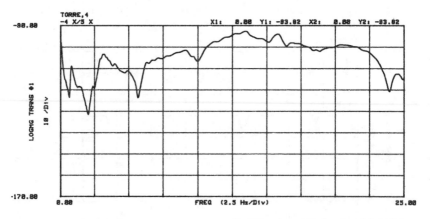

fig.6 Spectrum of the signal Level 4

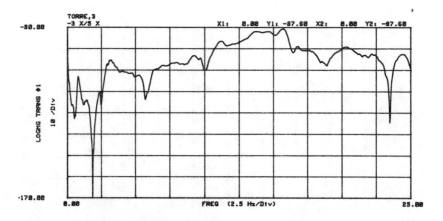

fig.7 Spectrum of the signal Level 3

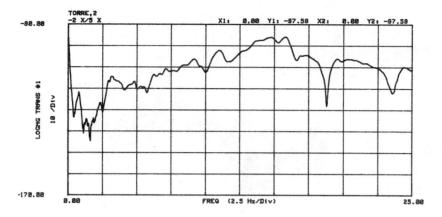

fig.8 Spectrum of the signal Level 2

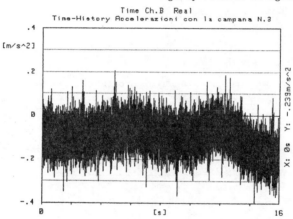

fig.9 Signal recorded with the bells

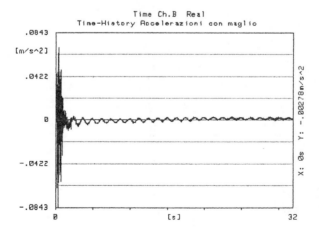

fig.10 Signal recorded with the impulse

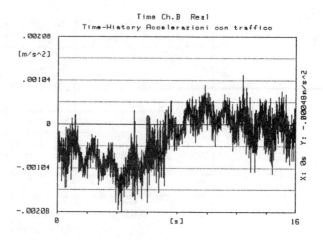

fig.11 Signal recorded with the traffic

With the frequency response functions obtained it was possible to construct the first three nodal forms of the structure.

The first three frequencies characteristic of the structure were identified as:

0.79 Hz, 3.09 Hz, 5.90 Hz

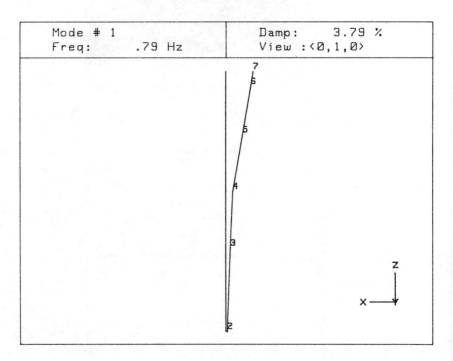

fig.12 First modal form

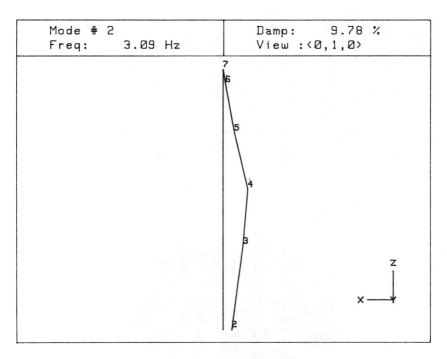

fig.13 Second modal form

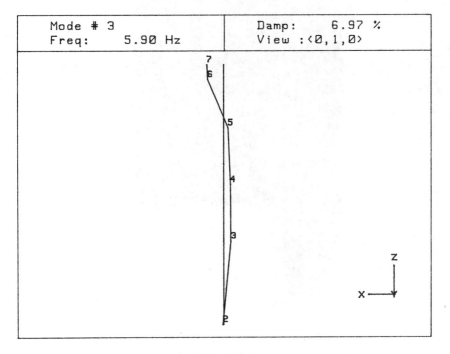

fig.14 Third modal form

5. NUMERIC MODELLING AND IDENTIFICATION PROCEDURES

The Finite Element numeric model for identifying the structural characteristics was created by using the well-known Ansys program, from the Swanson Analysis System, Inc. (Houston), which has a vast store of elements at its disposal, including "gap" elements with monolateral behaviour and has the possibility of carrying out analyses in the static and dynamic fields.

Using this program, a model of the structure in which the areas corresponding to the mullioned windows were defined in greater detail was constructed; in fact Ansys allows the elaboration of parts with more elaborate "mesh", as the program itself imposes suitable conditions on the outline

fig.15 Sub-model

For the   calibration of the model the dynamic tests were reconstructed by analysing two situations, one whole and one fragmented (with the vertical lesions).

The analyses carried out on the whole structure (unfractured) revealed the presence of relevant traction tensions corresponding to the areas that were in fact damaged, especially for the action of horizontal and dynamic loads.

The identification procedures, in particular the reconstruction with the model of the modal forms and of the values of the corresponding frequencies found experimentally, have revealed the importance of the present cracked state for dynamic behaviour of the structure and have made it possible to define the mechanical characteristics of the masonry.

One of the important results is the value obtained for the module of longitudinal deformability E of 60.000 Kg/cm^2 for the masonry.

All this made the calibration of two numeric models possible: one linear and one non-linear.

With the first some conditions of "exercise" load were examined, for which the hypotheses of "little displacement" may be considered acceptable.

A special study was made of the tensional and deformative states caused by its own weight and by the dynamic action of the bells, formulated as a time-history, produced by a variable force in a sinusoidal way.

Surveys were also undertaken for the study of the structure's response to time-history of dynamic actions simulating specific wind and earthquake conditions.

To evaluate the risk of the "limit situation of collapse" in which "non-linear" phenomenon such as the monolateral behaviour of the resistence of the masonry and the loss of the hypothesis of "little displacement" play a part, we have adopted on the other hand a "non linear" calculus procedure based on the simulation of the dynamic behaviour by means of a decomposition of the structure into rigid superimposed blocks and the study of the oscillations of the various "rocking" type blocks, according to the Blasi-Spinelli method [3].

The statistic evaluation of the seismic risk of the structure was made on the basis of the results of a significant number of project accelerograms.

CONCLUSIONS

The use of impulsive dynamic actions played a determining role, given also type of structure, in obtaining an exhaustive survey of the structural characteristics.

Through a comparison with the results of the numeric model, the dynamic test made it possible to define the complessive mechanical characteristics of the structure, in order to have a clear explanation of the cracked condition and of their fundamental importance in static and dynamic behaviour.

All the surveys carried out thus made it possible to define an informed consolidation project.

REFERENCES

1. Blasi, C., Spinelli, P., "Analisi dinamica di colonne formate da blocchi lapidei", II Convegno Nazionale "L'Ingegneria Sismica in Italia", Rapallo 1984.

2. ISMES, "Rilievo delle vibrazioni sulla Torre di Arnolfo in Palazzo Vecchio in Firenze", Enel/Cris Milano, Agosto 1987

3. Blasi, C., Spinelli, P., "Un metodo di calcolo dinamico per sistemi formati da blocchi rigidi sovrapposti" , Ingegneria Sismica, anno III N.1 gennaio-aprile 1986

Historic Buildings in the County of Santa Cruz and the Loma Prieta Earthquake of 1989

W. Bradford Cross, N.P. Jones

The Johns Hopkins University, Baltimore, Maryland 21218 - 2699, U.S.A.

INTRODUCTION

On Tuesday, October 17, 1989, at approximately 17:04 local time, a magnitude 7.1 earthquake struck northern California. The epicenter was 10 miles northeast of the city of Santa Cruz. This quake caused extensive damage throughout the San Francisco area: the Marina district suffered fires and building failure, one span of the Bay Bridge fell from its support, a 1.5 mile section of Interstate 880 (Nimitz Freeway) in Oakland (Cypress Section) collapsed, and major structural damage was reported from a number of locations in Santa Cruz county. The death toll has been estimated to be 67.

A team from The Johns Hopkins University was in the region affected by the earthquake within 24 hours of the event. It became immediately apparent that much of the damage to buildings in the County of Santa Cruz occurred in historic structures. This paper will describe observed damage to the historic resources of the county and provide comprehensive damage statistics for these resources. In addition, the response of the engineering and planning community will be examined, and important concerns regarding historic buildings will be addressed.

A BRIEF HISTORY AND DESCRIPTION OF THE COUNTY

Santa Cruz is California's second smallest county, with an area of 429 square miles (Figure 1). It is bounded by Monterey Bay and the Pacific Ocean on the west, and the Santa Cruz Mountains on the east. The area is known to contain several active earthquake faults — the most notable being the San Andreas Fault — which have contributed to the spectacular terrain of the region as well as the seismic hazard (EERI [4]).

The original inhabitants of the county comprised about 50 separate political groups and were all called Costanos by the first explorers to the region. The first such explorer, Juan Rodriguez Cabrillo, a Portuguese navigator, sailed up the California coast in 1542 under the flag of Spain. With news of the calm waters of Monterey Bay reaching potential settlers in the 18th century, Spanish interest in the region increased. Mission

Figure 1: County of Santa Cruz, California. ❧ Epicenter.

Santa Cruz was established on the banks of the San Lorenzo river in 1791, within what is now the City of Santa Cruz. Development continued with the establishment of Branciforte, a well-planned Spanish pueblo. Mexico gained independence from Spain in 1821 and made generous grants of land in the Santa Cruz area to loyalists.

In 1848, Alta California became a territory of the United States, including what is now known as the County of Santa Cruz. Original American settlers to the region included fur trappers and pirates. Later, the region's rich agricultural lands were exploited, and the redwood forests were harvested for their valuable lumber resources. Several capitalistic schemes were tried with varying success. Limekilns and powder works were established in the mid-19th century. Railroads were introduced to the county in 1876 to facilitate the transportation of lumber from the redwood forests. The recreational value of the county's Pacific coastline did not go unnoticed, and by the end of the 19th century resorts were being constructed in the cities of Santa Cruz and Capitola. Watsonville initially was a center for sugar beet production; that crop was later replaced by apples (Verardo and Verardo [8]).

The cities of Santa Cruz and Capitola continue to be major recreational areas to this day, while Watsonville still relies heavily on its agricultural economy, as does the remaining unincorporated county of Santa Cruz. There is one additional incorporated city within the County of Santa Cruz: Scotts Valley.

HISTORIC BUILDINGS IN THE COUNTY

The history of the County of Santa Cruz has provided the county with a rich and diverse architectural resource. A wide variety of structural types is represented, including adobe, wood frame, brick and stone masonry, lightly reinforced concrete, and steel. Buildings dating back to the Spanish era of Alta California can be found, as well as structures associated with the early American settlements, exquisite Victorian homes, turn-of-the century commercial buildings, classic recreational facilities, and buildings representing the new materials and technological developments of the industrial revolution. There are 33 county landmark districts and buildings on the National Register of Historic Places (National Park Service [5]). The county and incorporated cities have designated 1053 buildings as being historically significant with totals listed geographically as follows: County of Santa Cruz, 310; City of Santa Cruz (Survey Volumes I and II), 560; Watsonville, 106; Capitola, 76; and Scotts Valley, 1. It should be noted that the communities establish their own criteria for landmark designation, and hence the number of such buildings varies widely from one jurisdiction to the next. Data have been gathered by the authors for almost all of the buildings listed on these historic inventories.

The construction dates of these buildings range from 1791 to 1960; the "average" date of construction for historic buildings in the county is 1894. The pre-earthquake building stock can be broken into 5 general structural categories, depending on the predominant structural system: wood frame, 938; unreinforced masonry, 48; concrete, 21; adobe, 4; and steel, 2. In addition, there were 40 buildings whose structural type was not determinable from the data available to the researchers. Clearly, most of the designated historic structures in the county prior to the earthquake were wood framed residential buildings, though there were several significant unreinforced masonry structures.

Pre-Event Preservation Efforts

Preservationists had been quite active in the County of Santa Cruz prior to the Loma Prieta earthquake. Local historic commissions had been set up to manage the historic resources in the City of Santa Cruz and the unincorporated county. Tax incentives for the rehabilitation of National Register structures have been available from the Federal Government; some renovation work was spurred in the county when these incentives were offered.

The State of California adopted a State Historic Building Code (SHBC) in 1979, which provides regulations to preserve the *architectural* integrity of certified historic structures. Beyond the National Register and the California Registered State Historic Landmarks, local jurisdictions are free to perform their own historic building surveys and designate architecturally significant sites that should be protected by the SHBC. Unfortunately, there are no financial incentives offered to owners of structures designated "historic" under the SHBC, so certain communities, such as Scotts Valley, are reluctant to make such surveys (City of Scotts Valley [3]). Surveys were performed in the other political jurisdictions of the County of Santa Cruz, resulting in the protection of hundreds of buildings by the SHBC.

The greatest preservation effort within the county, and one recognized as a success nationally, was the conversion of a section of Santa Cruz City's downtown into the Pacific Garden Mall. Several streets were closed to vehicular traffic within the mall area, and a concerted architectural restoration effort was undertaken to revitalize buildings. The entire district was listed on the National Register of Historic Places (National Park Service [5]). There were key architectural landmarks in the mall, such as the Cooper House, a Richardsonian Romanesque Revival structure that originally had been the Santa Cruz County Court House but had been converted to offices, shops, and restaurants by the time of the Loma Prieta earthquake.

Other preservation efforts had been undertaken throughout the county. In Capitola, much of the old seaside resort town had been restored to its original condition, including many quaint woodframe houses along Soquel Creek. St. Patrick's Church in Watsonville, constructed from brick masonry, was a focal point of the local Catholic community and had been well maintained since its construction in 1903. Several adobe structures still exist within the county, mostly in the hands of private owners who carefully maintain the structures' historic integrity.

Unfortunately, as is the case in much of the country, little attention was paid to seismic retrofit when architectural preservation efforts were undertaken. Most of the buildings in the Pacific Garden Mall had been cosmetically restored, but only minor structural upgrading was performed, if any. At the time of the Loma Prieta earthquake, a structural retrofit was in progress at the Cooper House, but it was only partially complete.

Damage to Buildings During the Loma Prieta Event

Reports obtained from the Planning Department of the County of Santa Cruz record that 1084 structures were destroyed, 3354 structures suffered major damage (>$10,000), and 16286 structures suffered minor damage (<$10,000). These statistics include data from all the incorporated cities, as well as the unincorporated county. The total cost of structural damage in the County of Santa Cruz is estimated at $300 million.

Damage to Historic Buildings

Within the borders of the County of Santa Cruz the damage to structures varied considerably from location to location, depending on several factors including site conditions, distance from the earthquake's epicenter, structural type, construction details, and building configuration. Accordingly, the damage to historic buildings will be examined by region, delineated by the political boundaries of the unincorporated county and the incorporated cities. Countywide damage statistics (unincorporated county plus incorporated cities) are shown in Table 1. Buildings listed under "DEMO" (i.e., demolished) are also included in the column headed "MAJOR". It should be noted in general that, as expected, a greater percentage of unreinforced masonry buildings (URM) suffer major damage than other structural types. It is interesting to note, however, that minor damage occurs at roughly the same rate for URM as for other types of structures.

STRUCTURAL TYPE	TOTAL		EARTHQUAKE DAMAGE							
			NONE		MINOR		MAJOR		DEMO	
	#	%	#	%	#	%	#	%	#	%
Wood	938	89	725	77	150	16	63	7	14	2
URM	48	4	20	42	6	12	22	46	15	31
Concrete	21	2	17	81	3	14	1	5	0	0
Adobe	4	1	1	25	1	25	2	50	0	0
Steel	2	1	2	100	0	0	0	0	0	0
Unknown	40	3	31	78	5	12	4	10	1	2
TOTALS	1053	100	796	75	165	16	92	9	30	3

Table 1: Damage to Historic Structures — County of Santa Cruz (Countywide Totals including Incorporated Cities)

STRUCTURAL TYPE	TOTAL		EARTHQUAKE DAMAGE							
			NONE		MINOR		MAJOR		DEMO	
	#	%	#	%	#	%	#	%	#	%
Wood	289	93	211	73	56	19	22	8	2	1
URM	5	1	4	80	0	0	1	20	0	20
Concrete	8	2	7	87	1	13	0	0	0	0
Adobe	1	1	0	0	0	0	1	100	0	0
Steel	1	1	1	100	0	0	0	0	0	0
Unknown	6	2	2	33	2	33	2	33	0	2
TOTALS	310	100	225	73	59	19	26	8	2	1

Table 2: Damage to Historic Structures - County of Santa Cruz (excluding Incorporated Cities)

County of Santa Cruz The political division referred to as the County of Santa Cruz includes all the land within the county borders excluding that encompassed by the incorporated cities. Aside from a few small, unincorporated cities, such as Aptos, Soquel, and Felton, the area is predominantly rural and lightly developed. Historic buildings are officially designated in the County's *Survey of Historic Resources*. Damage to these structures is tabulated in Table 2. One of the most significant historic structures in the county, the Castro Adobe, saw major damage in the earthquake, and was red-tagged by the California Office of Emergency Services (OES). The involvement of OES and the tagging system will be discussed later. Overall, however, damage to historic structures was relatively light, with only 8.4% of the buildings suffering major damage. Of the five unreinforced masonry buildings, only one suffered major damage.

City of Santa Cruz The City of Santa Cruz is situated on the center of the county's coast, and straddles the San Lorenzo river. There are several architecturally distinct neighborhoods present. The city had been surveyed twice to find buildings qualifying for historic designation, and the results were published in the two volume *Santa Cruz Historic Building Survey* (Page and Assoc. [6], Allen *et al.* [1]). Table 3 shows the overall damage statistics for these buildings. Damage to historic unreinforced masonry buildings in the city was severe, with only 35% of the structures remaining undamaged.

STRUCTURAL TYPE	TOTAL		EARTHQUAKE DAMAGE							
			NONE		MINOR		MAJOR		DEMO	
	#	%	#	%	#	%	#	%	#	%
Wood	493	88	409	82	65	13	19	3	10	2
URM	31	5	11	35	4	13	16	52	11	35
Concrete	8	1	7	87	1	12	0	0	0	0
Adobe	2	1	1	50	1	50	0	0	0	0
Steel	1	1	1	100	0	0	0	0	0	0
Unknown	25	4	21	84	3	12	1	4	0	0
TOTALS	560	100	450	80	74	13	36	7	21	4

Table 3: Damage to Historic Structures - City of Santa Cruz

Damage in the downtown historic district, the Pacific Garden Mall, was extensive. An example of the type of damage suffered by historic buildings on the mall was the Cooper House, a beautifully detailed unreinforced masonry building. This structure lost portions of its second story wall, suffered severe cracking above arches at the facade, experienced bowing and collapse of several ceilings, and sustained cracking in some shear walls. More generally, unreinforced masonry failures in the earthquake were mostly a result of inadequate connection details between floor/roof diaphragms and brick masonry walls. The three fatalities in the city were located in the historic district on the Pacific Garden Mall: two when a brick wall failed at its roof connection and collapsed on the Santa Cruz Coffee Roasting Company, and one when a similar failure caused a wall to collapse into Ford's Department Store. In this earthquake, collapse due to in-plane shear failure was rare, though there were several URM buildings where the characteristic X-cracking associated with such a failure mode was evident. Wood structures fared much better, with over 80% surviving the earthquake unscathed; most of the damage suffered by the remaining 20% was in the form of (or due to) brick chimney failure. The two adobe structures in the city fared well: the worst damage was at the Craig-Lorenzana Adobe, where minor cracking and spalling was observed at the top of some of the adobe walls. The Neary-Rodriquez Adobe on School Street was undamaged, despite heavy damage to the masonry tower of the nearby Holy Cross Roman Catholic Church. It is interesting to note that despite the tragic losses of notable buildings on the Pacific Garden Mall, overall only 36 (6.4%) of the 560 buildings on the city's historic survey sustained major damage. This is mostly a result of the high number of wood frame structures on the survey (493).

City of Watsonville The City of Watsonville is located inland on the north banks of the Pajaro River, which also forms a border with Monterey County to the south. It has an old downtown civic and commercial district, surrounded by prime agricultural land. In general, buildings in Watsonville were harder hit than in any of the other incorporated cities, and historic structures were no exception (see Table 4). 59 (55.7%) of the city's 106 historic buildings were damaged in the earthquake, and 30 (28.3%) experienced major damage, compared with the overall totals above of only 92 out of 1053 (8.7%) buildings suffering major damage for the entire county. There was one fatality associated with the collapse of a brick parapet from the historic Oddfellows building: a woman was killed while putting change in a parking meter. A large percentage of the wood structures suffered major damage (27.8%). These unusually high damage totals were probably a result of poor soil conditions in the Watsonville area (EERI [4]).

| STRUCTURAL TYPE | TOTAL | | EARTHQUAKE DAMAGE | | | | | | | |
| | | | NONE | | MINOR | | MAJOR | | DEMO | |
	#	%	#	%	#	%	#	%	#	%
Wood	79	74	31	39	26	33	22	28	2	28
URM	12	11	5	41	2	17	5	42	4	42
Concrete	5	5	3	60	1	20	1	20	0	20
Adobe	1	1	0	0	0	0	1	100	0	100
Unknown	9	9	8	89	0	0	1	11	1	11
TOTALS	106	100	47	44	29	27	30	28	7	28

Table 4: Damage to Historic Structures - Watsonville

City of Capitola Capitola is on the Santa Cruz coast, about four miles east of the city of Santa Cruz. It was originally a resort town, founded in 1867, by Frederic Hihn. No major structural damage was observed to occur in historic buildings in the City of Capitola, where most of the buildings in the historic districts are wood framed. Four of the 76 (5.3%) historic buildings in Capitola saw minor damage. All of these were wood framed structures.

City of Scotts Valley There is only one structure in Scotts Valley that is a designated historic landmark: the Hiram D. Scotts House. It is a wood frame building and survived the earthquake without damage.

POST-QUAKE RESPONSE

Damage Evaluations

OES Assessments By the morning of October 18, volunteers from the California Office of Emergency Services (OES) were inspecting damaged structures in the County of Santa Cruz. These engineers, architects, and building inspectors came from all over the State of California, with a large number of inspectors being imported from the Los Angeles area. These inspectors were trained to provide emergency safety evaluations of buildings as per the Applied Technology Council publication, ATC-20 (ATC [2]). The intent of this document is to provide guidelines for the *rapid* assessment of structural *safety*. Red, gold, and green tags are used to post a building as unsafe, limited entry, or safe, depending on the level of damage and the likelihood of further collapse. Although the mission of the inspectors is clearly stated in ATC-20, the tagging procedure sometimes caused a great deal of concern throughout the county, where local owners and officials believed that the evaluations represented a final engineering judgement for the structure. In reality, the OES inspections were merely a rapid, practical means to provide for public safety in the post-event period, and they were not to be considered a final condemnation for any structure without further, more in-depth structural evaluations. Because of the misinterpretation of the role of the OES inspectors, some owners would not allow their property to be evaluated for fear of being "red-tagged". They believed that the application of such a tag would ultimately result in the demolition of their building. Unfortunately, in some cases, this fear was justified, when the local authorities quickly slated for demolition structures with red tags, even though such action was not the intent of the tagging procedure.

Santa Cruz City/County Inspectors Locally, City and County inspectors provided post-earthquake evaluations in the form of reviewing proposals for structural repairs or demolitions after the earthquake. Almost all of the proposals for earthquake repairs were granted. In the thirty days immediately following the earthquake, approval of demolition plans was granted by the City of Santa Cruz *without* review by the local historic commission. This resulted in most of the early demolitions of historic structures, especially those on the Pacific Garden Mall.

"Second-Opinion" Inspectors Expert engineering firms were called upon to perform detailed structural evaluations of some historic buildings that had been "red-tagged" as unsafe. The owners of one adobe structure in the unincorporated county would not allow OES inspectors access to their property, preferring instead to rely on the opinion of an engineer experienced in adobe construction. In the case of the Cooper House in Santa Cruz City, four teams of experts reviewed the damage to the structure, with varying levels of concern about the current safety of the building and the need for demolition.

Park Service Observation/Inspection The National Park Service sent a team of observers to the area damaged by the Loma Prieta earthquake on October 29. The team included architects, engineers, and photographers expert in the repair and rehabilitation of historic buildings. The team was sent primarily to observe and record damage to buildings and had no official power to make recommendations regarding the structural condition of damaged buildings.

FEMA Reconstruction Funding

The misinterpretation of the availability of Federal Emergency Management Agency (FEMA) emergency work funds contributed to some of the quick decisions to demolish structures shortly after the earthquake. There was a general belief that FEMA demolition funds would be available only for demolitions that took place within 30 days of the main shock. Actually, the applicable federal regulations for disaster assistance (4 CFR Part 206) allow up to six months for "emergency work". Emergency work includes debris clearance, shoring, fencing, and demolition.

Concerns Regarding Demolition

Within seven days of the earthquake, the National Trust for Historic Preservation was sending letters to the city officials of Santa Cruz warning against "hasty demolition of older buildings that might not actually be as unsafe as they appear." The removal of such structures can seriously effect the historic and aesthetic character of a community. Unfortunately, in the confusion following the earthquake, there was a desire to quickly remove damaged structures. The National Park Service recommends that there be closer interaction between their historic preservation experts and FEMA.

In the thirty days following the quake, there was no demolition review by historic resource commissions. Emergency legislation was passed in November of 1989, changing the California Public Resources Code to contain a provision assuring such review. This law has been successfully implemented in the County of Santa Cruz since November, 1989.

Recovery

Recovery from the earthquake damage within the county has been slow. Concerns regarding the safety of damaged unreinforced masonry structures have led to the demolition of 15 buildings in the county, more than half of them on the Pacific Garden Mall, including the Cooper

House. This represents 31.4% of the total historic URM building stock. Countywide, including the incorporated cities, 30 historic buildings of all structural types have been razed. One notable preservation effort was attempted at the County Bank building on Pacific Garden Mall, where an effort was made to jack bearing walls back to plumb. Unfortunately, the procedure was unsuccessful. The only portions of the building now remaining are the two free-standing walls.

CONCLUSIONS: LESSONS LEARNED FROM LOMA PRIETA

Expected Damage to Historic Structures

Clearly, historic buildings are often severely damaged during earthquakes, and the Loma Prieta event was no exception. The well-known poor performance of unreinforced masonry was once again verified in the County of Santa Cruz. Several important features of the damage to older buildings in the county are notable:

- There seems to be little correlation between the age of historic buildings and observed damage within the studied group. Since most of the structures in the survey were constructed before the implementation of rational aseismic design procedures, they all seemed to equally suffer the effects of the earthquake, with variables such as structural type and location playing a more significant role than age.

- Connection failures in unreinforced masonry structures played a major role in the failures of walls. Out-of-plane masonry collapse due to lack of adequate bracing at floor and roof levels was much more common than collapse due to in-plane shear failures. Some buildings suffered major damage because of collapse of an inadequately braced wall in an adjacent structure.

- Although major damage occurs more frequently in unreinforced masonry structures, minor damage occurs at roughly the same rate as for other structural types.

- Interior damage to plaster can be severe in wood structures, due to their general ductility. Loss of historic wall finishes can be expected.

- The most common type of damage in wood structures is the loss of a masonry chimney, with attendant structural damage.

- Stone footings, even those of apparently low quality, performed adequately.

Coordination of Engineering Inspection Effort

In the aftermath of an earthquake, it is necessary to provide quick, emergency evaluations of buildings to provide for public safety. The procedures delineated in ATC-20 may be adequate for all structures, but their role must be understood. The standards could be revised to account for the specific needs of historic buildings. Emergency inspectors, or local preservation agents, could be made aware of those buildings with historic significance, and special evaluations should be made of such buildings to guard against their demolition. It has been proposed that a fourth tag in addition to the standard red, gold, and green tags be used to mark historic buildings (Pichard [7]).

In the case of historic buildings, it is necessary to have expert engineers make detailed evaluations following the emergency inspections by organizations such as OES. In-depth analyses will provide for the most accurate assessment of the strength of the historic building and provide planners with the data required to make informed decisions for the community. The value of the structure to the history of the community at large must be taken into account, and weighed against the cost estimates for structural repair. Several opinions should be required for important structures, with the relative expertise of the investigators taken into consideration.

Required Demolition Legislation

Legislation to prevent rash demolitions of buildings should be passed throughout the country. California's demolition review provision for historic structures could be used as a model. Such review by independent historic commissions, comprised of citizens and professionals familiar with the local architectural history, is necessary to protect local historic resources. Unfortunately, this law was passed a few weeks too late to save several important buildings in Santa Cruz county.

Retrofit Sensitive to the Needs of Historic Structures

Finally, it must be recognized that retrofit is necessary to bring historic buildings up to acceptable levels of safety and performance. In addition to the 4 deaths in the county occurring as a result of the failure of historic buildings, a large number of people were injured in and around such structures. Realistic retrofit must take into account the particular needs of older materials and structural systems, *as well as* the important safety requirements of the community. Accordingly, structural engineers should be made familiar with the unique requirements of historic buildings and should be aware of the concerns of preservationists. Most of the building failures in the County of Santa Cruz could have been prevented by proper seismic rehabilitation. While simple lessons taught by previous earthquakes have been learned, they have not been implemented. Unreinforced masonry walls will fail at floor and roof connections if proper bracing is not provided. The strengths of existing connections must be analytically verified, and technologies for the seismic upgrading of these connections should be developed. For an historic building, it is necessary to intervene as little as possible in order to preserve its architectural character. Methods must be developed that fully exploit the existing capacity of the structure, so that retrofit procedures can be as unobtrusive as practicable. Considering the strengths of partition walls, infill walls, and analyzing/retrofitting entire blocks of structures will help to minimize required interventions.

ACKNOWLEDGEMENTS

The authors would to thank Pilar Marien of Santa Cruz County, Dan Costelc and Bob Rivers of Capitola, Pete Katzleburger of the City of Santa Cruz, Paul Kaneko of Scotts Valley, and Dicksie Allen of Watsonville, for generously providing information related to earthquake damage of structures in their respective jurisdictions. We would also like to thank Carol Nelson of Santa Cruz, who took time during the hectic week after the earthquake to escort one of us (WBC) to the Pacific Garden Mall. We especially acknowledge the invaluable assistance of Mickey Ryan of the Santa Cruz Historical Society and Blaine Cliver of the National Park Service, both of whom provided much of the factual data in this report.

REFERENCES

1. Allen, D., Chase, J., and Gordon, J., Santa Cruz Historic Building Survey, Vol. II, Department of Planning and Community Development, Santa Cruz, CA, 1989.

2. Applied Technology Council, Procedures for Postearthquake Safety Evaluation of Buildings, Redwood City, CA, 1987.

3. City of Scotts Valley, Personal Communication with Paul Kaneko, Associate Planner.

4. Earthquake Engineering Research Institute, Earthquake Spectra — Loma Prieta Earthquake Reconnaissance Report, Supp. to Vol. 6, El Cerrito, CA, 1990.

5. National Park Service, The National Register of Historic Places, National Conference of State Historic Preservation Officers, American Association for State and Local History, Washington, D.C., 1989.

6. Page, C.H. and Associates, Santa Cruz Historic Building Survey, Vol. I, Department of Planning and Community Development, Santa Cruz, CA, 1976.

7. Pichard, Pierre, Emergency Measures and Damage Assessment After an Earthquake, UNESCO CLT/84/WS/14, 1984.

8. Verardo, J. and Verardo, D., Restless Paradise — Santa Cruz County — An Illustrated History, Windsor Publications, Inc., Northridge, CA, 1987.

SECTION 2: STABILISATION, UNDERPINNING AND REINFORCEMENT

Stabilisation of the Round Tower, Windsor Castle, Windsor, Berkshire, England

J. Dawson

Hockley & Dawson, Consulting Structural Engineers

ABSTRACT

The Round Tower at Windsor Castle is a mass masonry structure standing on a man-made chalk mound dating from the 11th Century.

The works described in this paper were ordered after an investigation revealed that movement, due to instability of the mound, had caused cracking that occurred during the night of 27/28th January 1988.

INTRODUCTION

Windsor Castle is the largest (covering some 5 hectares) and most significant castle in England. It has been a royal castle since the time of William the Conqueror and is mentioned in the Domesday Survey of 1086.

Apart from the Tower of London, William constructed fortifications at Berkhamstead, Hertford, Ongar, Rayleigh, Rochester, Tonbridge, Reigate and Guildford, as well as Windsor, to protect the seat of government.

The Round Tower, standing on an artifical mound constructed by digging a dry moat and heaping up the displaced chalk in the centre to a height of some 15m, is of the type known as a shell keep.

Original fortifications utilised trimmed trees rammed into the chalk.

In the twelfth century, Henry II transported heath stone from Bagshot and started building stone walls to replace timber fortifications enclosing the castle.

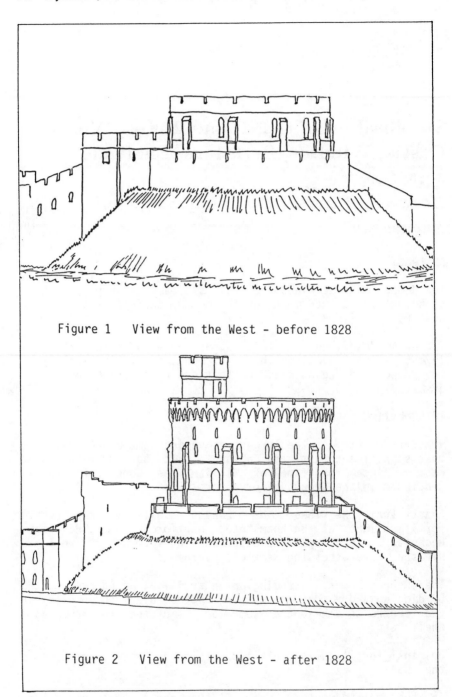

Figure 1   View from the West - before 1828

Figure 2   View from the West - after 1828

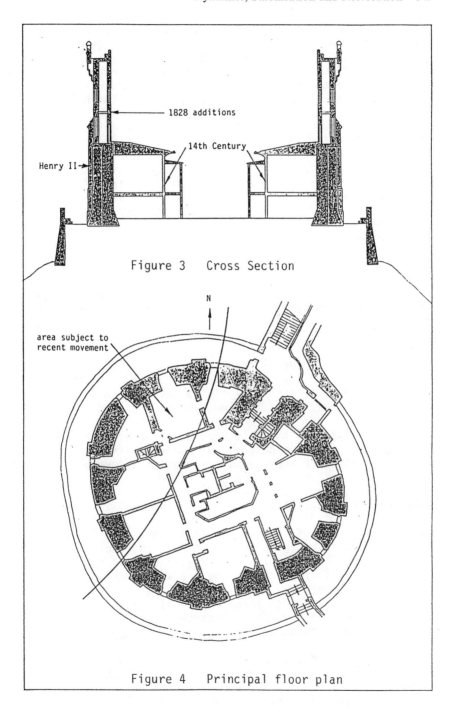

Figure 3   Cross Section

Figure 4   Principal floor plan

At this time the mound was some 100m diameter at base and 33m diameter at top. It is thought the mound shape (which is not a circle) dictated the Tower shape. The south access stair was also constructed. A well, excavated through the mound and chalk below to a depth of 50m and lined with stone for the top 18m was intended to provide water in time of seige.

In the 14th Century, a two-storey timber-framed residence was constructed (using 170 Oaks) within the Tower walls.

Apart from the installation of rainwater cisterns to eke out the water supply in the 17th Century, the Round Tower remained substantially unchanged until the walls were raised about 10m by Sir Jeffry Wyatville in 1828. He added an inner skin wall of brickwork to reinforce the old wall and provide a foundation for the new work.

CRACKING OF THE ROUND TOWER

The works described in this paper were ordered after an investigation revealed that movement, due to instability of the man-made mound, had caused the cracking which occurred during the night of 27/28th January 1989.

Examination of internal and external walls indicated that structural movements had been taking place for a long time, but the crack pattern related to the most recent movements suggested instability of the South-West quadrant.

Immediate steps were taken to monitor the newest cracks on a daily basis. All internal walls and ceilings and affected external areas were surveyed to provide an accurate record of the crack pattern.

GEOTECHNICAL INVESTIGATION

The composition of the mound fill and ground conditions in the area were investigated using eleven boreholes and five trial pits. The boreholes confirmed the mound to be composed of loose chalk fill placed on the chalk bedrock with a thin intervening layer of chalky topsoil at the surface of the bedrock (original ground level). Trial pits indicated the foundations of the Tower to be extremely shallow, in places only 0.2 to 0.3m below ground level.

Investigation indicated that the cracking resulted from movement of the Tower foundations due to instability of the underlying mound, this being constructed of loosely compacted chalk fill with very steeply sloping sides.

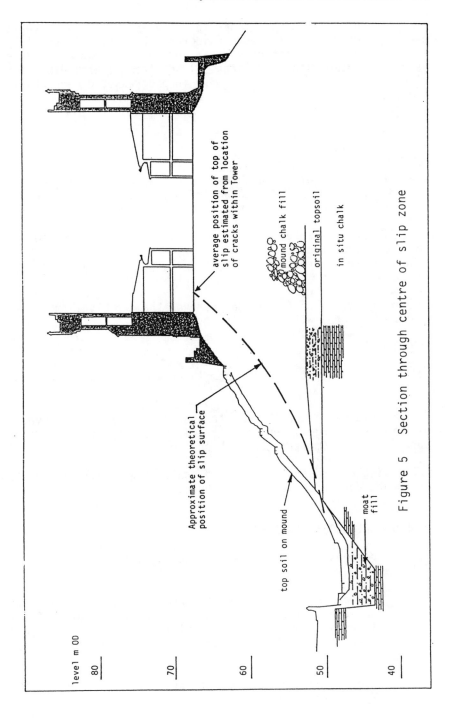

average position of top of
slip estimated from location
of cracks within Tower

mound chalk fill

original topsoil

in situ chalk

Approximate theoretical
position of slip surface

top soil on mound

moat
fill

level m OD

80

70

60

50

40

Figure 5   Section through centre of slip zone

Analysis of the mound indicated that stability had always been very marginal. It was considered that the instability was triggered by intensive rain during the night of 27/28th January coupled with additional load from scaffolding for stone cleaning works which were in progress. Old cracks in the masonry showed that similar movement of the mound had occurred in the past.

FIRST AID MEASURES

When the extent of the problem was realised it became obvious that design and implementation of remedial measures would take some time and during this time the Tower would be at risk. Ground drainage was installed in the mound slope to conduct surface water away and minimise water ingress thereby reducing the possibility of a recurrence of the high ground-water pressures that triggered the previous instability.

A decision was also taken to remove the archival material which was stored within the Tower.

MONITORING

Intensive observation of the Tower was carried out from an early stage.

This included accurate monitoring of:- cracks; levels; dimensions; targets on Towers walls (in three dimensions) borehole inclinometers (for sub-soil movement)

Monitoring records have indicated continuing small movements which are consistent with geotechnical analysis.

REMEDIAL MEASURES CONSIDERED

Eight options for remedial measures were considered as follows:-

1. **Do nothing to the Tower structure but, as a safety measure, discontinue the operational use of the Tower and remove all external loads.** (The least-cost solution with a definite risk of further slope movement and cracking).

2. **Remove the upper two storeys of the Tower.** (The Wyatville extension of 1828).

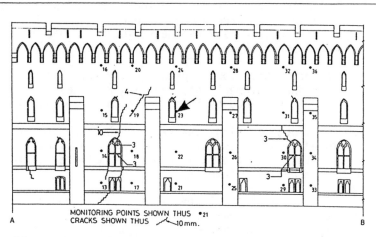

Figure 6   Developed elevation of cracked external wall

(see Figure 7)

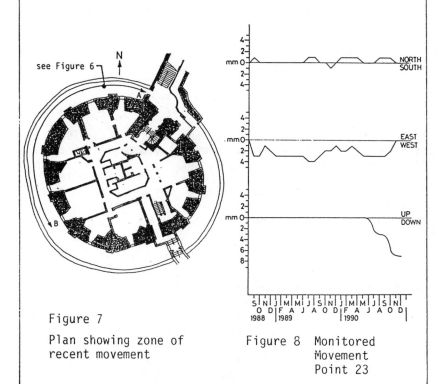

Figure 7

Plan showing zone of
recent movement

Figure 8   Monitored
Movement
Point 23

3. **Underpin the Tower using conventional piles.** (Provided a strong new support for the Tower foundations and achieved a reasonable improvement in mound stability.)

4. **Underpin the Tower using the Pali Radice system.** (Further movement of the Tower necessary before support provided by this system could be mobilised).

5. **Construct a ring beam around the Tower to widen its foundations.** (Similar to Option 3 with piles omitted, so that, for a similar order of cost the result would be technically inferior).

6. **Place fill on the lower parts of the mound slope, (and infill the moat).** (Provided a significant improvement in mound slope stability. Would not cater for excessive bearing pressures under the Tower wall. Would substantially alter the Tower setting).

7. **Grout-up the chalk fill in the mound.** (Inappropriate solution for this problem).

8. **Mechanically tie the mound slope with ground anchors.** (Inappropriate solution for this problem).

Option 3 was adopted as, of the options considered, it provided the best technical solution with minimal detrimental impact on the Tower and its environs.

The method of construction devised was also considered to provide gradual improvement in stability until final jacking relieved the mound of Tower loading.

UNDERPINNING THE TOWER WALLS

The underpinning system developed involved insertion of 50 concrete-encased steel needle frames to form a continuous ring beam under the Tower walls. This ring beam had the effect of lowering the foundations by 2m improving the temporary condition and permitting installation of 81 0.6 diameter reinforced concrete piles to transfer the Tower wall load down to rock chalk.

Procedure:

Figure 9.a   Set out position of 50 needle frames.

Figure 9.b   Install temporary works.

Figure 9.c   Insert first props of needle frames 'U'.

Figure 9.d   Using template insert second props, first diagonal and booms of needle frames 'U'.

Figure 9.e   Using template insert third props, second diagonal and booms of needle frames 'U'.

Figure 9.f   Using template insert fourth and fifth props together with other members in sequence to complete needle frames 'U'.

Figure 9.g   Using similar procedure widen excavations and insert needle frames 'V', fix reinforcement and encase with concrete on completion.

Following similar procedure, insert needle frame pairs 'WX' and 'YZ' and encase with concrete on completion.

Excavate 'dumplings' between needle frame pairs in sequence, fix reinforcement and fill with concrete.

At this stage the Tower foundations are in the form of a reinforced concrete ring beam 2m lower than the original construction. (The current stage).

Piling

Pile boring involves risk of vibration causing further damage to the Tower.

Installation and vibration monitoring of a working test pile determined acceptable vibration limits in advance of general piling operations.

Monitoring of mound and structure movement may also control piling operations in addition to vibration considerations.

Restriction of vibration limits and designation of construction techniques were intended to avoid unacceptable

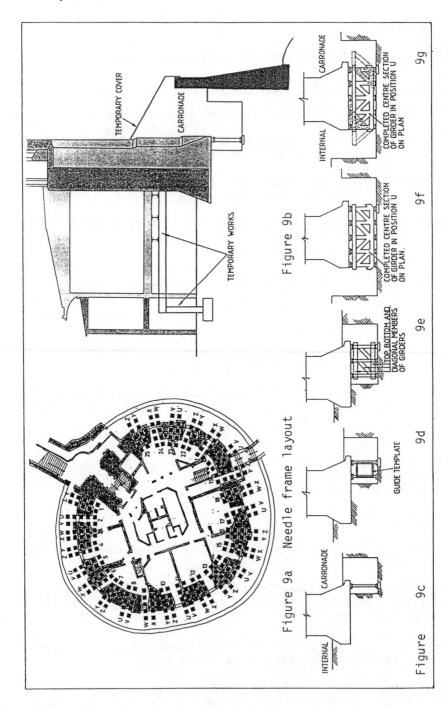

Figure 9a   Needle frame layout

TEMPORARY COVER

CARRONADE

TEMPORARY WORKS

Figure 9b

CARRONADE

INTERNAL

Figure   9c

GUIDE TEMPLATE

9d

TOP, BOTTOM AND
DIAGONAL MEMBERS
OF GIRDERS

9e

COMPLETED CENTRE SECTION
OF GIRDER IN POSITION U
ON PLAN.

9f

CARRONADE

INTERNAL

COMPLETED CENTRE SECTION
OF GIRDER IN POSITION U
ON PLAN

9g

settlement of the fill causing further cracking of the Tower as a result of, for example:-

(a) vibration-induced consolidation (compaction of the infill)
(b) vibration-induced movement of pre-existing slip plane
(c) overbreak around pile bore

The piling sequence was devised to provide support to the Tower Walls at the earliest opportunity, particularly in the area subject to recent movement.

Piling Installation

Vibration of structure and mound monitored continuously during installation of every pile.

Installation progress of all piles governed by vibration control of structure and mound.

Procedure:

Figure 10   Survey needle positions and establish pile positions.

Install test pile in Group G10 following instructions given by Assistant Resident Engineer.

Using two rigs install remaining piles in preliminary group G10.

Carry out integrity test on piles, cast and obtain approval of Supervising Officer.

Figure 11   Cast ring beams over pile Group G10 and fix projecting arms to needle frames. Have laminated packs available that may be installed quickly in an emergency.

Install laminated packs when concrete has achieved adequate strength.

Install piles to Groups G2 - G10 in sequence, concreting ring beam, fixing needle frame arms and inserting laminated packs as groups are completed.

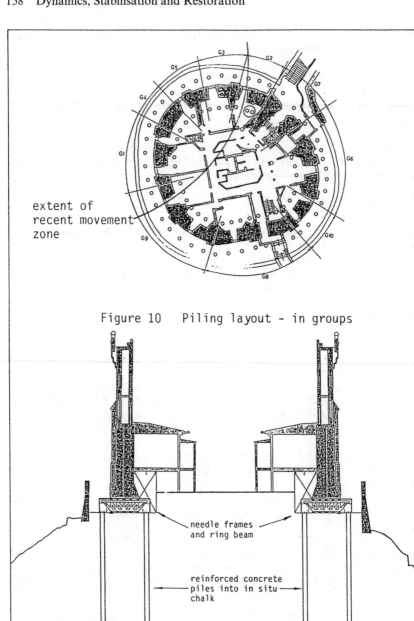

Figure 10   Piling layout - in groups

needle frames
and ring beam

reinforced concrete
piles into in situ
chalk

level of in situ chalk

Figure 11   Section on completion of underpinning

Jacking

To ensure that a substantial proportion of dead load is carried by the piles sequential jacking is necessary between needle frames and piled ring beam.

Summary

At the time of writing, installation of needle frames and concrete casing is complete and piling is due to commence. It is hoped that monitoring during the piling process will provide information on the vibration tolerance of the structure.

ACKNOWLEDGEMENTS

For permission to print this paper:

The Department of the Environment
The Property Services Agency

For help with history:

English Heritage

For Geotechnical notes:

C. J. Candler of Scott Wilson Kirkpatrick
& Partners - Geotechnical Consultants.

Application of Base Isolation on an Existing Unreinforced Masonry Building

R. Antonucci, R. Giacchetti

*Istituto di Scienza e Tecnica delle Costruzioni,
University of Ancona, Via delle Brecce Bianche,
Italy*

ABSTRACT

Base isolation represents a valid strategy for the
reduction of seismic risks, alternative to the classical approach based on the concept of ductility,
whenever the decrease of damage both to structural
and nonstructural components represents a design
parameter. In particular, such a strategy can be
advantageously applied in cases of strategic buildings where feasibility of the structure must be
guaranteed in emergency situations and the contents
represent an economical and/or cultural value to
be safeguarded. Among the available and already
widely experimented isolation systems, the one that
utilizes a combination of high damping rubber bearings and teflon sliders is presented. This system
has the advantage of being sufficiently rigid late-
rally to prevent the building movements under the
actions of the wind and of low intensity seismic sha-
kings (due to the effect of the friction developed by
teflon supports). Under medium and high intensity
seismic actions, once the friction threshold is overcome, the system changes the building, dynamics characteristics (decrease in fundamental frequency, increase in "equivalent" viscous damping for the effect
of hysteresis). The base isolation system utilized
for the rehabilitation design of the historical building "Villa Favorita" site of an Institute for economical studies is presented and the structural
response is also analyzed. A series of constructive
details and a cost analysis complete the examination
of the technique.

INTRODUCTION

Earthquakes are among the natural catastrophes over which mankind has no control. Even moderate earthquakes can cause loss of lives, and serious damage or loss of property. For several years, engineers have favored tying the building rigidly to its foundations. This, however, causes large forces to be tranmitted to the building. Ground motion is amplified in the structure and the roof response can be as high as 5 to 6 times the motion at the base.

Conventional seismic design relies on ductility. The effect of ground motion can be thought of as an input energy; this energy is transmitted to the structure. Part of it is transmitted back to the soil and the other part causes amplification. Structural and non-structural elements will deform beyond their elastic range. The distributed non-linear behavior is in fact partial damage that certain structures cannot afford.

Conventional design focuses on avoiding collapse. However, it is short of safeguarding the superstructure, non structural components, and loose contents. In many cases, the demand from the seismic design goes beyond avoiding collapse. Such a demand is encountered in the design of critical facilities like fire stations and hospitals. These are mostly needed directly after an earthquake. They must not only survive the earthquake, but also remain functional.

Another example of such a demand is represented by the existing historical buildings, seismically unsafe. In this particular case, the main concern would be to interfere as little as possible with the existing architectural layout and also to avoid damage to the architectural features.

A conventional retrofit might not provide the earthqhake protection needed. A strengthened building becomes stiffer. Its fundamental frequency is more likely to fall in the typical frequency range of ground motion. It will amplify the ground accelerations and be subjected to severe damage.

A NEW METHOD FOR SEISMIC DESIGN

Base isolation is a seismic design strategy based on partially detaching the structure from its foundations. This is realized by creating a horizontally soft interface at the base of the superstructure. As a result, the fundamental frequency of the isolated structure is very low, outside the range of frequencies of ground excitation. The controlling mode in the response is the one where the superstructure floats on its horizontally flexible mounts like a rigid body.

This technique transforms the shaking of upper stories into a gentle motion. The interstory drift is drastically reduced and the superstructure is most likely to remain elastic even under moderate to strong earthquakes. Small elastic strains will not affect the non-structural elements like plasters and ornamental details, and the gentle low frequency motion will not overturn and damage loose contents. Hence, base isolation meets the main three requirements of preservation: saving human lives, keeping the superstructure elastic, and protecting loose contents.

Several base isolation systems have been proposed and the choice depends on the type of application [1]. There are several requirements from a base isolation system. It must provide wind restraint, stability, and fail-safe capacity.

A commonly used system consists of multilayered elastomeric bearings, often accompanied by accessories for enhanced energy dissipation. Systems that consist of solely rubber bearings might be susceptible to large horizontal base drift which could cause bearing buckling or roll-out.

On the other hand, a purely sliding system can cause excessive drift once their sliding threshold is overcome, and they have no recentering capacity. A permanent base offset after an earthquake affects the functionality of the utility lines going into the building. Also, it causes dissymmetry in the seismic gap that the designer should create between the isolated structure and its corresponding ground structure. Another requirement an isolated structure should satisfy, is the presence of a rigid diaphragm at the base. The rigid diaphragm is very important to ensure that no differential movements will take place between the walls.

PROCEDURE FOR SEISMIC REHABILITATION

OBJECTIVES

The following illustrates the seismic rehabilitation of an existing unreinforced masonry building by base isolation. The system which has been used combines teflonstain-less steel sliders and rubber bearings. This system satisfies the main requirements discussed above and has other advantages. The rubber bearings are installed under the peripheral structural elements while the sliders are installed under the interior ones. The system has extensively been tested on the earthquake simulator of the University of California and results were presented by Chalhoub and Kelly [2].

THE BUILDING

The building to be retrofitted, is the Villa Favorita near the city of Ancona, Italy, (figure 1). The Villa was constructed at the end of the 18th century and represents a significant example of historic heritage because inside its rooms the surrender of the Papal States was signed after the battle of Castelfidardo which gave birth to the State of Italy.

From an architectural standpoint, the four-story building represents an original and organic archetype in that two main coaxial ring-shaped masonry wall systems, erected around a large inner area, are coupled by secondary radial masonry panels. Four clusters of small-to-medium size rooms are enclosed by the two rings while the master living quarters are located at the center (Figures 2, 3). Also, of some interest are the frescoes which decorate the walls and the vaults of several rooms (Figure 4).

From the engineer's standpoint, the interior masonry walls are either made of hand-hewn sandstone blocks interleaved every two or three layers by a horizontal layer of clay bricks or wholly made of brickwork, depending on whether the thickness is larger than or equal to one head. The perimeter wall is composed of an outer skin of clay bricks with joints sealed with "cocciopesto" and an inner panel made of sandstone blocks interleaved by layers of clay bricks. The first floor is partially carried by masonry vaults and partially by timber joists while the remaining floors and the roof are wholly carried by timber joists.

STATE OF CONSERVATION

At present, the building is abandoned and strongly degraded due to both the lack of maintenance and the effects of earthquakes that struck the Ancona area in the recent past. Furthermore, the first story shows evidence of diffused humidity coming up from the foundations.

THE REHABILITATION DESIGN PHYLOSOPHY

Once the building is restored, it will become the site of an Institute for Economical Studies. In consideration of its historic and artistic quality, the rehabilitation method has been chosen in such a way as to completely preserve the building's original and distinctive structural layout. The only new structural element will be the reinforced concrete slab at the ground level beneath which a ventilated basement will encase the utility lines. Particular attention has been paid to the interception of the upraising humidity. In order to accomplish the above-mentioned architectural and technical requirements and at the same time to provide the building and its contents with an effective earthquake protection against seismic damage, base isolation has been considered for the rehabilitation.

It is worth noting that some of the structural works (especially at the foundation level) that would have been necessary even in a conventional design make the base isolation option cost-effective as is shown in one of the next sections.

PRELIMINARY DESIGN OF THE BASE ISOLATION SYSTEM

The unreinforced masonry walls will be detached at their base from their foundations. This will be achieved by gradually cutting and jacking starting with the exterior walls and working inwards. The initial layout of the foundations with the recommended locations of the bearings and sliders is shown in Figure 5. Based on this layout, the maximum span of a base beam is limited to 3.00 m. Since vertical clearance is an important factor in such applications, sliders are an excellent choice because they can be installed within a very small vertical space. A teflon-stainless steel slider can be designed so that it doesn't occupy more than 0.04 m in the vertical direction. The rubber bearings will be installed at the periphery and the sliders will be installed at all the other locations. Only 50% of the live load is considered in computing the lateral load according to the current Italian seismic code (the whole load is considered in the vertical direction for the service load condition). The reduced vertical load carried by each bearing and each slider is shown in Figure 5 (the number in brackets is the dead load plus the live load). The total weight of the building is 49200 KN.

SIZING THE SLIDERS

The layout discussed in the previous section allocates to the sliding bearings a total weight of 30960 KN. Thus, they will carry about 63% of the total weight of the building. A similar system was tested on the shake table at the University of California,

Berkley where the sliders carried about 60% of the total weight of the structural model and good results where obtained [2]. Besides enhancing the energy dissipation capacity of the system, the sliders should ensure wind restraint under design wind loads. Based on the Italian code, the wind pressure acting on the projected area of the building is:

p = 74 daN/m2

leading to a total wind lateral force of 33940 daN.

The vertical load carried by the sliders is 30960 kN and, with a friction coefficient of 2.5%, the base shear threshold is 774 kN. Since 774 kN > 339.4 kN the structure will not slide under the wind load. The total number of sliders is 36. Two types of sliders have been designed. The former is sized for a vertical force of 900 kN, the latter for a vertical force of 620 kN. The plan dimensions of the sliders are respectively 0.36x0.36 m. and 0.30x0.30 m. A woven teflon fiber material WTF4 or WTF6 can be used in this case along with a mirror finish stainless steel plate (Figure 6).

SIZING THE RUBBER BEARINGS

The effective stiffness of the system, Keff, is shown in Figure 7. Denoting by Vt the design base shear, D the design base displacement, Kr the stiffness of the rubber, and Vs the base shear threshold, then:

Keff = Vt/D   and   Kr = (Vt - Vs)/D = Keff -Vs/D   (1)

The design displacement can be obtained from the SEAOC [3] formula:

D = 0.25 x ZNST/B   where: (2)

D = design displacement in metres,
T = period of the base isolated structure in seconds,
S = soil factor,
N = near field coefficient,
Z = zone factor,
B = coefficient related to the damping of the specific isolation system.

Assuming S = 1.5, N = 1.0, Z = 0,20 and B = 1.7, in consideration of the fact that the system with 63% sliders is expected to provide an equivalent viscous damping of about 30%, then D = 0.0448 T m. The fundamental period is obtained from:

$$T = 2 \pi \quad Wt/g \text{ Keff} \tag{3}$$

where Wt is the total weight carried by the isolation system and g is the gravitational constant.
Examining the site specific linear elastic design
spectrum (Figure 8) a period of 1.5 seconds is desirable to drastically cut down the spectral acceleration. Then the displacement at the center of masses
is D = 0,067 m, the required effective stiffness is
Keff = 88046 kN/m and the required rubber stiffness
is Kr = 76494 kN/m. The rubber stiffness has been
provided by 24 bearings. Thus, a typical bearing must
have a horizontal stiffness Kh = 3187 kN/m. Assuming
an IRHD 60 compound the shear modulus G at ambient
temperature is about 1.06 MN/m2. The required area A
of the rubber bearing can be obtained from:

Kh = GA/tr

    Where tr is the total thickness of rubber. The
total thickness of rubber, tr, is selected such that
the shear strain under the design displacement would
not exceed 75%. The total tr is then 0.067/0.75 =
= 0.0893, say 0.09 m. The requirement on the cross
section is then A = 0.270 m2. This is achieved with
a circular bearing, 0.60 m in diameter (Figure 9).

    In order to provide high vertical stiffness, a
shape factor s = 30 has been selected leading to a
thickness of a single rubber layer of 5 mm.

    The resulting vertical stiffness is then Kv =
= 13987.74 MN/mq, the maximum vertical load in a
bearing is 10500 kN and the vertical deflection is
δv = 0.00075 m which is very small.

    Thus, the bearings that will be used for this
application consist of 18 rubber layers, 5 mm thick,
interleaved by 17 steel shims, 3 mm thick, with two
limiting steel plates, 50 mm thick. The bearing is
shown in Figure 9.

    For the system illustrated in the preceding sec-
tions, the design base shear to be resisted by the
superstructure is provided by SEAOC as:

Vt = 1.378 Kmax D/Rw   (6)

    Where Kmax is the maximum effective stiffness of
the system and Rw is a coefficient that depends on
the structural configuration. In our case is Keff =
= Kmax and Rw = 6 for a bearing wall system in which
the lateral load resistance is provided by masonry
shear walls. Equation (6) leads to Vt = 1820 kN. This
is equivalent to a base shear of 0.037 Wt. For comparison, the base shear of the fixed base structure is
obtained using the Italian Code. The base shear coef-

ficient is obtained by the formula:

Vt/Wt = C * R * ε * ß

where C is the specific seismic zone factor, R the normalized inelastic spectral response depending on the structural period, ε the specific soil amplification factor, ß is a ductility coefficient depending on the structural configuration. In our case:

C = 0,07

R = 1 (for T = 0.1 H/B = 0.32 seconds where H is the height and B the maximum plan dimension of the building)

ε = 1.1

ß = 4 (for masonry structures), then:

Vt/Wt = 0.308 which is 8.3 times the base shear coefficient obtained with the base isolation system.

THE GROUND STRUCTURE

As discussed earlier, the design displacement is 0.067 m. In order that this amount of displacement be allowed, a gap has to be built all around the perimeter of the building. In our case an underground path has been designed (Figure 10) which might also be used for maintenance inspections and in the case of substitution of the bearings. In the same way, hollow spaces at the center and near the short side of the octagonal plan have been realized. Reinforced concrete elements have been designed, both at the top and at the bottom of each bearing. The upper element is formed by a reinforced concrete cross beam which has the twofold function of 1) connecting the reinforced concrete longitudinal side girders which are built in contact with the masonry walls at the foundation level and 2) diffusing the concentrate load (Figure 11) transmitted by the bearing. Tie rods have been placed across the beams in order to improve the masonry-to-girders connection. In order to diminish the compressive stress upon the soil at the bearing location, enlargements of the existing footing have been designed which may also be used as supports of jacks in the case that substitution of some damaged bearing after an earthquake be required. The separation of building from its old foundation will be obtained by sawing; the vertical clearance of 0.03 ÷ 0.04 m will be formed by a unique continuous cut. Before doing that, the rubber bearings and sliders will be placed on their seats. For this reason the

cross-beams, the plynths and the side girders are   to
be previously built. On the contrary, the   reinforced
concrete base diaphragm will be built later on.

COST ESTIMATE

The economic comparison between a   typical conventional seismic   rehabilitation   and   the base   isolation
technique is limited at the foundation level because,
from this   comparison it is   already possible to make
significant considerations. In fact, when it is   needed doing work   for eliminating the   upraising   humidity (diaphragm and humidity insulation) base   isolation becomes   economically   interesting even   without
considering the advantages for the superstructure due
to the decrease   in base shear.   As discussed in previous sections, the extra works in the base isolation
solution are: excavations, foundation   enlargements,
cutting of masonry, supply of   bearings and connected
works, the   reinforced   concrete   wall of the   underground path.   On the other hand, with   the separation
of the building from its old foundation, the humidity
problems will vanish and   so it is no   more necessary
to do   expensive   insulation work .   A cost estimate,
based on   the average   expenses   in Ancona, leads to a
35% cost increment   at the   foundation   level for the
base isolation solution.   This cost   increment   might
be compensated for by the   decrease   in the amount   of
work   at the upper levels.

CONCLUSIONS

One of the main issues in the preservation of   historical buildings is the interference with the existing
architecture.   Conventional   techniques   often affect
the configuration of the superstructure   because they
are based on direct strengthening of structural   components.   Base isolation concentrates the alterations
of the existing structure at its base. Minimal intervention is needed in upper levels.

Seismic rehabilitation by   conventional techniques
does not keep the structural and non-structural   components   from   undergoing   large deformations.   Large
cyclic deformations   dissipate the energy transmitted
from the ground   on the   expense   of partial or total
damage. Base isolation provides   the energy   dissipation mechanism at the base   and   drastically   reduced
the ductility demand from the superstructure.

The use of   a system   comprising   teflon-stainless
steel   sliders   and rubber   bearings   is   particulary
interesting   for masonry buildings   due   to a drastic
reduction of demolitions.

From an economical comparison (limited to the works at the foundation level) it is possible to show that the base isolation technique may be economically very valid even not considering the effect of the dramatic reduction of base shear (in our case 8.3 timer) that requires only minor strengthening.

Furthermore, since the rehabilitation of historic building often requires special elements (like a slab at the ground level), these elements may be considedered as a part of the base isolation system thus reducing the total cost of this technique.

REFERENCES

[1] Kelly James M., "Aseismic Base Isolation: Review and Bibliography," Soil Dynamics and Earthquake Engineering, Vol. 5, No. 3, 1986.

[2] Chalhoub Michel S., And Kelly James M., "Earthquake Simulator Evaluation of a Combined Sliding Bearing and Tension Controlled Rubber Bearing Isolation System," ASME Pressure Vessels and Piping Conference, Volume 181, pp.59-64, 1989.

[3] Structural Engineers Association of California, "Tentative General Requirements for the Design and Construction of Seismic-Isolated Structures". March 1989.

FIG. 1 VILLA FAVORITA

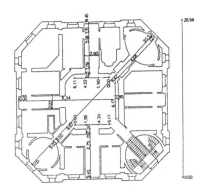

FIG. 2 PLAN

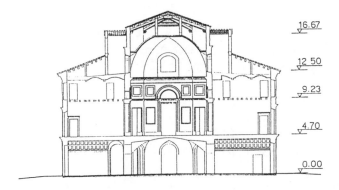

FIG. 3   SECTION

FIG. 4 THE FRESCOES WHICH
DECORATE THE WALL
OF VILLA FAVORITA

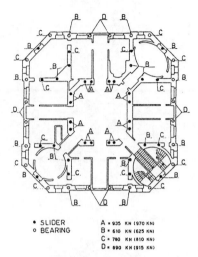

• SLIDER   A = 935 KN (970 KN)
○ BEARING   B = 610 KN (625 KN)
             C = 780 KN (810 KN)
             D = 890 KN (915 KN)

FIG. 5 LOCATION OF THE
        RUBBER BEARINGS,
        SLIDERS AND VERTICAL
        LOAD.

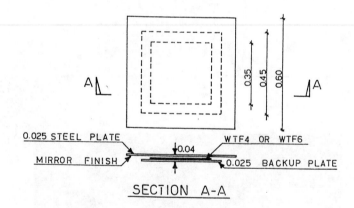

SECTION A-A

FIG. 6 SLIDER

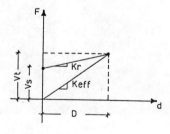

FIG. 7

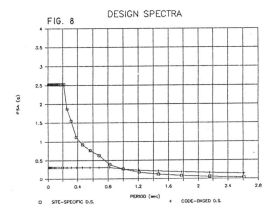

FIG. 8   DESIGN SPECTRA

SITE-SPECIFIC D.S.   CODE-BASED D.S.

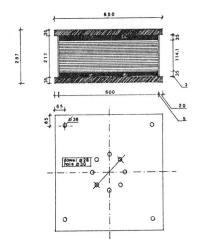

FIG.9   RUBBER   BEARING

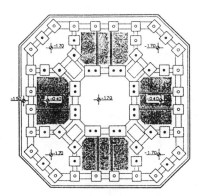

FIG. 10   FOUNDATION STRUCTURES
AND PATH AROUND THE
BASE OF THE BUILDING.

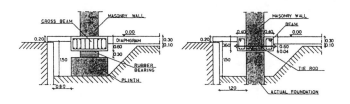

FIG 11   COSTRUCTIVE   DETAILS

Regional Groundwater Control for Two Zones Comprising Several Historical Buildings in Cairo/Egypt

M. Atalla, R. Fouad

EGY-TECH Group, Consulting Engineerings, Cairo/Egypt

ABSTRACT

Continuous rise of groundwater level has been noticed in Cairo
in the last two decades. The rise is mainly caused by surface
shallow groundwater from leaking watersupply and sewage systems.
Effect of groundwater on the existing historical buildings and
monuments in Greater Cairo is now a well known issue continuously discussed in the mass media. Hundreds of Islamic,Coptic
and Roman monuments some of which are from the first century
are badly affected by the groundwater. Regional groundwater
control is proposed for two zones of Greater Cairo comprising
several historical buildings and monuments namely : Old Cairo
and Elgamaliya-Elghoria. Four sections compose the presentwork:
Greater Cairo Scale , Regional Scale , Site Specific Scale and
Conclusions.

INTRODUCTION

Several monuments and historical buildings in Cairo suffer
from the effect of groundwater. Mosques , Churches , Synagogue,
fortresses , Palaces , Tombs , Walls and Gates are the usual
type of buildings to be restored and which are affected by
groundwater. The rise of the groundwater in many regions of
Greater Cairo cause serious problems to Pharaonic (Sphinx
for example) , Coptic and Islamic monuments.

In some monuments , the flooring is flooded , specially
if the monument's flooring is lower than the surrounding
streets. For monuments having the flooring higher than the
surrounding streets , basements and surrounding trenchs may
be permanently flooded. Humid flooring and walls , deteriorated
limestone walls are usual effects of the near or above flooring groundwater. Capillary water infiltrates through walls and
columns and when this water evaporates , salts are left
noticeably on the outer surface of the building elements ,
leading to deterioration of the walls.

Historical buildings in Greater Cairo are concentrated mainly in three regions : Old Cairo , comprising Jewish , Coptic and Islamic monuments ; Elgamaliya-Elghoria districts comprising hundreds of Islamic monuments , churchs and convents of Babzewela and others ; and Giza pyramids and Sphinx zone.

Regional concentration of monuments illustrates the necessity to tackle the problem of saving these monuments from the effect of groundwater on regional scale. FIG. 1 shows how one street Elmoiz Ldin Ellah includes several Islamic monuments which suffer from a damaging effect of ever rising groundwater. However , present practice in the restoration of monuments is based on monument by monument basis or what can be called site specific scale.

Phenomena of rising groundwater level in Cairo has been observed in the last two decades mainly due to leakage of the watersupply and sewage systems and new reclamation and hectic growth areas. East of the River Nile has groundwater levels higher than the River Nile indicating that the River Nile is acting as a drain. Seemingly , the increase in ground-water level suggests that the inflow feeding the groundwater is greater than the outflow drained to the Nile. The problem is reversed in the West of the Nile where the outflow due to pumping of the groundwater for daily use exceeds the inflow and falling groundwater level is observed.

According to the extensive study of the Scientific Research Academy and the Groundwater Research Institute [1] concerning the groundwater studies for Greater Cairo, the rise in the groundwater level in the East of the Nile was estimated to be from 0.25 to 2.0 m in the last two decades . On the other side West Nile the fall in the groundwater was estimated by the same authority [1] to range from 1.0 to 3.0 m due to the extensive pumping from wells in the West Nile side. In one specific site in Old Cairo the authors noticed that the ground-waterlevel has risen 0.6 to 1.0 m in the last three years.

As necessitated by these considerations , groundwater conditions and types are reviewed in the present study on both Greater Cairo scale and regional scale. Locations of the two chosen regions proposed for groundwater control namely : Old Cairo and Elgamaliya-Elghoria are shown in FIG. 2.

It is worth noting that adopting the site specific scale i.e. monument by monument groundwater control in regions comprising tens to hundreds of historical buildings is practic-ally impossible due to the surrounding conditions of each monument.

GREATER CAIRO SCALE

The River Nile divides longitudinally Greater Cairo (FIG. 2) into two sides : East Nile and West Nile. Geomorphology of

FIG. 1   Elmoiz Ldin Ellah Street monuments in Elgamaliya-
Elghoria Zone

Greater Cairo (FIG.3) is quite explained by two plateaus :
Elmokatem in East side and Pyramids in the West side and two
flood plains usually referred to as East Nile and West Nile.

The historical geography of the River Nile and how it was
much wider in the ancient times was described by El-Sohby and
Mazen [2] based on several extensive historical documents
describing ancient Egypt. Complete areas are now based on re-
filled chanels and birkas (lakes).Other areas have thick filling or made ground superficial layers up to 15-20 m with ruins
and debris. This thickness has been developed over several
centuries. However , Topography of Greater Cairo is quite
plain in the flood plain areas (18 to 25 m absolute level i.e.
above MSL at Alexandria) and quite high in the plateaus areas
(100 to 200 m) with piedmont slopes transion between them (30
to 40 m and 40 to 60 m).

Geology of Greater Cairo is illustrated by FIG.4.
Quaternary deposits composing the plains consist of silt and
clay river deposits with prevailing thickness from 8.0 to 10.0m
and maximum thickness reaching 20.0 m. This deposits unit is
overlain by filling or made ground with varying thickness
reaching in some areas 20.0 m . Underlying the silt and clay
unit are about 100 m layers of sand and gravel with interbeded
clay lenses followed by about 300 m of intercolations of

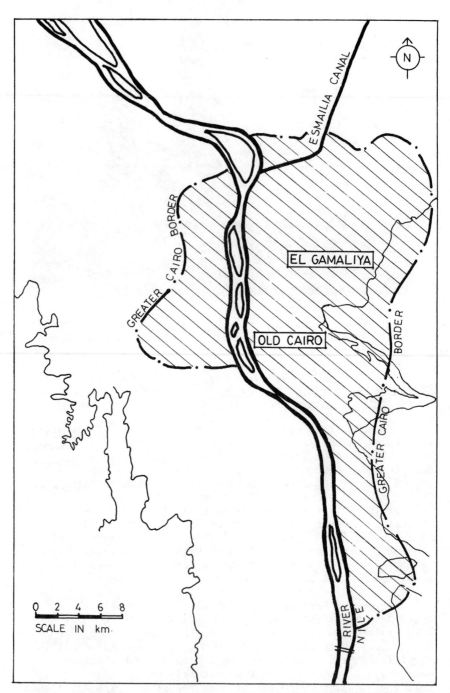

FIG. 2 : Location map of Greater Cairo indicating the two
considered zones.

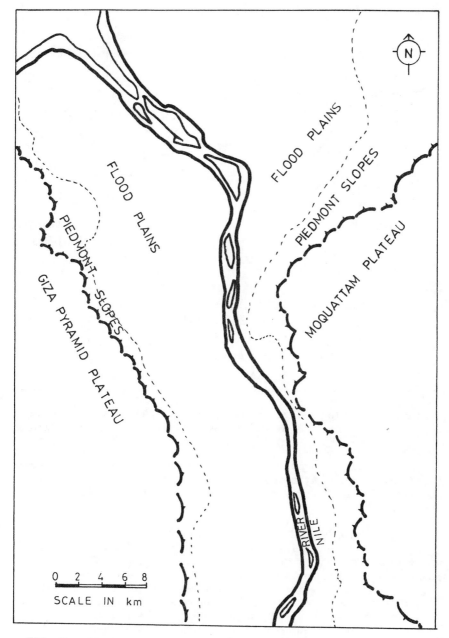

FIG. 3 : Geomorphology of Greater Cairo , Simplified from
        Reference [I].

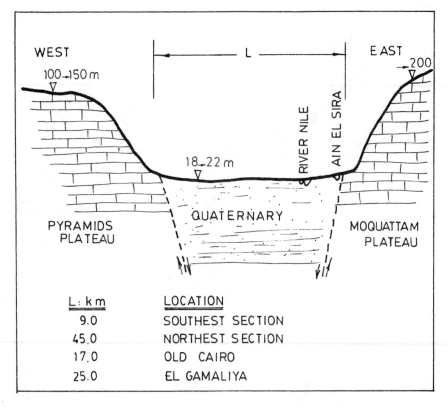

FIG. 4 : Geological Sections almost perpendicular to the
River Nile at different locations in Greater Cairo.

sand , gravel , and marl with layers of clay. Subsurface geology
of Elmokattem and Pyramids plateaus are described by Hefny and
Khalid [3] , El-Nahas , Mostafa and Abdeltawab [4], El-Sohby and
Mazen [5].

Hydrological studies of the Scientific Research Academy and
Groundwater Research Institute [1], Hefny and Khalid [3] managed
to draw contour lines of the groundwater levels in Greater
Cairo based on extensive observations of deep wells and piezometers , A map is worked out from these studies for the groundwater levels to be compared with the available data for the two
zones considered in the present study and the River Nile Level
at Roda Nilemeter near Old Cairo which is now almost constant
at 16.7 m .Groundwater levels shown in FIG.5 express the piezo-
metric head of deep piezometers and wells which are different
from another type of groundwater usually referred to as surface,
perched , or shallow groundwater mainly localized due to surface
leakage of watersupply and sewage systems. In the present study
the term 'perched groundwater' will be used throughout. There is
evidence that perched groundwater is higher by 0.0 to 2.0 m [1] .
However , the vertical groundwater movement and the connection
between the perched groundwater and groundwater is still unclear.

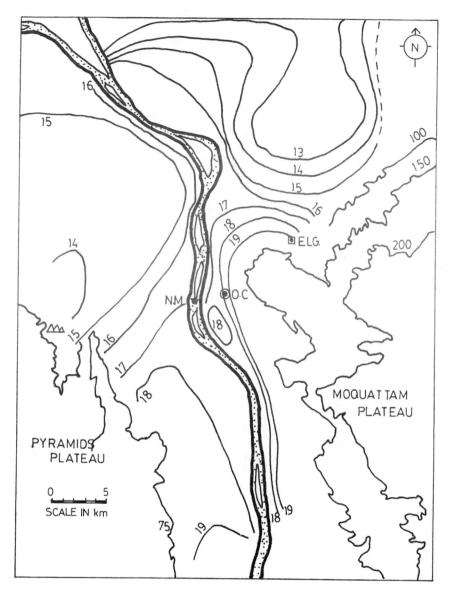

FIG. 5 : Monitored Groundwater Levels as compared with
Groundwater Contour Lines From Ref. [1] , not
taking perched Groundwater into consideration ,
● –Nilemeter at Roda 16.7 m
◉ –Groundwater at Old Cairo
▣ –Groundwater at Elgamaliya
◗ –Groundwater contours
〜–High topography contours

Specially in areas with practically impermeable clay layer, the
two types of groundwater are almost separated. Should the superficial layers be unsaturated and relatively permeable , the
groundwater movement would be downward.

REGIONAL SCALE

Study of the groundwater conditions in the two chosen zones is
based on installation and monitoring of multi-level piezometers.
Used piezometers are composed of a porous tip connected with
a P.V.C. tube to the ground level. Under, around and above the
tip exists a sand filter,above which there is an upper plug
of bentonite. Depths of piezometers porous tips below ground
level ranged between 7.0 to 15.0 m in Old Cairo and 4.0 to
16.0 m in Elgamaliya. Open pits had also been excavated to
check and monitor directly the surface groundwater level.

   Monitoring of shallow and deep piezometers and open pits
revealed the following groundwater conditions :
- In Old Cairo , no perched groundwater has been observed but
the usual gradient in the groundwater related with the groundwater movement towards the Nile;
- In Elgamaliya, a perched groundwater as measured by the
shallow piezometers and open pits is 0.0 to 0.8 m higher than
the groundwater level as measured by deep piezometers tip
of which is sunk below the clay layer.

   Soil conditions in both chosen areas , FIG. 8 and FIG. 9
explain why perched groundwater has been observed in Elgamaliya
zone while one level has been noticed in Old Cairo. Presence
of a practically impermeable clay layer in Elgamalia separates
the two types of water while the relatively permeable fill
layers and the fissured weathered limestone in Old Cairo
suggests a downward groundwater movement.

   Borehole logs had been cross checked with the geotechnical
maps and sections of Cairo in the studies of Shenouda [6] and
Mazen [7] which had been based on an extensive collected bor-
ings from different authorities. Similarly , the observed
groundwater levels are compatible with the Academy of Scientific Research study [1] as shown in FIG.5.

   Based on the above considerations,the proposed groundwater
control project (FIG.6 and FIG.7) consists of a net of secondary
and main underdrains collecting the perched groundwater and
a very limited -not exceeding 1.0 m - lowering of the groundwater level.Proposed type of underdrains is trench filters
containing a perforated P.V.C. tube or prefabricated filters.
Drainage lines lead to a huge ground tank.

   No where to drain the collected groundwater as the present
sewage system is much overloaded and even after the operation
of the huge new sewage Cairo project , the collected water would

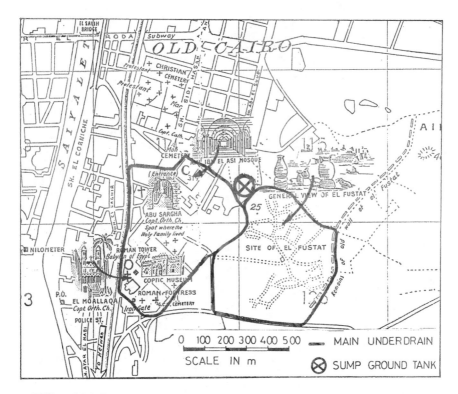

FIG.6: Old Cairo zone and the proposed groundwater control

affect the performance of this project.

Consequently , it would be appealing to retreat the collected groundwater and reuse it for green areas irrigation. Two big green areas projects are planned in the near future in two zones very near to the zones considered in this paper namely : Alfustat green area and Elmokkatem green area.

SITE SPECIFIC SCALE

Restoration of monuments due to the groundwater effect on the regional scale should be combined also with building by building consideration. Humid walls and floorings due to capillary rise is basically due to the absence of horizontal insulation in almost all the considered historical buildings. To reduce or prevent the infiltration of capillary water the following methods can be considered :
-Insertion of horizontal insulation ;
-Electrical methods using the principles of electrosmosis to
 reverse the direction of infitration ;
-Chemical slow injection suced inside the wall to create a
 sort of impermeable layer ;
-Filters, open trenchs and holes to reduce the humidity effect.

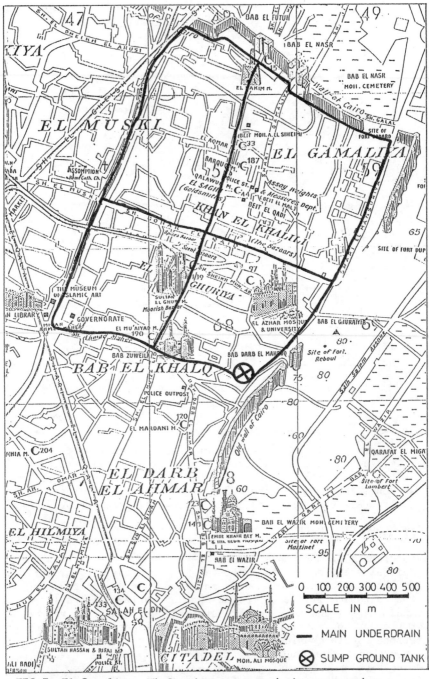

FIG. 7: El Gamaliya –El Ghuriya zone and the proposed

groundwater control project .

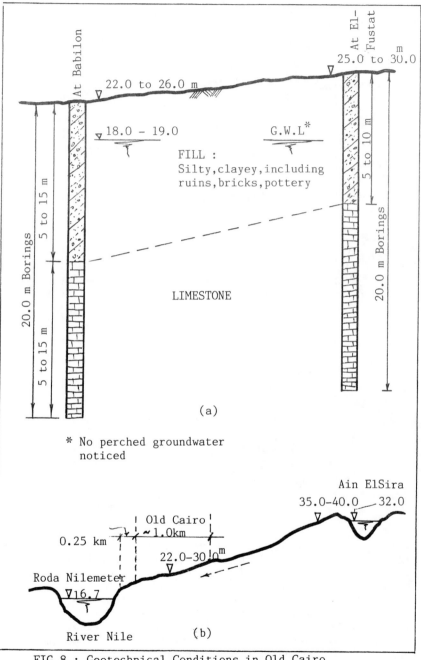

FIG.8 : Geotechnical Conditions in Old Cairo
(a) -Soil Conditions (b) -Groundwater Conditions

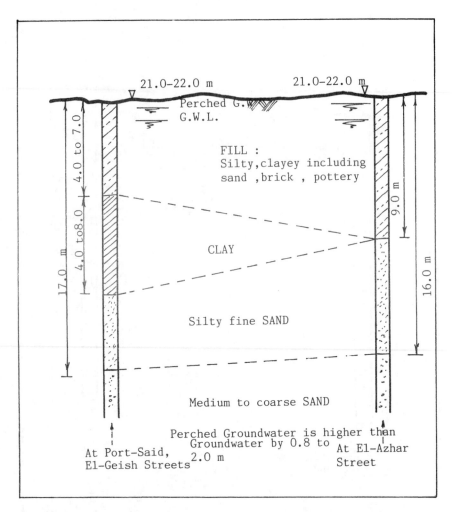

FIG. 9 : Geotechnical Conditions in Elgamalia-Elghoria Zone

Out of the four mentioned approaches, the already adopted in Elgamaliya monuments is the inserion of an insulating thin layer by evacuating the wall block by block. The same technique can be adopted using a hammerised steel plate cutting the wall part by part. With respect to floorings ,the technique of flooring filter is adopted to reduce the capillary rise to few millemeters in the highly permeable gravel or no-fines concrete. Should any rise happen in the groundwater , the accumalated water would be drained from below the floorings.

CONCLUSIONS

Regional groundwater control in areas with high concentration

of monuments may be the single feasible way of draining the
ever rising ground water in the considered zones. Naturally ,
any improvement in the state of leakage of water supply and
sewage systems would assist the solution and lessen the
quantity of water to be drained. The drainage of groundwater
has to take care of both perched groundwater and groundwater
specially if the flooring of the monument lies below the
groundwater level .

Chances of using the retreated drained water are considered
in a separate study .Limited chemical analyses of groundwater
are available to the authers and intensive hydrochemical analyses and the method of retreatment are recommended for future
studies. Irrigation of the green areas to be realised in the
near future very nearby the considered two zones -Alfustat
and Elmokkatam green areas- from the retreated shallow groundwater could be very realistic and feasible target.

The double purpose proposal -saving the monuments and a
source of water for green areas seems to the authors a quite
appealing way of thinking.

REFERENCES

1.Scientific Research Academy and Water Research Center.
Groundwater Studies for Greater Cairo ,Cairo,1982.

2.El-Sohby,M.A. and Mazen,S.O.Historical Development of
Greater Cairo Subsoil, Proc.of International Symposium of IAEG
"The Engineering Geology of Ancient Works , Monuments and
historical Sites",Vol.3,pp.1427,Athens,1988.

3.Hefny,K. and Khalid,J.B.General Hydrological Conditions of
Greater Cairo Area,Water Science Journal,6th issue,Cairo,1989.

4.El-Nahas,F.,Mostafa,A.R. AND Abdeltawab,S.Geotechnical
Characteristics of Limestone Formations of Gebel Elmokkatam
Area,Proc.1st. Alexandria Conference on Structural and
Geotechnical Engineering,pp.9,Alexandria , 1990.

5.El-Sohby,M.A. AND Mazen,O.Geological Aspects in Cairo Subsoil Development,Proc.X ICSMFE,Vol.4,pp.2401,San Fransisco,85.

6.Shenouda,N.G.A Comparative Study of the Soil Formation at
Cairo, MSc.Thesis,Cairo University,1973.

7.Mazen,O.Geotechnical Properties of Subsoil in Greater Cairo,
Ph.D. Thesis, Al-Azhar University , 1983.

SECTION 3: RESTORATION OF INTERNAL AND EXTERNAL STRUCTURES

Computer Approach to a Consolidation Problem

L. Bussi, F. Rampa

Civil Engineers, Rome, Italy

ABSTRACT

Within the strengthening now being carried out at the Galleria Borghese of Rome, there is a problem with two barrel vaults gravely damaged that are being held by supporting walls.

This paper reports the results of the studies on these vaults and the strengthening work being carried out by means of examining the geometrical configurations, the building material structure and the data of the analysis of the numerical models.

HISTORICAL OUTLINE

The internal struggles and disorders that tormented Siena towards the middle of the XVI century pushed a city nobleman, the famous jurisconsult Marcantonio Borghese (1504-1574), to the decision to leave his native country and move to Rome, thus starting the period of his family's greatest fortune.

Marcantonio's firstborn, Camillo, became Pope as Paul V and loaded all his relatives with honours and riches, especially the nephew Scipione Caffarelli who was adopted by the pontiff - thus being able to use the name and the coat-of-arms of the Borghese family - and rose to cardinal dignity. Extremely rich, enormously keen on art and brilliant patron, Cardinal Scipione Borghese decided to start a collection of art work that

even today carries his name and has been defined
"the queen of the world's private collections". For
it he wished a worthy location: the task was
entrusted to the papal architect Flaminio Ponzio
and, on his death, to Giovanni Vasanzio (Van
Santen), who between the years 1613 and 1615,
erected the "Casino Borghese" in the exhuberant and
richly decorated style that was typical of him, a
style deriving from his past as an ebony carver.

The building, whose typology pertains to the style
of the Roman villas, of which the Farnesina and the
Villa Medici are typical examples, was built in the
inner gardens of Villa Borghese - once known as
Villa Pinciana - and, as quoted by Manilli, was
erected and placed like an "Island", that is free
on the four fronts. The front of the building had
a central portico with five Doric arches, and, on
the second floor, a loggia again with five arches
painted in frescos by Lanfranco; two small squared
towers located on the rear side, then, were
dominating the three floors of the building
(fig.1).

The second half of the '700 saw the beginning of
the internal decoration, handled by the architect
Antonio Asprucci, assisted in this work by several
artists, and on that occasion the necessary
strengthening was carried out, enclosing the loggia
on the second floor and transforming it into the
present day "sala XIV" (also known as Lanfranco's
hall).

In 1902 the Borghese property was acquired by the
Italian State which gave the garden to the City of
Rome to turn it into a public park and used the
villa as a Museum. On the ground floor the
collection of modern statues was placed: included
in these were Bernini's group "Plutone and
Proserpina", "David" and "Apollo and Dafne", to say
nothing of the world famous "Paolina Borghese" by
Canova; then, on the second floor, was the rich art

gallery with works by Tiziano, Correggio, Raffaello, Caravaggio and many other great artists.

DESCRIPTION OF DAMAGES BEFORE RESTORATION
The first of the damage at the Galleria Borghese began to emerge towards the middle of this century with cracks on the towers and on the floors; then they got worse and became more serious with cracks appearing on the architraves, material ejection from the pillars of small sections, relative rotations between structure elements, marble covering breaking , etc.; so the strengthening plans could not be postponed any longer.

As a result, inquiries were held to investigate the origin of the damage, and, among these, the geological research that revealed this discovery: at -13 m. level from the springline the subsoil that made up the foundations of the building was involved in a system of latomies of Etruscan origin, with vaults, underground passages, piers and galleries in tufa; furthermore those structures appeared deeply degraded by infiltration of meteoric waters.

Furthermore, it was ascertained that the construction was not, as it might appear at first sight, "hanging" on these cavities, but that the builders had provided the inner part of the latomies with supporting walls corresponding exactly to the walls of the building, thus to carry out the necessary formwork for the wells, that, in this way, became real deep foundations that crossed the empty underground passages.
More inquiries, aimed at defining the foundation typology, showed a differentiated situation regarding the perimetral masonry placed on deep foundation arches (in Italian"barulle"), in respect to inside walls based superficially and isolated among them.

INITIAL STRENGTHENING WORKS

The initial studies identified the different behaviour of the ground involved by heterogeneous systems of foundation methods and the collapse at the latomies level, as the principle causes of failures; so the first stage of the strengthenings, now finished, below ground level, included a regulation through canalization of the meteoric waters, before free in the percolation; then, the riveting and the reinforcement of the latomy vaults and the construction of concrete frames - where necessary - to stiffen the latomy area of the isolated foundations of the building (Portico); finally, the realization of a perimeter curb at the base of the construction as a preventive action against the further residual settlements.

The work was completed providing the superficial isolated foundations with a transferring system of the loads to a deep underground level and carrying out rigid connections with the remaining deep perimetral foundations. This was allowed by adopting the technique of the micropiles dimentioned according to the results of the geotechnical analysis performed (realization that presented the double advantage of operating in adherence to the old wall structure and limiting the disturbances using special machinary).

THE VAULTS IN THE BASEMENT
Once the building had been stabilized at the foundation level, in the second phase of the work, which is now in progress, the problem of the two barrel vaults emerged. They are located in the basement and symmetrically positioned on the plan, and situated above them, on the ground floor, is the museum full of statues which increased the weight,in particular the floors of rooms I and II (Paolina Borghese's hall and David's hall) and rooms VII and VIII (the Egyptian room and the room of the dancing Faunus) (fig.2).

These vaults, exactly alike in dimension and

structural scheme, placed on the perimetral and central walls, presented a severely lowered geometric configuration, showing furthermore, identical cracking episodes, so emphasizing the same cause of the damage. Moreover,these vaults are surrounded by supporting and stiffening walls both longitudinal and transversal.

The necessity to utilize all the available spaces of the underground area, as they were originally created, through the demolition of the protection walls, together with the use of upper floor for museum purposes, made a structural strengthening necessary for the elements of the vaults. This structural strengthening was determinated also by means of an accurate analysis of the numerical models.

ANALYSIS OF THE NUMERICAL MODELS
The analysis of the numerical models, carried out in the hypothesis of elastic behaviour with the F.E. method making use of the calculation code SUPERSAP , consisted of various phases through the definition of representative models of the vaulted masonry structure and, afterward, of this together with the proposed strengthening work.

In this way, the first scheme showing the masonry vaults has been defined by means of a spatial mesh of nodes and 3-D finite elements (characterized by the four nodes at the extremities) with variable thickness and plate-shell behaviour (fig.3).
 Following, the constraint scheme has been defined through several approximations to achieve positive results in agreement with the real condition: header walls of the vault, able to prevent lowering at the end points, have been modelled as horizontal rollers; at the impost of the vaults hinges have been placed along the base generatrix and some vertical rollers, finally, to simulate the restraint provided to the transversal deformations by the massive piers (fig.4).

The mechanical characteristics of the masonry have been deduced by a diagram of a loading test carried out with flat jacks, thus obtaining a module of longitudinal elasticity E = 12650 kg/cmq (E = 1265 N/mmq), and a rupture stress of σ_r = 29,24 kg/cmq (σ_r = 2,92 N/mmq), always in the hypothesis of linear behaviour, with the Poisson coefficient ν = 0.3 and γ = 2 t/mc.

Once geometry, restraints and mechanical parameters have been defined, the structural response for two distinct load conditions have been estimated:
1) dead weight,
2) live load + dead weight.
The first system of forces (dead weight), introduced as node loads, takes into account both the weight of the vault as well as the support materials and the marble covering of the upper floors.
The state of the structural deformation caused by this load has been considered irreversible because of the building technique based on the gradual loading of the vault during its realization.
Thus, the settlements noticed in the keystone are of reduced magnitude (0.19 cm. in the keystone in the vault's centre) such as the two axial lines still coincide before and after applying the mentioned load; moreover, the vault results completely compressed, except for some edge effects produced by the presence of the spandrel walls, with maximum compression stress in the order of σ_c = 3.45 kg/cmq (σ_c = 0.345 N/mmq) .
Following, we have evalued the effect on the same model of its own weight and with the addition of an live load of 600 kg/mq evenly distributed; such live load, according to Italian law, isn't punitive towards the structure for the presence of the heavy loads formed by the sculptural marble groups at the overhanging floor, often exactly on the keystone.
In this new load condition the deformations increased sensibly (0.276 cm. always in the

keystone in the vault's centre, fig.5) and the stress results too high and incompatible with the mechanics peculiarities of the "masonry" material.

Once the necessity of a strengthening of the vault - to increse the resistant section and to modify the lowered profile - was realized, and for not to strongly characterize the environment from an architectural point of view, it has been decided to utilize a concrete countervault with thickness varying from a minimum of 10 cm. in the keystone to a maximum of about 25 cm at the imposts; this new concrete structure so presents variable stiffness, influencing the stress redistribution.
   To evaluate properly the interaction between the two vaulted structures, the masonry one and the other built up with concrete, a supplementary model has been created through the introduction of a second mesh to model the concrete vault at the intrados of the masonry existing one. Afterwards the model was completed by inserting trusses between the corresponding nodes in the two meshes of the vault (fig.6).

Also for this model two loading conditions have been examined to determine the response of the double structure: the first system of external forces simulated the effect of the live load on a parallel system, masonry vaults and concrete countervault, for which the deformations due to the dead weight of the walls were deleted because these had already occured; the second, on the contrary, considered the limit hypothesis of masonry collapse with the entire transfer of the loads to the concrete countervault; this is possible considering the module of longitudinal elasticity of the masonry $E = 0$.

This second analysis phase shows the presence of this concrete countervault, realized to consolidate the old crumbling masonry structure, bears a considerable reduction of the deformations (0.0266 cm. in the above-mentioned node in the keystone: therefore a reduction of 90%).

Finally, as regards the limit hypothesis of masonry collapse with the entire transfer of the loads to the concrete countervault, it has been found as this one, also with high deformations, is perfectly able to provide the necessary carrying capacity (fig.7-8).

ACKNOWLEDGEMENT
The authors gratefully acknowledge the invaluable help of the prof. Paolo Rocchi, designer of the consolidation works, for the use of his project.

Paper in Conference Proceedings

1.   Rocchi P., Ruggieri G.,Consolidamento e restauro della Galleria Borghese in Roma, analisi, studi, ricerche come metodo per le definizione degli interventi, Proceedings of the III course ASS.I.R.C.CO, Catania 1988.
2.   P.P.Rossi, Analysis of mechanical characteristics of brick masonry tested by means of non-destructive in situ tests, 6th International Brick Masonry Conference, Rome 1982.

fig.1

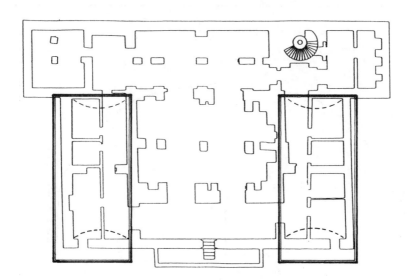

GALLERIA BORGHESE

Piano cantine

fig.2

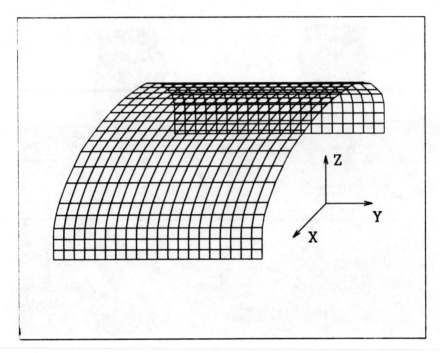

fig.3

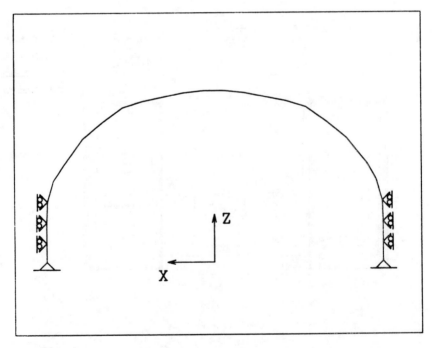

fig.4

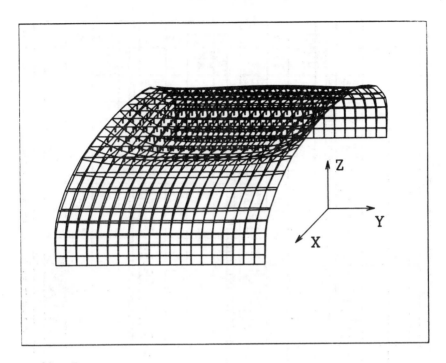

fig.5

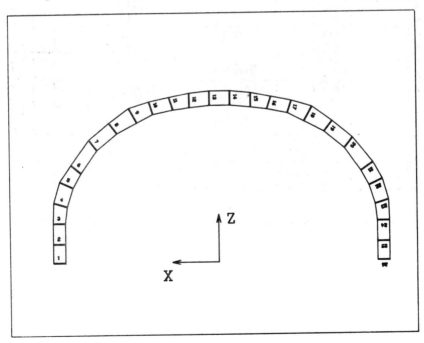

fig.6

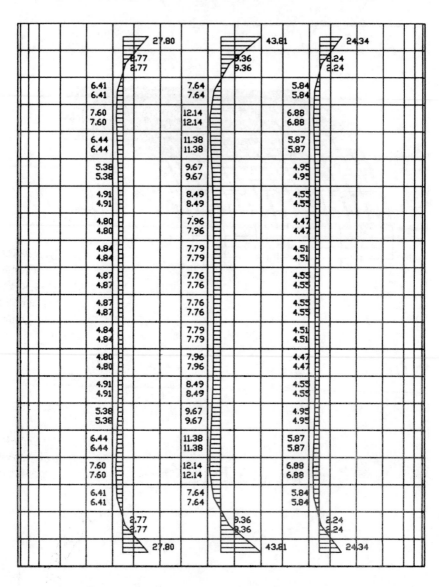

fig.7 - Concrete vault: membrane stress Sxx

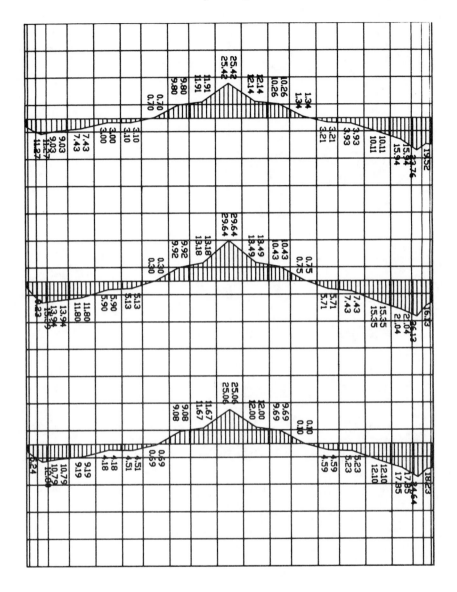

fig.7 - Concrete vault: bending stress Mxx

Lacock Abbey: Conservation of Stonework to Sharington's Tower

G.M. Seymour

Purcell Miller Tritton and Partners, Architects, 14 St. Clement Street, Winchester, U.K.

BACKGROUND

The thirteenth century nunnery of Lacock Abbey was acquired by William Sharington, a courtier of Henry VIII at the time of the Dissolution of the Monasteries. In converting the Abbey into a private house, the church was destroyed, but Sharington preserved most of the remaining mediaeval buildings around the cloisters.

William Sharington had a keen interest in architecture and considerable artistic taste. At that time, the French Renaissance was a major inspiration in England and was favoured by the Court. Sharington added an outer court-yard in domestic vein and displayed his liking for classical architecture in the remodelling of parts of the interior, the windows, the rather eccentric chimneys, and, most notably, the octagonal tower on the south-east corner, where the new influence in decorative detail is much in evidence. To execute the work on the tower, Sharington employed John Chapman, who had worked on royal buildings for Henry VIII.

The tower is three storeys in height with a Muniment Room or Strong Room on the first floor and a belvedere on the second floor approached from a parapet wall walk. A small turret staircase leads from this room to a flat roof surrounded by a balustrade which is a wonderful vantage point with views across the River Avon. In both rooms he placed octagonal stone tables reflecting the form of the building and their pedestal bases are richly carved to the highest quality.

The combination of the patronage of Sharington and the considerable abilities of Chapman have resulted in the highly individual characteristics of the carved detail to be found in the tables, the scrolled brackets or consoles which appear beneath the window sills and the heads of the lights, and in the unusual vaulted ceiling over the Strong Room.

THE STONE VAULT - INVESTIGATION

In 1983, a Quinquennial Survey carried out by Purcell Miller Tritton & Partners on behalf of the National Trust identified a considerable amount of decaying stonework on the external faces of the tower, particularly at the cornices, balustrade, and the domed roof of the turret. Internally, rusting iron dowels had caused particularly difficult problems within the vaulted ceiling/second floor.

The vaulting consists of a series of eight pendants reflecting the octagonal form of the tower with a ninth in the centre. The circular pendants flare outwards at the top and the stonework above links together to form complex interlaced vaulting. At the bottom of each pendant hangs a

Figure 1-Section through the tower

carved stone boss incorporating Sharington's initials and scorpion crest. The bosses are each suspended on the end of an iron dowel, and it was the fall of one of these bosses in 1978 which resulted in the closure of the Strong Room to the public.

Close inspection, assisted by the National Trust Statuary Workshops, revealed that damage to the bosses and pendants caused by the rusting of the dowels had worsened considerably since 1978 when tell-tales were applied to the cracks, the iron having increased in diameter by up to 25%.

The extent of the iron fixings within the pendants could not be seen, but the size of the dowel, together with the provision of washer and wedge, suggested that the fixings had a more elaborate function than holding the bosses in place.

The use of a metal detector, with a range of approximately 300mm in stone, seemed to confirm that the dowel extended through the pendants to just below the paving of the room above. A view through a hole drilled in a natural flaw 220mm above a boss seemed to confirm this. Further investigation by the use of radiography was considered but not taken up in the knowledge that inspection of the stonework beneath the paving of the floor above

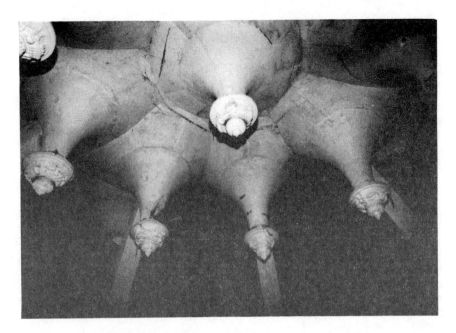

Figure 2-The vaulting before repairs

would be made possible by the impending removal of the table for repairs.

Treatments for the conservation of ferrous metals in an advanced state of decay generally require the metal to be worked on in isolation from other materials. Rust inhibitors or converters have to be applied directly onto the metal; in addition they are generally acidic and will stain stone. These factors, together with the knowledge that the iron fixings were in a relatively advanced state of oxidisation, suggested that even if access to the dowels were possible, metal conservation treatments would only have limited success.

The requirement to remove the iron dowels and fixings was unavoidable, followed by repairs to the stone. The dowels had been run in lead, and their removal would not be easy. There was also concern not to upset the delicate balance of inter-related forces within the vaulting in carrying out the repair.

Before decisions could be taken on the remedial work, a measured survey was carried out, and a drawing produced to show the position of joints between stones and the thickness of the floor. Further information was added regularly to the drawing as dismantling revealed more.

Removal of the table, and the taking up of the central area of paving above the pendants, confirmed the extension of the dowels through the ceiling, with a duplicate top fixing of washer, wedge and molten lead as found below.

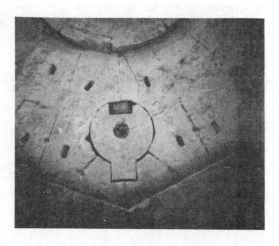

Figure 3-The floor above showing the drum above one of the pendants

Though tarnished, the upper end of the dowels was not as decayed as that below, leading to speculation that a damp atmosphere beneath (possibly aided by a hard cementitious render around the inside of the tower and lack of ventilation) was the cause of metal decay.

At this time simple structural analysis became possible. The weight of each of the pendants was taken by the dowel which was fixed above a circular stone drum located above the pendant. The wedge shaped keys (one forming a side extension to the drum, the other a separate stone), would have tightened under this weight so increasing compression in the floor which acted as a whole to span the room below. It was interesting to observe, during the removal of the pendants, that little or no compression was found to exist in the arched braces which appear to act to throw weight down onto the consoles in the eight corners of the octagon. Clearly, the transference of forces is very much dependent upon careful fine jointing and keying of the stonework, and craftsmanship in this respect was excellent. (Detailed analysis of the way the forces act was not considered necessary to effect repair.)

THE STONE VAULT - REPAIR

Initial attempts to release one of the pendants by removal of the wedge in the drum above and by sawing through the dowel below the pendant provided little effect, the stonework being held very tightly in position by the rusting iron and lead. There was sufficient gap between the pendants and the bosses for there to be little risk of damaging the stone.

The decision was made to remove the 20mm diameter iron dowels by the use of a 50mm diamond tipped core drill held in a

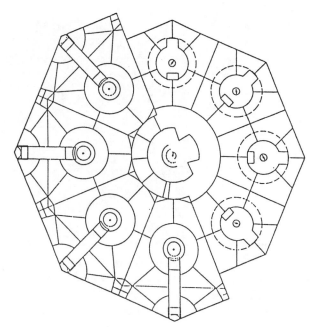

Figure 4-Plans of the vaulting: left - from below
                                right - from above

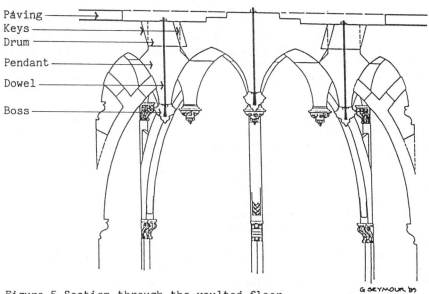

Figure 5-Section through the vaulted floor

vacuum-fixed jig from the floor above. This would remove not only the dowel but the lead which surrounded it. In carrying out this operation, the pendant would no longer be suspended and would thus be removed.

Work started on one of the pendants, and temporary structural support was given to the vaulting above the pendant by a specially designed steel ring suitably protected against the stone, supported on two adjustable props on the scaffolding.

Figure 6-The damage caused by the rusting iron dowels

The core drill penetrated about 300mm before the pendant became detached below. The reason for this became clear when a horizontal joint was revealed between the top of the pendant and a quite separate drum above it, which incorporated the wedge shaped keys.

Having removed the pendant much more of the floor construction became visible and further information could be added to the measured survey drawing. The pendant itself was taken to the National Trust workshops at Montacute for repair by John Salter where the removal of the remaining iron was made easier because the pendant had been quite severely shattered by the action of the rust.

To prevent further opening of the cracks during the removal of the dowel, the pendant was gripped by bands of nylon webbing and the dowel was removed by means of long drill holes set beside it. Stainless-steel turn-down cramps were set in polyester resin to tie the cracks at the top of the pendant, and dowels embedded in polyester resin placed in at angles further down held the lower cracks in place. The pendant repaired in this manner was considered in good enough condition to support itself again and to support the surrounding stones.

Having successfully removed one of the pendants, further supporting rings were made up so that three of the pendants could be removed and transported to the workshop at a time. Fortunately most of the shattered fragments from each pendant were re-usable because the breaks were clean, a polyester resin being used to piece them back together. In one or two instances, however, the base of the pendant was missing or so badly fragmented that new stone was necessary, and stone from the mine at Limpley Stoke was used which proved an excellent match to the original stone from Hazelbury near Box.

In reconstructing the floor, the iron was replaced by 25mm diameter stainless-steel threaded studding, with nuts and large washers let into the stone top and bottom which allowed the studding to be tightened gradually so as to bring the pendant accurately into place. About 75mm was left protruding below the pendants in readiness for the attachment of the bosses. Stainless-steel was chosen in preference to other non-ferrous metals for the replacement dowel because of its consistent good quality (phosphor-bronze being known to corrode in certain instances) and because it was readily available in the required threaded form.

Figure 7-The method of propping the pendants

Figure 8-The tower after repairs

CONSERVATION OF THE BOSSES

Recording was by photography and drawings. To ensure exact repositioning following conservation, lines were drawn by tensioning string from each boss to its opposite, the lines passing under the central boss.   Pencil marks recorded the tangential point of each boss that faced the centre.

Removal of all the bosses was by sawing through the dowels at the joint with the pendant. Bands of masking tape prevented further cracking of the bosses during this operation.   The section of iron that remained dovetailed into each boss by lead grout was carefully drilled out, and the cavity cleaned out with acetone to receive new fixings.

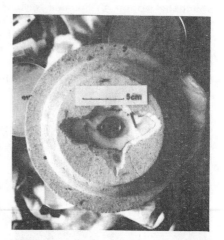

Figure 9-One of the finely carved bosses

Figure 10-One of the bosses showing the threaded socket in position

Cracks were stitched with stainless-steel dowel polyester resin and the bosses gap-filled with putty lime and stone dusts with earth colours added for toning.   Polyester resin was chosen because it is a reversible material (it can be dissolved in methylene-chloride.)

Re-fixing of the bosses was made possible by the fitting of a stainless-steel tube internally screw threaded to fit onto the protruding 25mm O.D. studding beneath the pendants. The tube was an adaption of a socket fixing for concrete casts for buildings. Welded onto the tube were two spigots that branched out into the boss providing extra stability for the fixings.   The fixings were held in place by polyester resin with staples of stainless-steel over the spigots.

Re-hanging the bosses was simply a matter of screwing the bosses onto the protruding dowels beneath the pendants and turning the bosses until tight onto the pendants and with their pencil marks once again facing the central boss.

With the bosses safely returned, the joints were grouted with putty lime and stone dust in a mixture of 3:2 and all the stone surfaces given a light swab of water and sponge. It was not found necessary to use any cleaning agents. The paving on the floor above was re-laid on a bedding of lime and sand and the table conserved and returned to its position. After a period of eleven years it was at last possible to re-open the Strong Room to the public.

THE GARGOYLES - CONSERVATION AND REPLICATION

There are seven stone gargoyles sited just below the parapets on the outer corners of the tower (the eighth corner being occupied by the turret stair). Each is carved to represent the head of a beast, some real and some mythical.

Whilst the condition of these gargoyles was found upon close inspection to be remarkably good after four centuries of exposure, some of the finer detail had eroded to a point where continued exposure may result in total loss in the near future. Based on the premise that these details should not be lost, alternative approaches to conservation were discussed with English Heritage and The National Trust, and a suggestion that the existing gargoyles be taken down and placed in museum conditions, with replacements built in, was rejected in favour of conservation of the gargoyles in-situ and replication of them in stone.

Figure 11-One of the gargoyles after conservation

Figure 12-The completed replica of the same example

Conservation was carried out by first cleaning the stone by a combination of water washing and air abrasive techniques. Friable stone was consolidated with applications of sulphated lime water and lime mortars and, in two cases of severe friability, consolidation was achieved by local application of a stone strengthener.

Finally, a shelter coat of putty lime and stone dust was lightly applied to protect the surface.

The carving of the replacement gargoyles   Whilst the scaffolding was in place for more general stonework and leadwork repairs, three sculptors were invited to produce carved maquettes of one of the gargoyles in competition.   Sculptor Peter Smith of Glastonbury produced an interpretation which was considered to be the closest both in detail and in spirit to Chapman's work.   He then produced maquettes of the remaining six in polyurethane foam, and numerous careful measurements and photographs were taken.   Carving in stone followed, a process made lengthy by the need to transfer dimensions from the maquette and the experimental modelling of missing detail initially onto the maquette.   This largely mechanical process was aided by the sculptor's growing appreciation of Chapman's work and of his style and techniques.

The Strengthening of Stone Masonry Walls with Grouting

M. Tomaževič, P. Weiss, T. Velechovsky, V. Apih

Institute for Testing and Research in Materials and Structures, Dimičeva 12, 61109 Ljubljana, Yugoslavia

ABSTRACT

The influence of compressive strength of the grout on the seismic behaviour of stone-masonry walls has been investigated. 8 specimens injected with 4 different types of mixes with different compressive strength have been tested by subjecting them to constant vertical and cyclicly acting horizontal load. Although the values of the compressive strength of the grout varied from 6.8 to 32.5 MPa, no significant difference in the behaviour of the tested specimens has been observed. The wide range of values of compressive strength of the grout did not influence the shear strength of stone-masonry walls. This will make easier the development of mixes designed for special purposes, which often have additives which significantly reduce their compressive strength.

INTRODUCTION

The walls of old masonry buildings in historical urban and rural nuclei in the region are generally built of two outside layers of uncoursed stone, with an inside fill consisting of smaller stones. Sometimes, the walls are homogeneous, with bigger stones and bricks distributed over the entire volume of the wall. Lime mortar is used as a bonding material in both cases, the quality of which depends on the quality of the aggregate: in the case of pure sand, good quality of mortar has been achieved. In the case of clay or earthy sand, however, the mechanical properties of the mortar and masonry are usually poor.

The load-bearing capacity of stone masonry is usually not sufficient to ensure buildings have the adequate degree of seismic resistance. Consequently, the stone masonry walls should be strengthened. Because of the method of construction of stone and mixed stone-and-brick-masonry walls, many void parts exist in the walls which are uniformly distributed over their entire volume. Therefore, as the most efficient method, the strengthening of such walls with systematic filling the voids by injecting the cement grout into the walls is most frequently used in the process of renovation of buildings in historical urban and rural nuclei.

Injecting the grout into the stone-masonry walls has one major advantage as a strengthening procedure: the intervention is invisible and ideal for structural strengthening of historical monuments, where the principles of preservation and restoration of cultural monuments should be taken into account, which severely limit the application of many other possible technical interventions and do not permit the reconstruction or replacement of structural elements.

However, if the walls are covered with frescoes and other decorations, even the applicability of grouting the walls is limited because of the requirements of art historians and conservators. Namely, the use of any binding material which would damage the paintings because of chemical reactions developed during the process of hardening, is not permitted. Unfortunately, Portland cement which is the basic constituent of the normally used grout mix, is a material of such kind.

Since grouting is the only way for strengthening the masonry walls of historical buildings without changing their exterior, adequate materials should be developed in order to replace the Portland cement, or the negative effects of the cement on the decorations should be reduced to an acceptable level. Both, the reduction of quantity of cement in the grout mix and special materials and additives which replace the cement in the mix reduce the compressive strength of the grout. The influence of the reduced strength of the grout on the seismic behaviuor of a masonry wall, however, has not yet been investigated. In this paper, the results of experimental investigations in the influence of the grout's strength on the seismic behaviour of the grouted stone-masonry walls, carried out at the Institute for Testing and Research in Materials and Structures (ZRMK) in Ljubljana, Yugoslavia, will be presented and discussed.

RESEARCH PROGRAMME

The influence of injecting the stone-masonry walls with grout consisting 90% of Portland cement and 10% of Pozzolana, which is added to the mix to ensure plasticity during the grouting procedure, on the seismic behaviour of walls has already been investigated [1,2, and 3]. Good results have been obtained with such a grout which normally has compressive strength several times greater than original mortar of the stone-masonry. Since systematic research is needed in order to develop the mixes which would meet the criteria for both, strength and chemical properties (the investigations are under way and their results will be reported in one of our future papers), the decision was made to investigate the influence of the low strength grout on the seismic behaviour of walls in the first phase. In the case of adequate results, the strength requirements could be relaxed which would make the development of a mix meeting the chemical requirements to be suited for injections of decorated walls easier .

The walls of old stone-masonry houses in historical urban nuclei are frequently humid. Therefore, in order to improve the standard of living in such buildings, attention should be also paid to the problems of humidity and a simple way to protect the walls from moisture in the case of renovation should be developed. One of the possible methods for humidity protection of stone and mixed, brick-and-stone-masonry walls is injecting the walls with a grout which consists hygrophobic additives. In such a way, both load-bearing and physical characteristics of the masonry are improved at the same time. Since several kinds of hygrophobic additives are available on the market and are successfuly used for humidity protection in the last several years (some were developed at ZRMK), decision was made to investigate the effect of such additives, which reduce the compressive strength of the grout in all cases, on the seismic behaviour of injected walls.

In the first phase of investigations, 10 specimens have been constructed and injected with 5 different types of grout mixes, some of them especially developed within this research project, some already in use for strengthening the walls for a longer period of time. The composition of grout mixes is presented in Table 1.

Table 1: Composition of mixes used for grouting the stone-masonry walls

Designation of grout mix	Designation of wall	Quantity (in kg)				
		Cement	Pozzolana	Water	Quartz dust	Additive
A	A-1, A-2	90	10	70	–	–
B	B-1, B-2	90	10	70	–	10 (a)
C	C-1, C-2	70	10	60	30	10 (a)
D	D-1, D-2	70	10	60	30	10 (b)
V	V-1, V-2	70	5	70	30	1.4 (c)

The mix type A is used for grouting the stone and mixed stone-and-brick-masonry walls in normal conditions (pure cement mix). In mixes B, C, D, and V the quantity of cement is varied and three different additives (a, b, and c) which are all based on the salts of stearic acid, are added.

Although the experiences show that it is difficult to reproduce existing masonry walls in the laboratory, even though very thorough chemical and mechanical tests of mortar and other constituent materials have been carried out, the specimens have been constructed, grouted and tested in the laboratory. Original stone and bricks were used, taken from the walls of an historical building and the composition of mortar was determined by chemical analysis (a 1:2 lime mortar was used). An experienced mason, familiar to historic masonry has built the specimens. Since the specimens were not aimed at the determination of the load-bearing capacity of the original stone-masonry, a small quantity of cement was added to the lime in order to obtain strength in a shorter period of time.

The specimens were built on the reinforced concrete foundation blocks (120x59x20 cm) with a r.c. bond-beam (100x50x20 cm) on the top of the walls. All walls were built in the same way, with special care taken for the uniform structure of the masonry and distribution of bonding stones. The courses of stones were not levelled with bricks. Crushed parts of bricks were only used as the infill material in the middle part of the walls. Two specimens (designated V) with dimensions 120x50x100 cm have been built for the vertical compression tests, i.e. for the determination of the elastic modulus and compressive strength. Eight specimens (designated A, B, C, and D) with dimensions 100x50x100 cm have been built for the seismic resistance tests, i.e. for the determination of tensile strength, shear modulus, ductility and energy absorbtion capacity. Before injecting the grout, injection tubes have been built 10 cm deep into the joints between the stones, 30 - 40 cm apart, on all sides of the walls. The injection tubes were fixed with fast binding mortar, which was also used to cover the joints between the stones in order to prevent the outflow of the suspension during the injecting process. The pressure of 2 - 3 bar was used in order to inject the grout into the walls.

In Table 2, the values of the compressive and bending strength of the mortar and grout on the day of the tests are given. As the indication for the porosity of masonry the consumption of the grout during the injecting of individual specimens is also given.

DESCRIPTION OF TESTS AND TEST RESULTS

By subjecting the walls V-1 and V-2 to the step-wise increased vertical compression in a 5 MN testing machine, the stress-strain relationships of the strengthened masonry at compression have been determined (Figure 1). The basic parameters obtained by means of the vertical compression tests are the compressive strength f_c (the average stress in the horizontal cross-

Table 2: Mechanical properties of mortar and grout

Designa-tion of wall	Designa-tion of grout mix	Mortar		Grout		Quantity (kg)
		Compressive strength (MPa)	Bending (MPa)	Compressive strength (MPa)	Bending (MPa)	
A-1	A	3.7	1.1	32.5	1.9	83
A-2	A	4.2	1.2	32.5	1.9	59
B-1	B	3.2	0.6	19.7	1.6	29
B-2	B	3.3	1.0	19.7	1.6	50
C-1	C	3.0	0.7	6.8	0.6	51
C-2	C	3.1	1.1	6.8	0.6	57
D-1	D	2.6	0.8	12.8	1.7	54
D-2	D	3.0	0.9	12.8	1.7	23
V-1	V	8.9	-	15.9	4.2	74[*]
V-2	V	3.7	-	15.9	4.2	72[*]

[*] The volume of the specimens V was 20% greater than the volume of specimens A, B, C, and D

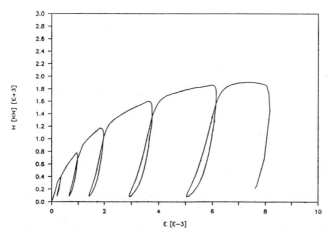

Figure 1. Stress-strain relationships obtained during vertical compression test of wall V-2

section of the wall at the maximum attained vertical load) and the modulus of elasticity **E** (secant modulus at 1/3 of the compressive strength). The values are given in Table 3.

A special test set-up (Figure 2) has been used to determine the seismic resistance of the specimens designated A, B, C, and D which keeps the

**Table 3: Compressive strength and modulus of elasticity obtained by
vertical compression tests**

	V-1	V-2
Compressive strength f_c	4.24 MPa	3.18 MPa
Modulus of elasticity E	2100 MPa	1385 MPa

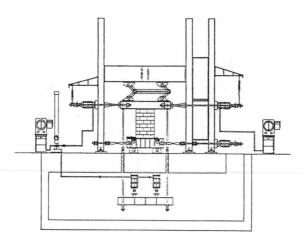

Figure 2. Test set-up

upper and lower boundary of the walls parallel during the tests. All
specimens were subjected to constant vertical load (500 kN), which caused
the normal stresses of the magnitude 1.0 MPa (approximately 25-30 % of
the compressive strength of the strengthened masonry, determined with
vertical compression tests of the walls V-1 and V-2) in the walls' horizontal
cross-section, and to cyclicly acting, step-wise increased horizontal load.
Tests were displacement controlled. At each displacement amplitude, lateral
loading was repeated three times in order to obtain information about the
strength and stiffness degradation and deterioration at repeated lateral
loading (Figure 3).

LVDT's have been used to measure the relative displacements between
the upper and lower part of the specimens. Lateral loads, correspondimg to
the programmed displacements, have been measured by means of load cells
at the bottom part of the support beam. Strains in the masonry in both
diagonal directions have been also measured (Figure 4). Typical example of
hysteretic relationships between the relative displacements and lateral loads
recorded during the test is shown in Figure 5.

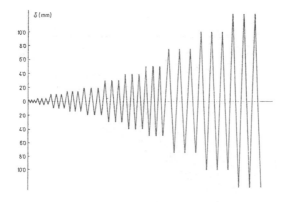

Figure 3. Typical loading history

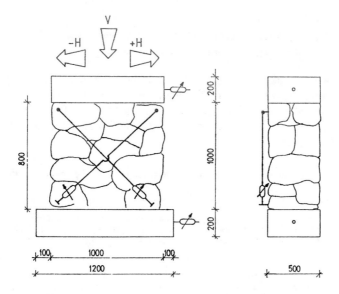

Figure 4. Instrumentation of specimens for seismic resistance tests

As expected, all walls failed in shear. In all cases, cracks were mainly diagonally oriented and were first observed at the lateral deformation of 3.0 - 4.0 mm. Because of the poor quality of stone which was used for the construction of old buildings in the historical part of the city of Ljubljana, some cracks occurred in the joints between the stones, some, however, passed through the stones. The cracks became wider at the increased amplitudes of lateral load and substantially opened at the repeated lateral load reversals. In most cases, vertical cracks also occurred in the middle section of the walls, indicating the separation of the two outer layers of the

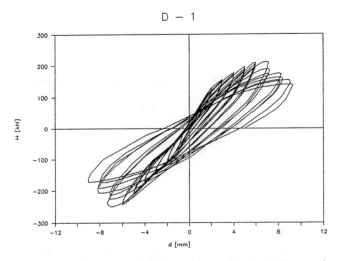

Figure 5. Typical lateral load - lateral deformation hysteresis
loops, obtained during the seismic resistance test

masonry, which took place despite injecting the walls with grout which has virtually filled all the voids in the walls and made the masonry a more homogeneous material. Consequently, the separation of the two layers caused significant stiffness and strength deterioration at the repeated lateral load reversals.

Table 4: Strength and deformability characteristics of the grouted walls

Designa-tion of wall	Tensile strength f_t (MPa)	Effective stiffness K_e (kN/mm)	Shear modulus at E_{max} G_{min} (MPa)	Shear modulus at E_{min} G_{max} (MPa)	Ductility factor d_u
A-1	0.30	64.69	156	160	2.60
A-2	0.30	83.85	194	200	3.44
B-1	0.36	48.85	115	117	2.20
B-2	0.37	52.31	119	122	2.41
C-1	0.20	53.85	133	137	2.58
C-2	0.42	57.98	139	142	2.52
D-1	0.33	57.25	134	137	2.72
D-2	0.39	60.89	144	148	3.13

Test results are summarized in Table 4. All parameters which define the lateral load-bearing capacity and deformability of the walls subjected to seismic loads (tensile strength f_t, effective stiffness K_e, shear modulus G and ultimate ductility factor d_u) have been evaluted on the basis of the measured relationships between the deformations and forces by using the well known equations developed for seismic resistant design of masonry structures (4). Shear modulus was evaluated by taking into account both extreme values of the modulus of elasticity, given in Table 3.

Looking at Table 4 it can be seen that all tested specimens can be classified into a single group, although they have been strengthened with grouts of different mechanical properties. The average value of the tensile strength of the set of all 8 specimens is 0.33 MPa, with standard deviation of 0.07 MPa and coefficient of variation equal to 21 %. It can be also seen that the value of the modulus of elasticity does not influence the magnitude of the shear modulus.

It can noticed, however, that the walls grouted with pure cement grout (specimens designated A) are stiffer than the walls injected with the grout with hygrophobic additives. By comparing the average values (walls A on the one side, and walls B, C, and D on the other), a difference of more than 30 % can be seen. Considering the ultimate ductility factor (as a measure of the capability of the walls to carry the vertical load although damaged at large lateral deformations), no significant difference can be observed.

The above observations can be clearly seen in Figure 6, where the hysteresis envelopes obtained during the seismic resistance tests of all walls are compared. In Figure 6, the average hysteresis envelopes, obtained by testing the two specimens of the same type, are compared.

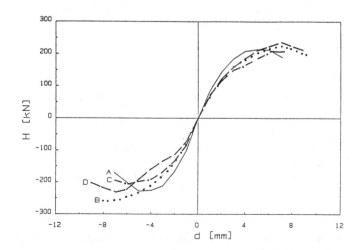

Figure 6. The comparison of hysteresis envelopes obtained during seismic resistance tests of all walls

CONCLUSIONS

The seismic resistance of stone-masonry walls, strengthened with injections of different mixes of grout, has been experimentally investigated by subjecting the specimens to a combination of constant vertical and cyclicly acting lateral load. The behaviour of specimens grouted with usually used cement grout has been compared to the behaviour of specimens grouted with four different other types of grout with different quantities of cement and hygrophobic additives. Although the compressive strength of different grout mixes varied from 7 to 32 MPa, the analysis of test results has shown no significant difference in the behaviour of specimens subjected to seismic loads. In all cases, the same degree of improvement in the seismic behaviour of the walls has been observed.

As can be seen in Table 5, the results of these tests are in good agreement with some typical previous results obtained at ZRMK and other parts of the country.

Table 5: Comparison of strength and deformability characteristics of the grouted stone-masonry walls

Description of walls	E (MPa)	G (MPa)	f_c (MPa)	f_t (MPa)
These tests	1761	141	3.71	0.33
Uncoursed stone, pure sand [5]	2744	154	2.14	0.25
Uncoursed stone, pure sand [6]	3098	89	–	0.23
Mixed masonry [3]	–	450	–	0.19

Note: [3] average value of 2 walls, compressive strength of the grout 24 MPa,
[5] average value of 6 walls, compressive strength of the grout 33 MPa,
[6] 1 wall, compressive strength of the grout not known.

The test results indicated the possibility of further reduction or substitution of cement in the grout with other adequate materials. Since the strength of the mix is no more the most important parameter (the lower bound of the stength, however, is limited with the strength of the original mortar in the wall), the development of mixes which will meet both, the requirements of restoration and conservation of historical monuments and the requirements of earthquake resistant design, will become easier.

ACKNOWLEDGEMENTS

The research described in this paper was financed by the Foundation for Innovations of the Ministry of Research and Technology of Slovenia and by the SCT Corporation of Ljubljana. The financial support of both of these organisations is greatfully acknowledged.

REFERENCES

1. Turnšek, V., Terčelj, S., Sheppard, P. and Tomaževič, M. The Seismic Resistance of Stone Masonry Walls and Buildings, 6th European Conference on Earthquake Engineering, Vol.3, Dubrovnik, 1978, pp. 75-82.
2. Tomaževič, M., Sheppard, P. The Strengthening of Stone-masonry Buildings for Revitalization in Seismic Regions, 7th European Conference on Earthquake Engineering, Vol.5, Athens, 1982, pp. 275-282.
3. Sheppard, P., Tomaževič, M. In-situ Tests of Load-bearing Capacity of Walls of Old Masonry Buildings, 4th National Congress on Earthquake Engineering, Vol.2, Cavtat, 1986, pp. 85-92 (in Serbo-croat).
4. Turnšek, V., Čačovič, F. Some Experimental Results on the Strength of Brick Masonry Walls, 2nd International Brick-masonry Conference, Stoke-on-Trent, 1971, pp.149-156.
5. Tomaževič, M, The Effect of the Montenegro Earthquake of April 4, 1979 on Masonry Buildings, Report ZRMK, Ljubljana, 1980 (in Slovene).
6. Stankovič, V. The Seismic Vulnerability of Old Urban Nuclei and Cultural Monuments, Doctoral Disertation, Institute for Earthquake Engineering and Engineering Seismology, Skopje, 1987 (in Serbo-croat).

Unity Temple: Investigation and Repair

H.J. Hunderman, S.J. Kelley, D. Slaton

Wiss, Janney, Elstner Associates, Inc. Chicago, Illinois, U.S.A.

ABSTRACT

Unity Temple, designed by Frank Lloyd Wright and completed in 1907, is constructed with a structural system comprised almost entirely of reinforced, cast-in-place concrete. The incorporation of an exposed pea-gravel exterior aggregate is one of the first uses of an architectural concrete finish in the United States. The original design of the concrete elements of the building has significantly affected the serviceability and appearance of the structure. Cracking and deformations have been noted over the life of the structure. Previous repair programs involved coating the exterior walls with a polyvinyl acetate bonding agent during the 1960s. In the early 1970s, the original exposed aggregate surface was removed from most of the exterior wall area and a shotcrete coating was applied. This paper describes the original construction, previous repair programs, and current investigation program. The recently-completed investigation was implemented to evaluate the existing condition of the original materials and the newer shotcrete surfaces, and to determine appropriate methods of repair and restoration for this historic structure.

INTRODUCTION

Frank Lloyd Wright's Unity Temple in Oak Park, Illinois, was completed in 1908, and is widely recognized as an important early use of architectural and structural concrete in the United States. The structural system of the Temple was constructed almost entirely of reinforced, cast-in-place concrete. The incorporation of an exposed pea-gravel aggregate finish on the concrete is one of the first such applications of that type of architectural concrete finish in the United States.

The growth of the concrete industry in the late nineteenth century encouraged applications of concrete in engineering in the United States and abroad, while architectural use of the material was still limited. The varying qualities of natural cement, high cost of imported portland cement, lack of understanding of the strength and durability of the material, and resistance to its appearance all contributed to its limited use for architectural construction.

This paper will review the technology of Unity Temple's construction, the history of problem and deterioration of the material, and the previous repair attempts. The techniques used in the recent investigation and testing of the concrete performed by Wiss,

Janney, Elstner Associates, Inc. (WJE) will be defined; the results of the investigation reviewed; and the design for the repair examined.

Figure 1. This photograph of the west facade of Unity Temple was published in the Ausgefuhrte Bauten und Entwurfe von Frank Lloyd Wright in 1911.

FEATURES OF THE ORIGINAL DESIGN

Unity Temple consists of two building masses; the larger (Temple) is used for worship and the smaller (Unity House) is used for social gatherings. The main structural support system for each building mass consists of four large, hollow concrete piers located near the four corners, and cast-in-place concrete, load-bearing exterior walls. The roof and floors of the Temple are supported by cast-in-place concrete beams and slabs. Some of the larger beams are constructed with steel beam sections embedded in concrete.

At the time that Unity Temple was constructed, reinforced concrete construction was governed by an array of patented systems. The character of the Unity Temple specifications and drawings that are still extant and the absence of reinforcing details suggest that the concrete system used was a patented system. The patent for the system used has not been identified and the amount of engineering used to develop the system, if any, is not known.

Although reinforcing bars were utilized in the United States as early as 1878, specification standards for reinforcing bars were not developed until 1910, after Unity Temple was constructed. Early reinforcing bars were smooth round or square steel bars in structural, intermediate and hard grades, or cold twisted steel. The specified minimum yield strengths of structural, intermediate, and hard grades were 33,000, 40,000, and 50,000 psi respectively. Structural grade was normally used unless otherwise specified. The Unity Temple specifications did not specify grade.

The original design specifications describe the concrete materials that were to be used in the structure and the size and placement of the reinforcing steel. The elements of the building that resist compressive stresses, such as foundations, walls and piers, were specified to be constructed with a material referred to as "stone concrete." This was a normal-weight concrete fabricated with portland cement, sand, and limestone aggregate. Elements that resist flexural stresses, such as roof and floor slabs and the Temple overhangs, were specified to be constructed with "cinder concrete." This is a lightweight concrete fabricated with portland cement, sand, and soft coal cinders.

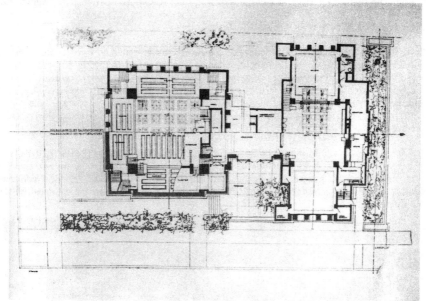

Figure 2. This plan for Unity Temple was published in the <u>Ausgefuhrte Bauten</u> in 1911. The drawing includes a reflected ceiling plan showing the skylights.

The original structural specifications identify the scope of work in terms of performance; however, complete structural drawings for the building may never have been prepared. The Contractor may have been responsible for the design of the individual structural elements of the building. The floor slabs were to be poured monolithically with the supporting beams, and were specified to carry 100 pounds per square foot (psf) of superimposed live load. However, it is believed that the live load capacity was changed during the design or construction process to 150 psf. The roofs were specified to support 50 psf of live load. The span lengths for the roof and floor slabs were specified not to exceed 22 feet. All floors in the building were specified to have a maximum deflection of 1/800 of their span length. Load testing of the floors by loading to twice their service load capacity was to have been done within 15 days after their construction. It is not known if these tests were actually performed.

"Surfacing mortar" was specified for the exposed surfaces of the building. It was originally specified to be made up of one part portland cement, and three parts crushed red granite. At the initiation of the construction process, it was decided to use pea gravel aggregate rather than red granite.

The manner in which the exterior walls of the building were placed is of interest when evaluating the performance and durability of the concrete. The concrete was specified to be placed in six-inch high layers, extending horizontally with a maximum of 1'-6" laid up in a 24-hour period. This method of construction was probably used to facilitate application of the exposed aggregate finish on the exposed surface of the concrete, and to eliminate the need for form ties through the walls. It had the additional benefit of minimizing shrinkage cracking of the concrete. This method would also encourage proper consolidation of the concrete, provided the concrete was a workable mix. The exposed aggregate finish on the surface of the exterior walls was specified to be completed by removing the wood forms immediately after the concrete had achieved its initial set, and floating the surface gently with a carpet-covered float to expose the pea gravel aggregate.

PREVIOUS REPAIR PROGRAMS

In the early 1960s, all exterior concrete surfaces of the building were coated with a polyvinyl acetate-based bonding agent. This treatment was apparently implemented in response to observed areas of cracking and spalling of the concrete where reinforcing steel was corroding. The bonding agent may also have been applied to provide additional adhesion between the exposed aggregate particles and the cement paste in the walls. Application of this material obscured the original exposed aggregate texture of the concrete surfaces.

A much more ambitious rehabilitation program was undertaken in the early 1970s, also in response to cracking and spalling of the exterior concrete. This program consisted of removing areas of distressed concrete and applying a pneumatically-applied concrete coating ("shotcrete") to most of the exposed concrete elements on the exterior of the building.

Figure 3. Shotcrete was applied to the grit-blasted surfaces of Unity Temple in the early 1970s, after the cracks had been cut out and filled and other repairs to the concrete surfaces had been completed.

The shotcrete was applied in a layer one-half to three-quarter inch in thickness. Prior to application of the shotcrete, the wall surfaces were abrasively blasted to remove as much as possible of the coating that was applied in the early 1960s and to provide a better mechanical bond. The abrasive blasting completely removed the original exposed-aggregate wall surface in all areas treated.

The shotcrete application was selected to closely match the original exposed aggregate texture of the exterior concrete walls. The shotcrete mixture was created using locally available pea gravel to match the appearance of the original aggregate used in the walls. The coating was troweled to the required thickness and then was finished with a float to a level surface. After curing, the shotcrete was lightly sandblasted to exposed the pea gravel aggregate. Shortly after completion of the shotcrete rehabilitation program the exterior exposed concrete surfaces were treated with two applications of linseed oil. Approximately four years after the initial application, the linseed oil coating was reapplied.

THE CURRENT CONCRETE INVESTIGATION

Investigation Scope of Work

The current investigation was initiated in response to continuing deterioration of the exterior concrete. The purpose of this work was to provide an assessment of the condition of the exterior concrete surfaces of the building; to investigate the causes of existing distress; and to determine methods for repairing the distress and prolonging the life of the exposed concrete elements.

The scope of the concrete investigation and testing performed over the past two years has included:

- A complete hands-on survey of the exterior surface to record all cracking, delamination, spalling and other deterioration.

- Sounding of the concrete to detect delamination, and use of magnetic devices to locate reinforcing steel in those concrete elements.

- A program of selective removal of the concrete to determine the location, size, configuration and condition of the reinforcing steel in a representative area of the roof and overhang on the Temple portion of the structure.

- Laboratory tests on samples of the concrete to determine the characteristics of the material and the degree of deterioration. Concrete cores were removed from the roofs, exterior walls, floor slabs, and Temple overhangs for laboratory testing.

- Structural analysis of the roof slabs and roof overhangs based on the survey, inspection openings and laboratory testing. Measurements were taken to document the deflection of the roof slabs in a number of locations including the overhangs.

- Basic water permeance tests to indicate the degree to which water penetrates the surface and can attack the reinforcing.

Visual Inspection

The visual inspection addressed the exterior concrete surfaces of the walls and overhangs. Since the shotcrete application 15 years ago, cracks have developed in the concrete of the exterior walls. Some of these cracks are readily visible, while others were identified only through a close-up survey of the exterior surfaces of the building. The shotcrete itself was found to be generally in good condition, with only isolated areas of partial delamination from the underlying concrete. A few cracks were found to extend only through the shotcrete layer. No obvious freeze-thaw deterioration of the shotcrete was found.

The concrete soffits were found to be in much worse condition than the walls. The soffits have numerous cracks that run perpendicular to the building facade. Delamination and spalling of the concrete is evident in these areas, particularly on the Temple portion of the building. One of the most severely spalled areas is at the southwest corner of the Temple overhang, where large areas of concrete have spalled off and corroded steel is exposed.

Figure 4. Cracks have reappeared in the exterior walls since the 1973 repairs. As shown in this photograph, the cracks were highlighted with chalk during a recent crack mapping survey of the building.

Through the use of a metal detector and examination of steel exposed at spalled areas, reinforcing bars were detected running perpendicular to the edge of the overhang. Some of these bars are one inch diameter, twisted square reinforcing bars, while others appear to be one-half inch diameter, smooth round bars. The bars are irregularly spaced from eight to sixteen inches on center. The bars are of varying lengths, and extend to about two feet to about five feet from the fascia. These bars appear to turn up into the slab or edge beam along the fascia. There are two round bars running parallel with the fascia, located approximately five and ten inches from the edge of the overhang. There is approximately two and one-half inches of cover below the bars. The reinforcing bars running perpendicular to the fascia apparently hook over these two bars and turn up into the slab or edge beam.

Inspection Openings
In response to the conditions observed and to perform a structural analysis of the roof slabs, a program of selective removal of the concrete was conducted to determine the

location, size, configuration and condition of the reinforcing steel in representative areas of the overhangs.

It was discovered that the southwest corner of the west overhang has deformed downward 4.2 inches from the point where the overhang meets the wall of the building. The northwest corner and much of the west face is consistently 2.3 inches lower than the base elevation. On the south overhang, the southeast and southwest corners are about 3.3 inches below the base elevation.

Three inspection openings were made through the roofing and concrete roof slab. The openings were framed and temporary covers installed for weather protection. Approximately the top six inches of the roof was found to be covered by a "cinder fill" that was originally installed to provide drainage. This material could be easily removed by hand and the pick hammer. A trench was excavated running perpendicular to the reinforcing bars in each of the inspection openings. The structural concrete was easily removed with the lightweight hammer.

Concrete Coring and Laboratory Testing
A simple hand held coring device was used to remove the cores. The concrete did not appear to be very dense, and it was possible to cut through 12 inches of concrete in the overhangs in a few minutes, indicating its softness. Twelve cores were removed from the roof slab, of which six were drilled through the entire 12 inch thick overhang. The top quarter to third of the roof concrete specimens crumbled when they were removed from the coring bit. In addition, two cores were also removed from the interior floor slabs so that the condition of the roof and floor slabs could be compared. Two cores were also cut into the exterior walls. These cores were taken where cracks in the concrete existed to determine the depth of the cracking and how the cracked related to the shotcrete finish.

At the location of one of the wall cores, a crack had apparently existed before the 1973 shotcrete application. This crack had been cut out at that time and patched with new concrete. The patch was then covered with the shotcrete. The concrete was found to have recracked along one side of the patch material at its intersection with the original material. The second wall core was also cut through a crack in the wall. At this location, a large area of poorly consolidated concrete was identified.

Laboratory examination of the specimens included petrographic evaluation and chemical testing. The laboratory testing indicated that the condition of the roof concrete is particularly poor. The original water-to-cement ratio of the concrete was found to be high, which resulted in a porous, structurally weak paste. The paste is almost entirely carbonated and therefore offers little or no protection to the embedded reinforcing steel. The chloride content in the specimens was found to be at or above the threshold for corrosion of embedded steel. The severity of carbonation and the presence of deleterious substances such as chloride can promote the corrosion of embedded reinforcing steel. The roof concrete in particular is very permeable, allowing moisture to penetrate to significant depths. Evidence of damage from cyclic freezing was pervasive.

By contrast, the cinder concrete floor slab samples were found to be undistressed. While the water-to-cement ratio of these cores was similar to that of the roof slab concrete, the floor concrete was found to be only partially carbonated and no evidence of freeze-thaw damage was observed.

Several of the concrete core samples removed during the investigation were tested for compressive strength. The values obtained ranged from 1,258 to 2,485 pounds per square inch.

Structural Analysis

A structural analysis was performed on the structural slab which makes up the west cantilever. All dimensions, thicknesses, weights, sizes, and placements upon which the model was based were derived from measurements taken at inspection openings. Material strengths were based upon the results of concrete cylinder testing. A compressive strength of 1,300 psi was utilized for the strength of the cinder concrete, based upon the results of WJE testing. The cinder fill material was found to have little strength and was not considered as a part of the structural system. The strength of the steel reinforcing bars was assumed to be 33,000 psi based on historical data. The bars were assumed to be detailed in such a manner that they were 100 percent effective in composite action with the concrete.

A dead load of 100 psf was based upon actual loads obtained from measurements of the roof slab components. A live load of 20 psf was derived from local codes. Calculations were performed in accordance with American Concrete Institute (ACI) publication 318-89, "Building Code Requirements for Reinforced Concrete." The analytical model proved problematic because of the unusual placement of the reinforcing. The results of the evaluation yielded issues of concern for further study.

DISCUSSION AND CONCLUSIONS

The shotcrete coating that was applied to nearly all exposed surfaces in the early 1970s has performed relatively well. However, cracking of the structural concrete has resulted in associated cracking and deterioration of the shotcrete surface. The vertical cracks in the walls are probably due to shrinkage and thermal movement in the structure. The localized cracks in the walls that are not distinctly horizontal or vertical may be related, at least in part, to differential shrinkage of he concrete in regions of high and low paste content, or areas of inconsistent consolidation. The inadequacy of steel reinforcing to control shrinkage may also have contributed to the cracking.

The roof slabs and overhangs are in poor condition. The effect of exposure to the weather on the roof slabs and overhangs is indicated by the undistressed condition of the floor slabs which are constructed of the same materials. The reinforcing that is embedded within those concrete elements has corroded and caused distress in the surrounding concrete. The high degree of permeability to water penetration found in the specimens from the roof slab has contributed to cracking and spalling of the soffits. Lightweight concrete is generally much more permeable than normal-weight concrete, and also tends to carbonate at a faster rate than normal weight concrete. It is also possible that deleterious substances such as calcium chloride in the lightweight "cinder" concrete have contributed to corrosion of the embedded reinforcing steel bars.

Numerous repair schemes were considered for the overhangs. Any appropriate repair scheme will require replacement of the fascia and repair of the original soffit surface. Repair schemes that would have an obvious negative aesthetic impact, such as the addition of columns to support the overhangs, were not considered. Nor were schemes such as suspension cables that would set up alternate load paths for the cantilever loads and introduce unanticipated stresses into other portions of the structure. Replacement of the structural cantilever with materials other than concrete was studied. These schemes entailed difficulty of implementation, drainage problems, susceptibility to future deterioration, and related long-term maintenance problems, and were therefore rejected.

Replacement of the structural cantilever utilizing cast-in-place concrete offers distinct advantages over other schemes. This system utilizes replacement with "in-kind" materials, and the repair implementation is uncomplicated. Repair methods within this category range from salvaging portions of the existing concrete to completely removing and replacing the overhang.

The selected repair program will be designed to minimize the disturbance to the interior of the church. Protection procedures for adjacent building elements, such as the ornamental columns and leaded glass windows, will need to be carefully implemented. Deteriorated concrete materials and corroded reinforcing bars will be removed to prevent future maintenance problems. The goal of the repair program will be to re-establish the structural integrity of the overhang while recreating the historic appearance of the structure.

REFERENCES

1. Hunderman, Harry J. and Stephen J. Kelley. Investigation of the Structural Concrete at Unity Temple, Oak Park, Illinois, WJE No. 891699. Chicago, Illinois: Wiss, Janney, Elstner Associates, Inc., November 5, 1990.

2. Hunderman, Harry J., Deborah Slaton, and Stephen J. Kelley. Unity Temple Historic Structures Report. Chicago, Illinois: Wiss, Janney, Elstner Associates, Inc., July, 1987.

3. Hunderman, Harry J., Stephen J. Kelley, and Deborah Slaton. Investigation of Concrete at Unity Temple, Oak Park, Illinois, WJE No. 881352. Chicago, Illinois: Wiss, Janney, Elstner Associates, Inc., June 26, 1989.

4. Hunderman, Harry J. and Thomas L. Rewerts, "An Analysis of the Performance and Service Life of the Concrete Structure of Unity Temple, Oak Park, Illinois," Service Life of Rehabilitated Buildings and Other Structures, Special Technical Publication 1098, edited by Stephen J. Kelley and Philip C. Marshall. Philadelphia, Pennsylvania: American Society for Testing and Materials, 1990.

Church of St Clement, Sandwich, Kent, England: Installation of a Peal of Six Bells in the Norman Tower

A.E. Stocker, L. Bridge

Purcell Miller Tritton & Partners, Architects, 9 London Road, Sevenoaks, Kent, U.K.

ABSTRACT

St Clement's, the Parish Church of Sandwich as fitted its status once possessed a peal of five bells, cast by John Hodson of London in 1672, but these were removed with the bell frame in 1866. One bell was retained, augmented by a carillon of tubular bells and these were in use until a few years ago. In 1988 the parish was offered a light ring of six bells weighing 2.3 tons with an iron frame which had been removed from St John the Baptist Church in Kirkheaton, Yorkshire, where a new ring of eight bells was to be installed. The paper describes the installation of the bells and frame in the Norman tower of St Clements church. Cost was an important factor as well as conservation of the existing fabric and the need for completion by Sunday 20 May 1990.

INTRODUCTION

Sandwich is a small town, close to the east coast of Kent and one of the Cinque Ports (which in fact number more than five). During the thirteenth century it was the chief harbour for the export of wool from England. As King Edward III (1327-77) had no standing naval force he granted these Cinque Ports special privileges in return for providing ships and men for his service.

Sandwich was built at the mouth of the river Stour which gradually silted up and the port became virtually landlocked. Trade declined, the town lost its importance and has since remained almost static. The result is that its original character has been conserved and it is considered to be one of the finest mediaeval towns in Europe.

There were three churches in Sandwich at that time St Clement's, St Mary's and St Peter's. Only the parish church, St Clement's is still in use; the other two are in the care of the

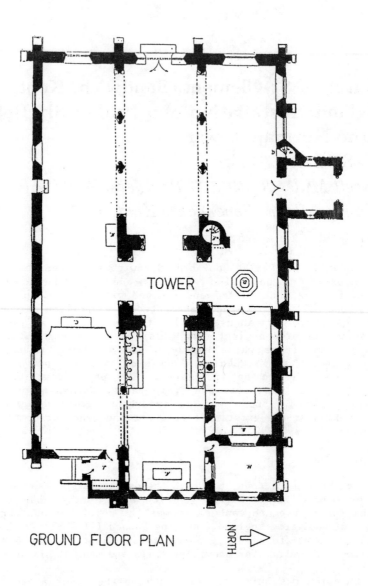

GROUND FLOOR PLAN

Fig. 1

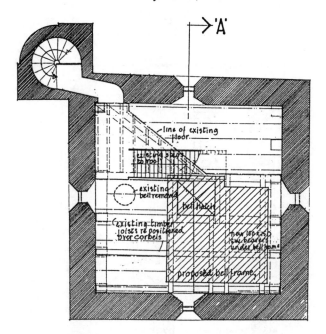

Plan at second floor level [Belfry]   B-B

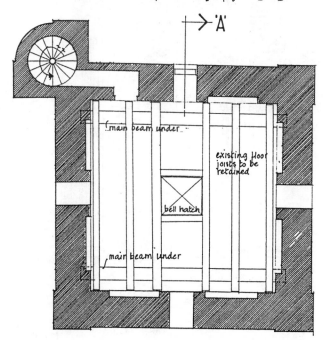

Plan at first floor level [Ringers' floor]   C-C

Fig. 2

NORTH

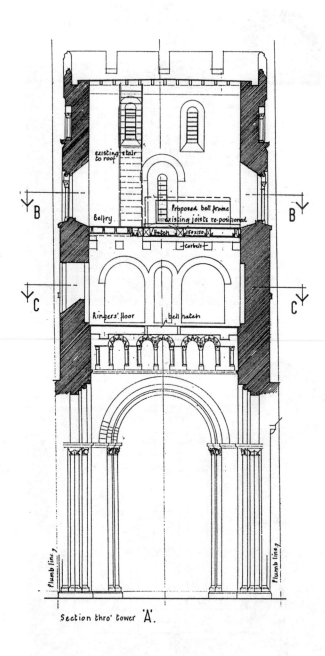

Section thro' tower 'A'.

Fig. 3

Redundant Churches Fund.

St Clement's church is on the east side of the town near the south bank of the river Stour and its large square Norman tower is a prominent feature of the town.   The tower is the only remaining part of the earlier church on this site.   The chancel and chapels date from the thirteenth or early fourteenth century, the nave was rebuilt in the fifteenth century and at the same time the aisles were increased in width, changing the original cruciform plan to a rectangular one (fig.1).

The tower which was built in two stages in the early and mid-twelfth century is square on plan 25'6"x 25'6" (777.2 x 777.2cm) and 65'0" (1981cm) high, with walls 3'9" (114.3cm) thick at the base (Figs. 2 & 3).   It is built of Caen stone, brought by sea from Normandy, with three tiers of arcading incorporating narrow windows on the outer walls, and crenellated parapet walls. The former steeple was removed in 1670-3 and the parapet walls date from the restoration in the nineteenth century.   The tower is carried on four large corner piers with round-headed arches between which open into the chancel, nave and aisles.   The first floor level in the tower 32'0" (975.4cm) above ground floor level is approached by a stone spiral stair in the north-west corner. From this floor fixed timber ladders lead to a mezzanine floor and then to the roof of the tower.

In June 1988 Purcell Miller Tritton & Partners were asked by the Rector, Canon David Naumann, to look at the structure of the tower and see if it would be possible to install the bells (which had already been purchased by the Central Council of Church Bell Ringers Rescue Fund for Redundant Bells and were stored in the nearby church of St Peter in Sandwich).   Peter Ross of Arup Research & Development was asked to give a preliminary report on the feasibility of hanging and ringing the peal of six bells.

ENGINEER'S REPORT

Peter Ross reported in November 1989 that the tower was of robust construction although it showed signs of some distortion with lateral spread at the springing of the arches.   The north and south arches were partially infilled, apparently during the rebuilding in the fifteenth century (although this may have been done to accommodate the change in the layout of the roofs which took place at this time).

Tie-rods had been inserted on the inside faces, just above the arches to counteract lateral spread.   This work was done about fifteen years ago but no details were available.

There were cracks and distortion in the masonry above the

ground floor arches and at higher levels, which was not surprising in view of the age of the masonry, but nothing was seen that was of serious concern.

The first floor of the tower which was supported by two main beams running east to west was sagging noticeably and needed further investigation. Some of the openings in the walls at this level had been filled in. The second floor level was marked by a row of robust stone corbels on the north and south walls and the area was bridged by timber beams of considerable size (30 x 23cm).

When considering the suitability of the structure for installing the bells the actual weight of the bells 2.3 tons is a small factor. When bells are rung in the English manner, i.e. swung in almost a complete circle, large horizontal forces are produced. It is necessary to consider not only this dynamic load but also the possibility of its amplification due to resonance.

The maximum lateral force is produced when all the bells are "fired" that is rung simultaneously. This rather unmusical activity should be proscribed and this would not be considered an unreasonable restriction by bell-ringers. During ordinary change ringing there is an averaging out of the lateral forces which reduces the peak value.

The iron frame in which the bells were to be hung is of the "saw-pit" type in which all the bells swing in the same direction. Although the tower itself has approximately the same stiffness in all directions additional strength in the east-west direction was provided by the arcades which terminate each end in buttresses. It was suggested that the bell-frame should be orientated so that the bells swing east-west to take advantage of the increased stiffness of the masonry to help counteract the resonance.

The other major lateral load on the tower was the force of the wind acting on the masonry above roof level. Hurricanes such as that experienced in this area in October 1987 produced loads which are of the same order as the equivalent dynamic loads of the bells and the tower has withstood these for approximately 800 years.

To summarise: if the bells are mounted to swing east-west and they are not "fired" or rung during high winds then their installation and use for change-ringing should not distress the tower.

To carry the project further it would be necessary to examine the existing beams and corbels at second floor level,

examine the existing beams and corbels at second floor level, check the bell-frame and propose a method of mounting.   The existing beams will probably need adding to and the stiffness of their support would have to be considered as it is most important that the frame is safely and rigidly held in position.   The existing cracks in the tower structure should be surveyed and recorded.

On the basis of this encouraging report it was decided to proceed with the project although the finance available for the work was very limited.

DESIGN

At this stage it became necessary to involve other groups beside the architect, engineer and client.   The Whitechapel Bell Foundry in London (one of the two remaining foundries in England) was asked to comment on the design and quote for the work involved. This foundry under various names has been at work continuously since 1420 and the bells from Kirkheaton were cast there in 1805 and 1819 by Thomas Mears, Whitechapel.   Mr Alan Hughes of the Whitechapel Bell Foundry confirmed that the Kirkheaton bells, fittings and framework were generally in a fit state for re-use. However, he had reservations about the proposals on two counts, mechanical and acoustic.

From the mechanical point of view he emphasised that any ring of bells must be supported rigidly in a rigid tower.   Any horizontal movement in excess of 1/32" (.076cm) at gudgeon level would have an effect on the ease with which the bells could be rung and the accuracy with which they could be struck with the clappers.

The question of the acoustics also concerned him as the ringers would be close to the bells which could sound uncomfortably loud unless effective sound insulation could be introduced.

The architect and engineer discussed these problems particularly Mr Hughes' suggestion that the bell-frame should be supported in a grillage of new steel beams let into the walls of the tower instead of using the existing timber beams and stone corbels for support.   Peter Ross pointed out that up to the nineteenth century bells were rung supported by timber bell-frames fixed to timber beams.   He was confident that an acceptable level of rigidity could be obtained by securely fixing the existing timber beams and providing raking struts below them. The architect and the Diocesan Archaeologist were both anxious to avoid any unnecessary disturbance of the masonry of the tower which would be inevitable if a grillage of steelwork was

saving led to the adoption of Peter Ross' scheme for using the existing structure as far as possible.

Although the proposed arrangement was not ideal from the acoustic point of view it was not possible to introduce the conventional "Silence Chamber" between the Ringing Room and the Belfry due to lack of space. Compensating insulation in the form of a heavy floor and ceiling would be provided to help to overcome this problem.

The Whitechapel Bell Foundry quoted for carrying out all the work connected with the bells and bell-frame but considerable sections were in fact undertaken by volunteers led by Mr Peter Romney of the Kent County Association of Change Ringers, working closely with the Foundry.

CONSTRUCTION

A local builder W C Gregory was already working at the church, carrying out repairs to the fabric so he agreed to do the necessary builder's work prior to the installation of the bells. Scaffolding was erected in the tower base in January 1990 to allow for inspection and repair of the existing first floor of the Ringing Room. It was known to be in poor condition so all the floorboards were taken up and the ends of the two main supporting beams exposed by removing the mortar. The existing timbers were all defrassed and thoroughly treated with insecticide. Two lengths of 12" x 4" (30.5 x 10.2) steel channel sections the width of the tower with angled cleat plates were installed to strengthen the floor. The central trap (to allow the bells to pass through) was enlarged to 3'9" x 3'9" (114 x 114cm) and new panels and 2" (5.1cm) thick trap doors fitted.

The casing to the two main supporting beams was decayed and had to be renewed with 3/8" (.9cm) plywood stained to match the ceiling of the tower base. Decayed panels in this ceiling were repaired using sound timber salvaged from the beam casings.

A new floor was laid in the Ringing Room using 6" x 2" (12.7 x 5.1cm) floor boarding with ¼" (.6cm) ply tongues fixed to new 4" x 4" (10.2 x 10.2cm) firring pieces. All new timber was treated with insecticide before fixing.

By mid-February work had started on the Belfry floor where the existing timber beams were repositioned, parallel to the south wall of the tower and bearing onto the stone corbels. The beams were fixed to the walls with large cleats and M26 Parabolts. M30 bolts were used to fix the cleats to the timber and a tight fit was specified. Resin anchor bolts were used to fix the beams to the corbels below. A raking strut was fixed to the underside of each end of the beams about 3'6" (114) in from the wall and secured to the wall above the Ringing Room floor using 6" x 3" (15 x 7.5cm) bearers fixed with 2no. M30 Parabolts. The bell-frame was positioned in the south east corner over these large beams.   Care had to be taken that the bell ropes passed through the floor boarding and not the beams although the position of the bell ropes was largely pre-determined by the layout of the bell-frame.   The northern area of the floor was infilled with new 7" x 2" (17.8 x 5.1cm) joists covered by 1¼" (3cm) T&G boarding.   A new bell trap was formed in the centre of the floor at the north west corner of the bell-frame, above the trap in the floor of the Ringing Room below.

The Belfry floor was insulated with mineral wool and a plasterboard ceiling was fixed to the underside of the new and existing joists.   The ceiling immediately below the bells may be removed to allow for servicing.   The openings in the walls of the Ringing Room were closed to help prevent sound penetration into the roof spaces.

Meanwhile, the bell-frame had been assembled and its details checked.   In December 1989, it was transported with the bells and fittings by volunteers to the Bell Foundry in London.   Here the frame was cleaned and painted and a girder foundation constructed for it.   The ringing fittings were overhauled and tested.

The bells, fittings, frame and sub-frame were returned to St Clement's and installed by Peter Romney and his team with the assistance of the bell-founders.   The one remaining bell, made by Hodson, was also re-hung.

A band of ringers had been gathered and trained and the bells were rung on 15 April, Easter Sunday morning.

On Sunday 20 May 1990 Her Majesty Queen Elizabeth the Queen Mother, Lord Warden of the Cinque Ports was present at the service held for the Dedication of the Bells.

CONCLUSION

The bells have been successfully installed and their effect on the tower structure will continue to be monitored.   There are some problems with the acoustics so it may be necessary to introduce additional sound insulation between the Belfry and Ringing Room.

The results which have been achieved after tremendous efforts by a large number of people, mostly volunteers, are commendable.   If secondhand materials and voluntary labour had not been used the cost of approximately £25,000 would have

not been used the cost of approximately £25,000 would have certainly been doubled.

ACKNOWLEDGMENTS

Client   The Reverend Canon D Naumann & the Parochial
                  Church Council of St Clement's Church,
                  Sandwich

Architects   Purcell Miller Tritton & Partners
                  9 London Road
                  Sevenoaks, Kent, TN13 1AH

Engineers   Arup Research & Development
                  13 Fitzroy Street
                  London, W1P 6BQ

Contractor   W C Gregory
                  High Street, Wingham
                  near Canterbury, Kent

Bell-founders   Whitechapel Bell Foundry
                  32-4 Whitechapel Road,
                  London   E1 1DY

Repair of the Terra-Cotta Facade of Atlanta City Hall

C.L. Searls, S.E. Thomasen

Wiss, Janney, Elstner Associates, Inc.
Emeryville, California, U.S.A.

ABSTRACT

The Atlanta City Hall, constructed in 1930, is a 15-story
concrete framed, terra-cotta clad building. By the 1980's, the
terra cotta was severely decayed with cracks running the full
height of the building and extensive spalling of terra cotta.
A preservation and renovation program of the building was
undertaken by the city of Atlanta. WJE performed field and
laboratory tests to determine the cause of the failure and
designed repairs for the terra-cotta cladding. The 2.3 million
dollar exterior restoration was completed in 1990.

INTRODUCTION

Architectural terra-cotta cladding was used extensively in the
United States between 1900 and 1930. The use of terra cotta
coincided with the building of American cities and the
development of the steel framed high rise. Terra cotta provided
a technique for mass producing a cladding material to imitate
stone, in America, where the tradition of carving stone masonry
is not as strong as in many European countries. In later years,
the beauty of terra cotta itself was recognized and it was
produced in vivid colors for use in art deco style buildings.

BUILDING DESCRIPTION

The Atlanta City Hall, built around 1930, was designed by a
local architect G. Lloyd Preacher and Company. The neo-gothic
structure, shown in Figure 1, has a 12 story tower rising atop
a 3-story base. The building frame is cast-in-place concrete.

Terra-Cotta Construction
The terra-cotta cladding consists of fired clay blocks with a
glazed face and with web stiffners in the back. A typical block
is 450 mm x 300 mm in size and the face is 30 mm thick with

the webs extending back another 70 mm. The blocks were fabricated by hand pressing clay into wood molds. After removing the clay from the mold, the glaze, an aqueous solution of metal salts, was sprayed onto the unfired clay. Three glaze colors were used on each block to imitate the appearance of stone: a beige background color under two stipple coats of white and yellow. After glazing, the blocks were fired to cone 4 to 5 (about 1130°C). They were then ready for shipping to the site and installation on the building.

The terra cotta was supported vertically on steel shelf angles bolted to the outside edge of each floor slab, as shown in Figure 2. A back-up wall of masonry was constructed along with the terra-cotta cladding. Horizontal support was provided by Z-shaped steel straps anchored into a slot in the edge of each terra cotta block and placed into the back-up wall. Large ornamental units had multiple anchors. As was common practice at the time, neither expansion joints nor flashings and weepholes were provided.

INVESTIGATION OF DISTRESS

Terra cotta is generally a durable material but many older terra-cotta clad buildings are in need of repair after years of neglect. The terra cotta at the Atlanta City Hall was severely deteriorated by the early 1980's because of inherent defects in the original installation and because repairs and maintenance

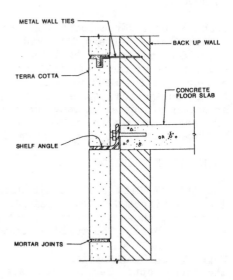

Figure 1. Atlanta City Hall.

Figure 2. Terra Cotta construction.

over the years had been done piecemeal without addressing the cause of distress.   A series of field and laboratory investigations were undertaken to determine the causes of the distress.

Field Investigation
Visual observations were made of the entire building facade from scaffolds and from street level using binoculars.   Crack locations marked on elevation drawings were studied to detect failure trends.   The condition of the terra-cotta glaze and the mortar joints was spot checked from swing stages.   Exploratory openings were cut into the walls to inspect shelf angles, wall ties and the condition of the back up wall.   At the same time, terra-cotta samples were removed for laboratory analysis.

Field Observations
Several types of failures, as shown in Figure 3, were common throughout the building facade:

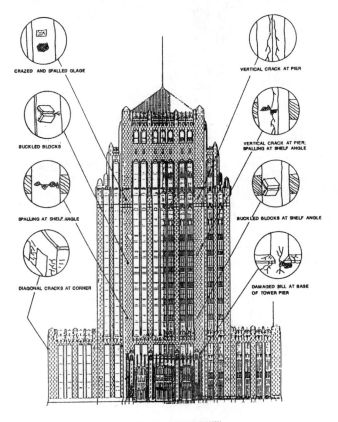

ATLANTA CITY HALL - FRONT ELEVATION

Figure 3.   Typical types of terra-cotta failures.

1.   Buckling of terra-cotta blocks occurred in the tower piers, both immediately above the shelf angles and between floor levels, as shown in Figure 4, and some pieces had broken off the building. The buckling occurred when the terra-cotta blocks in the piers could no longer support the high compressive stress caused by expansion of the terra cotta.

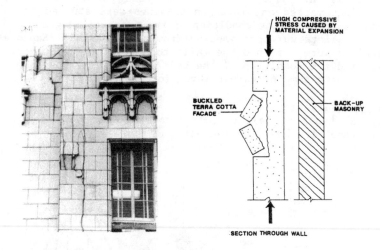

Figure 4.   Buckling and cracking of terra-cotta piers.

2.   Vertical cracks were seen in the tower piers near the concrete columns.   When the terra cotta expands horizontally, as shown in Figure 5, vertical cracks develop near the pier corner, and isolated corner pieces of terra cotta rotate and become loose.

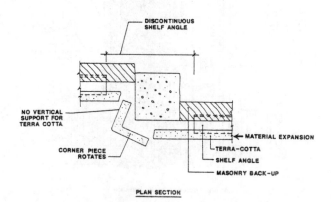

Figure 5.   Cracking of terra-cotta piers.

3. Some shelf angles were missing, others had corroded away
    and all of them stopped 2 to 3 feet short of the wall
    corners. The uneven vertical support, especially at the
    corners, caused extensive vertical cracking from shear
    failure between supported and unsupported terra cotta.

4. Terra-cotta blocks had crushed at the base of the tower
    piers due to high compressive stresses.

5. Rust scale expansion at the toe of the shelf angle caused
    cracking and spalling of the terra-cotta blocks just above
    and below the shelf angle, as shown in Figure 6.

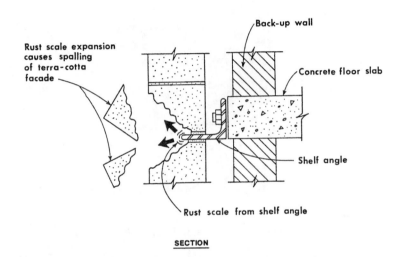

Figure 6. Shelf angle corrosion.

6. Parapets had cracked due to thermal expansion and an
    absence of expansion joints.

7. Mortar joints had apparently deteriorated in the past and
    this had resulted in water leakage. The repair had been to
    smear sealant across the joint – in the mistaken belief
    that this would solve water infiltration problems. The
    sealant, which never worked, had attracted black dirt,
    giving the building a checkerboard appearance.

Strain Relief Test
Thermal and wet/dry cycles both cause permanent expansion of
terra cotta. This lengthening in a building without expansion
joints can cause high compressive stresses. Field observations
indicated that a high level of stress existed in the cladding.

Strain relief testing was performed to measure the magnitude and direction of these built up stresses. Electrical resistance strain gages were attached to the terra-cotta surface and the gages were read. Then the terra-cotta block, with the gages attached, was cut loose from the wall and the gages were read again, as seen in Figure 7. The change in gage reading is a measure of the strain in the block. The stress in the block is then found by multiplying the measured strain difference by the modulus of elasticity of terra cotta, as determined by laboratory tests.

Figure 7.   Strain Relief Test.

The strain relief testing indicated a build up of vertical stress in the tower piers, increasing from the top of the building towards the base. Horizontal stresses were not significant. The maximum recorded vertical stress was 11.07 MPa (1606 psi) at the base of the tower piers.

Another strain relief test was performed to determine the feasibility of relieving the vertical stress by cutting horizontal expansion joints. A joint was cut below a shelf angle for the full depth of the terra cotta and the full width of a pier. Cutting the joint relieved the built up stresses, but the sudden release of stress during the cutting caused cracking adjacent to the joint and several blocks almost exploded during the stress release.

Laboratory Examination

Petrographic Analysis A petrographic examination revealed that the clay material was of good quality without significant deterioration of clay body or glaze.

Compressive Strength The compressive strength of 1-inch cubes was determined in accordance with ASTM C-67.   Strengths of 64 MPa (9300 psi) to 99 MPa (14300 psi) were obtained.   These strengths are typical for good quality terra cotta, indicating the strength of the clay has not significantly degraded.

Absorption Tests to determine 24 hour rates of absorption of glazed and unglazed specimens showed that the glazed units absorb water at the rate of about 15% of the absorption of unglazed samples. The absorption of water into the clay causes irreversible expansion of the material. It also makes the terra cotta susceptible to freeze-thaw damage.

Thermal Coefficients The thermal coefficients of expansion of the clay and of the glaze, determined experimentally from individual gaged samples of material, were found to be compatible. This might account for the good condition of the glaze and the small amount of glaze spalling observed.

CAUSES OF THE TERRA COTTA FAILURE

The terra-cotta facade of Atlanta City Hall had suffered distress and deterioration much the same as many other similar terra-cotta buildings constructed in the early 1900's.   The causes of the distress can be summarized as follows:

1.   The wall was constructed without expansion joints.   The long-term shrinkage of the concrete columns and concurrent thermal and moisture expansion of the terra cotta had created high compressive stresses in the facade.   These stresses caused crushing and buckling of the terra-cotta blocks, especially at the lower floors where the weight of the facade was greatest. Horizontal expansion of the terra cotta caused vertical cracks near the building corners.

2.   The terra cotta was supported on shelf angles at each floor level but some of the original angles had been omitted, other angles had corroded away and none of the supports extended all the way to the building corners. This caused vertical displacement cracks between the supported and un-supported sections and some of these cracks extended through 15 stories from the ground to the roof.

3.   Significant amounts of water were penetrating into the wall through cracks, spalls and open mortar joints, and causing corrosion of the steel shelf angles. Expansion of the rust product confined by adjacent terra cotta blocks resulted in cracking and spalling of the terra cotta. Bulging terra cotta at the toe of the shelf angles created locally unstable conditions.

4.   Water entering the terra cotta had also caused glaze
     spalling partly from freeze-thaw action and partly from
     salt formation below the glaze as the water again
     evaporates. However, the amount of glaze spalling at
     Atlanta City Hall was considerably less than is normally
     seen on terra-cotta claddings of this age.

RESTORATION

The project involved a total restoration of the City Hall,
inside and out. The exterior facade work, which cost $2.3
million and took 15 months to complete, included the following:

Expansion Joints
Horizontal expansion joints were cut into the terra-cotta
cladding below selected shelf angles, as shown in Figure 8, in
order to release the built-up stresses in the wall. Cutting was
started from the top of the building where stresses were lowest
and progressed downward. Even so, some damage to the terra
cotta occurred as there was an uneven release of pressure during
the cutting. The blocks immediately above and below the
expansion joint were anchored with stainless steel rods prior to
the cutting. A flexible sealant was used to fill the newly cut
expansion joint, as shown in Figure 9.

Figure 8.   Cutting Expansion Joint.

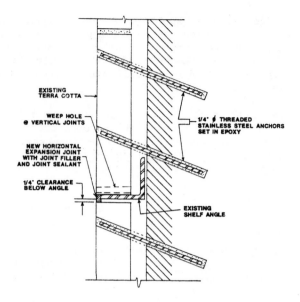

Figure 9. New horizontal expansion
joint at existing terra cotta units.

Terra-Cotta Supports and Anchors
Corroded or missing shelf angles and wall ties were replaced
with new steel material. Neoprene flashing was added above the
new shelf angle and weep holes were installed in vertical
joints.

Joints
The restoration called for 100% repointing of all terra-cotta
joints in order to remove the sealant that had been applied over
the joints and in order to restore the watertightness of the
facade. The removal of the dirt covered sealant turned out to
have the greatest effect of any repair on improving the
appearance of the building. Repointing was done with a
traditional cement-lime mortar, nearly white to match the
original mortar color. Mortar was used in all joints (except
expansion joints) since it allows any water trapped in the wall
to dissipate.

In-situ Repairs
Instead of replacing entire blocks, small cracks and spalls were
repaired in-situ. Cracks were cleaned out and filled with a
colored mortar. At wide cracks, the mortar was coated to match
the terra cotta glaze. Epoxy injection was used only where
structural strength had to be restored, for example, at a
cracked ornamental unit. Spalls were prepared and patched with
a polymer concrete. Stainless steel bolts and wire were used to
reinforce larger patches.

Both large and small spalls were coated with a 100% acrylic paint to match the original terra cotta glaze. Many colors were required to match the variety of original terra cotta colors found on the building. Glaze spalls, where only the thin layer of glaze had come off over a small area, were patched with a natural cement mortar and coated.

New stainless steel threaded rod anchors set in epoxy were installed in areas where the existing terra cotta anchors were suspect. The balustrade at the roof parapet was strapped and braced. Finials and other ornamental pieces were secured to their base with stainless steel anchors.

Replacement of Terra-Cotta Blocks
Damage to the terra cotta was more severe than seen on many other buildings of the same age, and the restoration required replacement of a large number of terra-cotta blocks, as shown in Figure 10. The most extensive damage was on the 12 story tower. For speed and economy, polymer concrete was used to fabricate the 1501 replacement pieces for this part of the building. The damaged blocks were removed, numbered, measured and replaced with blocks cast in a field factory set up near the building.

Figure 10. Damaged terra-cotta blocks removed for replacement.

Most of the damaged blocks were simple rectangular shaped pieces and the contractor used stainless steel forms with two sliding sides so that the size of the block easily could be adjusted. After removing the blocks from the forms and cleaning off the form release agent, the blocks were coated with the same acrylic paint used for the in-situ repairs, and then installed on the building, as shown in Figure 11.

Figure 11. Installation of new polymer
concrete blocks.

New terra cotta replacement blocks were installed at the
three-story building base, which is the most visible part of the
City Hall. Some 466 replacement blocks used for this part of
the building were manufactured in California and shipped to
Atlanta.

Prior to fabrication the contractor submitted a series of trial
samples using different glaze formulas and methods of glaze
application. The replacement blocks were installed with shelf
angles and stainless steel anchors, as shown in Figure 12.

FUTURE MAINTENANCE

As part of the restoration, a maintenance program was
prepared for the client. The program describes the procedures
and the materials used for the present restoration and it
delineates maintenance procedures and schedules.

Figure 12. Installation of new
terra-cotta blocks.

Reinstatement of Twin Spires at Faversham Almshouses Chapel, Faversham, Kent, England

J. Coath

Purcell Miller Tritton & Partners, Architects,
9 London Road, Sevenoaks, Kent, U.K.

ABSTRACT

The twin spires of the Chapel at Faversham Almshouses, constructed in 1863, were removed in 1964 because they were thought to be structurally unsound. Some four years ago the Trustees of the Almshouses took the decision to reinstate them. This paper describes the investigation of the existing structure and the original form of the spires, and the process of designing and constructing the new spires. The aim was to return the chapel to a form that respected the original design concept by reinstating the missing elements with minimal disturbance and intervention to the remaining structure whilst integrating current standards of construction and adopting modern design philosophy where appropriate.

INTRODUCTION AND HISTORICAL BACKGROUND

Faversham is a small town on the North coast of Kent and is of historic interest especially with respect to its provision of Almshouses. Between the early Seventeenth century and the mid-Nineteenth century the generosity of former Faversham residents led to the establishment of four separate Almshouse foundations. In 1614 Thomas Mendfield provided an Almshouse for six poor widows in Preston Street; in 1636 John Foade left his house in Middle Row to be used for a further three poor old widows; in 1721 Thomas Napleton left his estate to the town to found a Hospital at Tanner's Green for six poor men and by 1840 when Henry Wraight died he had established an Almshouse in Abbey Street for six dredger men, or their widows, and provided for a further six widows or spinsters at Mendfields Almshouses in Preston Street.

With the aim of combining these four Almshouses a scheme was put to, and approved by the Court of Chancery in 1856 for "the erection on some eligible site within the town of Faversham, thirty suitable Almshouses containing accommodation for thirty poor persons, with a chapel adjoining". The Trustees were authorised, as soon as the new Almshouses were erected and occupied, to sell the four empty buildings to defray the cost.

An initial design produced in 1860 by Mr Hussey, Architect, envisaged thirty separate houses and a chapel on ground in

Napleton's Orchard but the Lord Chancellor would not approve this plan as he thought that "all persons should be able to get to the chapel under a covered way".   The Trustees then arranged a competition which was won by Hook & Wheeler of Brenchley (Fig. A). The dominant feature of the winning design was the covered arcade that provides a sheltered route from each house to the North and South entrances of the chapel. This created a strong cross-axis to the chapel and the two entrance vestibules were surmounted by steep stone spires on open arcaded drum bases which serve to reinforce it visually. This arrangement forms a very unusual and innovative composition and the spires are an essential part of the whole ensemble.

A tender of £9,483 for the superstructure of all the buildings from G W Chinnock of Southampton and another of £1,300 for the foundations from Lewis Shrubsole of Faversham were accepted and a Clerk of Works named T Cloutman was appointed. The foundation stone was laid on 19 July 1862 and the building was completed and occupied on 1 August 1863, just over one year later.

It is on record that the stonework of the spires was eroding badly and giving cause for concern by 1930 when a "miracle treatment" was used to "prevent" further erosion. However, in 1964 the Trustees were advised that the two spires and drum arcades below, were dangerous and that it would be wise to have them removed. Despite protestations from the Faversham Society they were taken down and the plinths capped with concrete at a cost of £2,140 and the stones were disposed of without any detailed records being taken. The possibility of reinstatement in the future was obviously not contemplated at that time.

In 1979 the Trustees learnt of the munificent bequest of the latest in a line of Faversham's benefactors, Peter Head, which was for repairs to the chapel. This meant that consideration could be given to the reinstatement of the spires and in 1987 Purcell Miller Tritton & Partners were asked by the Trustees to prepare outline proposals for the task, one hundred and twenty four years after the construction of the previous spires.

Fig. A   The Hooker and Wheeler Design 1862

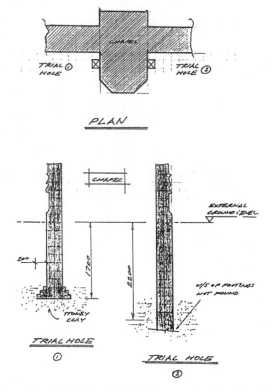

Fig. B   Structural Engineer's record sketch of the foundations
from the trial pits

INVESTIGATION OF THE ORIGINAL STRUCTURE AND FORM OF THE SPIRES

One of the original contract drawings showing the spires and chapel stonework and dated 1862 is still in the possession of the Trustees. This was initially examined by the Architect and seemed to show that the spires were constructed in stone four to five inches (10-12.5cm) thick and supported by slender octagonal drum arcades, the column shafts of which were only some six inches (15cm) thick. The plinth appeared to be constructed in brickwork of varying thickness with corbelled projections and a thin cladding of about four to five inches (10-12.5cm) of stone on the outside face.

Although this drawing clearly shows the general appearance of the original design, the type of stone used was not noted on the drawing and it did not give much detail of the construction or carved decoration.

A preliminary sequence of work was presented to the Trustees as follows :-

1 a) Investigation of the existing structure - survey the existing structure to see if it is in good condition and adequate to carry the proposed loading. Some investigation of the foundations may be needed and possibly calculations by a structural engineer.

   b) Investigation of the design - research into the detailed appearance of the spires from old photographs, drawings and other documentary evidence, and examination of the existing structure.

2   Design of the replacement of the two spires - method of construction, choice of stone and possible simplification of some of the details, weatherproofing the open area and preventing birds from roosting in or on the spire.

      Consultation with local authority; Listed Building Consent would be needed as the building was probably listed after the Spires were removed.

3   Detailed drawings, Specification and estimates - for approval by the client followed by competitive tendering from stonemasons and general contractors with experience of this type of work.

4   Construction and completion - it should be possible to control the total cost as the number of unknown factors will be few and the new stone can be accurately costed.

This was accepted and the investigation and design procedure began.

A scaffold was erected around the existing Southern plinth and the stonework was cleaned. The existing stonework at the top of the plinth was found to be in a very eroded condition and the ashlar cladding above the main eaves-level cornice had suffered from inconsistent differential weathering. The stone used was identified as a coarse grained shelly limestone, generally light brown or cream in colour but with areas of blue/grey tint, probably from one of the Bath quarries. A measured survey of the South plinth was carried out, photographs taken and the scaffold was then removed. A visual inspection of the inside face of the two brickwork shafts, which supported the spires and pass through the chapel to the ground, was carried out to assess the structural condition and possible extent of repairs that would be necessary to the existing structure. The brickwork was found to be roughly built and some minor fractures were recorded but their general condition seemed quite sound. A trial pit was dug near to the base of each shaft, a record of the foundations taken and then they were filled in (see fig.B).

As well as the 1862 contract drawing the Trustees provided photographs taken just before the spires were demolished in 1964 but these were unclear and only provided a general impression of the form and construction. Subsequently the Faversham Society lent the Architects various photographs taken in 1930 and around 1900. Although these were also too indistinct to give an accurate record of the details, they did show that the decorative finials and crosses, which appeared on the contract drawing, did not exist at that time and may not have been included in the original building as intended.

DESIGN OF THE NEW SPIRES, AIMS AND STRATEGY

As there was evidence for the previous form, the primary object in the design of the replacements was to explore the option of replicating them as accurately as possible. Outline design drawings were prepared (Fig. C), based on the documentary details and showing all of the original features, including the intended decorative finials and crosses at the top of the spires.

The open drum arcades posed particular design problems when attempting to keep them aesthetically correct while considering them in context of 1990's technology and standards. Firstly, the slender nature of the stone structure at that point could not satisfy current structural design criteria if it was not reinforced in some way. Secondly, the stone column shafts are vulnerable to natural wind erosion and even if they could be the only structure element at that level (as they were in the

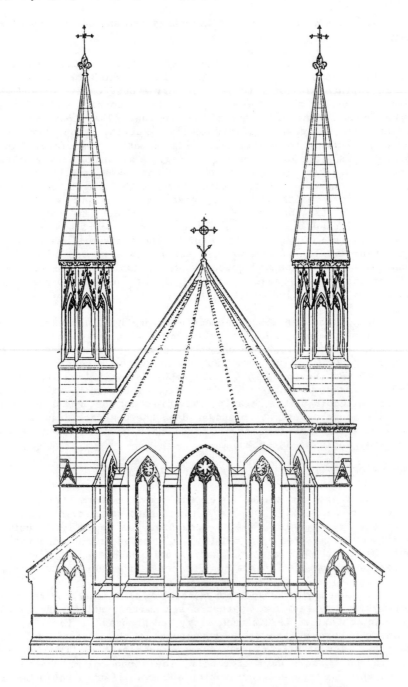

Fig. C   First Outline Design Scheme : East Elevation

originals) it would be very difficult to replace or repair any of them, when this became necessary in the future, without seriously affecting the overall stability of the spire above.   Thirdly, leaving the arcades open to weather and birds creates a maintenance problem that would be difficult to overcome.   To solve the first two points the Structural Engineer devised a stainless steel and reinforced framework to act as a relieving structure in combination with the stonework (Fig. D).   The only alternative to the metal frame solution was a solid masonry drum in the centre of the arcaded section of the spire.   This would have interrupted the clear view through the structure which was felt to be in the spirit of the original design.   The stainless steel and concrete framework as designed extended to a lower level in the shafts to bypass the top levels of existing brickwork which could not be proved to be of adequate strength. The framework also anchored a post-tensioned tie-bar which connected to the boss at the top of the spire and introduced a compressive stress into the stone skin.   The stone column shafts were tied back to the stainless steel posts with cramps.   It was decided that any rainwater entering the openings of the arcade should be collected in a box gutter and taken to the ground via a hopper head and rainwater pipework, rather than being allowed to spill over the outer stonework of the plinth.   Covered hatches and fixed ladders in the shafts would provide easy access to the spires for maintenance and inspection.

On the basis of this outline scheme the stonework was measured and a detailed cost estimate produced by a firm of specialist Quantity Surveyors.   A figure in the region of £400,000 was arrived at and presented to the Trustees by the Architects, who pointed out that this was the cost of reinstating the original design as near as possible but if this was prohibitive in terms of cost, other design options could be investigated and a ceiling figure should be given to the Architect as a basis.   The Trustees resolved that a ceiling figure of £250,000 be worked to and other options should be investigated.   The Architects redesigned the spires in a simplified form with less decorative stonework and roofs constructed in timber with lead cladding instead of stone (Fig. E). Apart from substantially reducing the cost, the revised design was thought to compliment the scale and character of the existing chapel as well as, if not better than the original design. Certainly the reduced amount of decoration on the spires seems appropriate when compared with the chapel itself.

Structurally the revised scheme was similar to the previous one but had some crucial differences. Mainly, the overall height and weight of the structure were reduced by about 20%.   This meant that the stainless steel and concrete relieving frame could bear on the existing structure at a higher level.   To accommodate

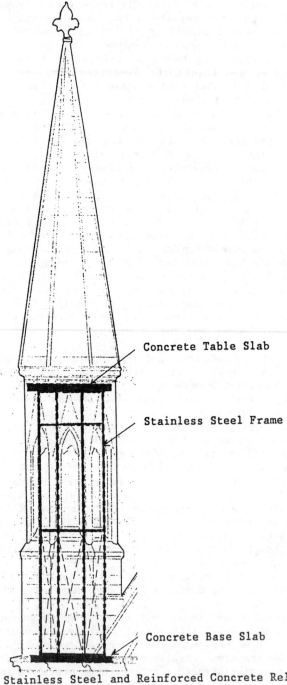

Concrete Table Slab

Stainless Steel Frame

Concrete Base Slab

Fig. D   Stainless Steel and Reinforced Concrete Relieving
Frames

Fig . E   Second Outline Design Scheme : East Elevation

this change it was decided to carefully dismantle and rebuild the top 10 feet (300cm) of the existing plinths allowing for replacement of stonework that had eroded excessively (estimated to be approximately 50%).

An 8" (20cm) thick insitu reinforced concrete slab was to be cast across the rebuilt shaft-top with a hatchway incorporated into it and this would act as the base slab for the relieving framework and tie the brickwork structure together. It was agreed to show the bottom ends of the 4" (10cm) square x ¼" (0.6cm) thick stainless steel box section posts cast into the base slab and a 6" (15cm) thick table slab cast onto the top of the posts. The posts at both ends would be connected together with a 6" x 3/8" (15cm x 1.0cm) steel ring plate fillet welded to the box sections and cast into the concrete. As in the previous design the stonework of the drum arcades would be fixed to the posts by means of stainless steel cramps. All stainless steel was specified as 316 grade.

The spire roofs are conventionally constructed with 6" x 4" (15 x 10cm) S.C.4 grade sawn softwood rafters. The feet are fixed to the concrete table slab with bolted stainless steel cleats (Fig. F) and the tops are connected to a wrot hardwood boss by means of stainless steel locating dowels and a 2½" x ½" (6.25 x 1.25cm) stainless steel strap band. The rafters are strutted at mid-span with 5" x 2" (12.5 x 5cm) softwood intermediate members fixed with bolted cleats and a horizontal diaphragm in 3/4" (1.8cm) thick W.B.P. plywood, closely cut round the rafters and fixed to the top of the intermediate struts acts as wind bracing. Further wind bracing is provided by the boarding which is 6" x 1" (15 x 2.5cm) wrot plain edged softwood fixed horizontally with ½" (1.25cm) gaps to allow ventilation to the back surface of the lead cladding. In addition to the timber structure the structural engineer specified cross-bracing to the lower half of the spires. This was in the form of ½" (1.25cm) diameter stainless steel rods connected in the centre with threaded stressing blocks and at the ends with plates bolted to the fixing cleats.

The cladding to the spires is 7/8lb (Code 7) continuous cast lead supplied by Midland Lead, laid with a herringbone pattern of hollow roll joints on the flat surfaces and hollow king rolls at the junction of the slopes.

The Phosphor Bronze finials (Fig. G) which top the spires were cast in 7 pieces and T.I.G. welded together then precisely drilled to accept the Naval Brass crosses which were then welded into position. The vertical stem of the cross is made of 1" (2.5cm) diameter bar and projects below the finial by approximately 2 feet (60cm) to provide a locating pin for the

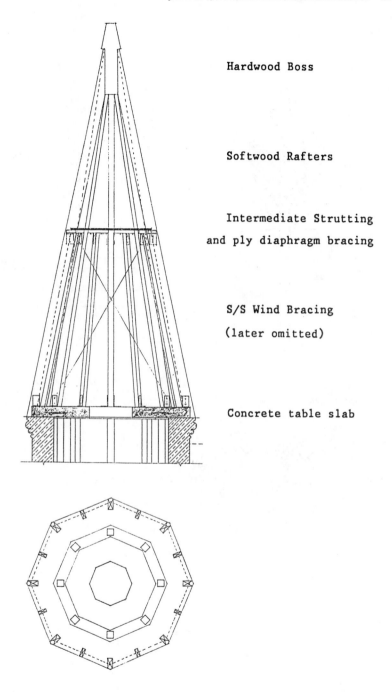

Hardwood Boss

Softwood Rafters

Intermediate Strutting
and ply diaphragm bracing

S/S Wind Bracing
(later omitted)

Concrete table slab

Fig. F   Section and Plan of Timber Frame to Spire

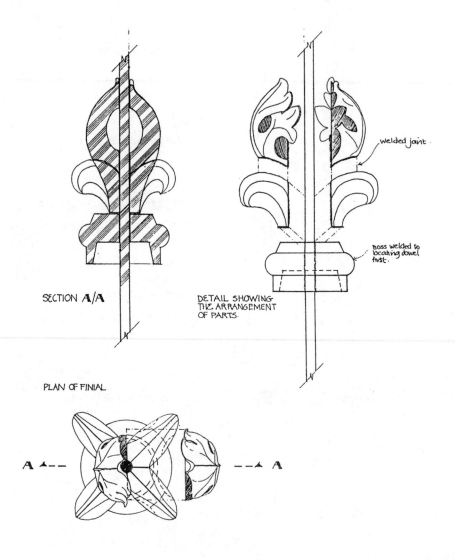

SECTION A/A

DETAIL SHOWING
THE ARRANGEMENT
OF PARTS.

welded joint.

Boss welded to
locating dowel
first.

PLAN OF FINIAL

A ◄ ──   ── ◄ A

Fig. G   Detail of Phosphor Bronze Finial

whole finial assembly which sits into a lead-lined socket in the
hardwood boss at the junction of the rafters. The crosses have
hand-crafted leaf decoration with the veins of the leaves beaten
into the brass sheet. This demonstrates the attention to detail
given to this project by the skilled tradespeople when one
considers that they rose to 80 feet (2400cm) above the ground
when they were installed in late November 1990 and cannot be seen
in detail from the ground.

CONCLUSION : REMEDIAL REPAIRS AND DESIGN CHANGES CARRIED OUT
DURING CONSTRUCTION

The construction started on site in April 1990. Once the
scaffold had been erected and careful dismantling of the tops of
the existing plinths began a more detailed survey of the existing
structure was carried out by the Architect and Structural
Engineer together. It became clear that the stone cladding
varied in thickness and was mostly only 3" (7.5cm) thick,
sometimes as little as 2" (5.0cm) and the brickwork skin was
generally thicker than at first thought and incorporated sections
that corbelled out over the chapel in the plane of the roof
structure. It was decided that further dismantling and
rebuilding was going to disrupt the existing building-fabric
unnecessarily. A series of remedial repairs and relieving, or
reinforcing, measures were specified which included building
further brickwork on the chapel walls to tie the corbelled
section back-to and by-passing some of the load from the new
structure above. Approximately 20 stainless steel straps were
bolted across fractures and weak points in the existing
brickwork, other cracks were filled and the entire inner surface
was cleaned down, covered with stainless steel expanded metal
lathing and rendered with a 1:2:9 lime/cement/sand render to
consolidate the rough friable surface and reinforce the structure
as a whole. This reduced the amount of cutting-out and
stitching-in of brickwork and meant that the thin stone cladding
could be replaced where necessary by piecing-in new stones.

It was found that the stainless steel box section for the
new frames was to be imported from Germany. The steelwork
fabricator warned the main contractor of a potential delay of 12
weeks. The main contractor requested that to mitigate any
possible delay to his programme, the reinforced concrete slabs be
pre-cast and the stainless steel frame bolted to them instead of
being cast-in. This meant that the sequence of work above the
frames could continue as soon as the frames were installed and
would not be disrupted by the formwork and insitu concrete work
that was going to follow. This was agreed, on the understanding
that any extra cost was met by the contractor. As it was, the
delay on the supply of the steel was not as great as anticipated
and the change in design meant that the job was in fact two

months ahead of schedule.   Two interesting points arose out of this change.

Firstly, the entire superstructure was able to be pre-fabricated on the ground in sections, then hoisted and fixed into position in a matter of hours, and secondly, the stainless steel cross-bracing which was found to be unnecessary on the timber structure was fixed to the stainless steel frame to give it extra stability and allow the spires over to be fully loaded before the stonework to the drum arcades was installed.   This produced two further fortuitous advantages.   Firstly, the temporary stability at times of repair would be even greater than first planned for and an unexpected delay in the supply of stone for the project had no affect on general progress.

The stonemason experienced difficulty in obtaining the Clipsham Limestone, specified by the Architect, of a consistently good quality.   It comes from a small quarry and supplies can be variable in quality when ordering large quantities.   Due to the location and exposure of the building, every effort was made to obtain a stone with a reasonably consistent durability, although of course stone is a natural material and will erode with time. The aim was to match the existing stone on the building as closely as possible in both colouring and consistency while trying to avoid the uneven erosion that had occurred previously. After some delay a stone from the base beds of the Stoke Ground Quarry, near Bath, was obtained and proved to be a suitable alternative.

The stonework was completed, the lightning conductors installed and the scaffold was struck in mid-December 1990, and the spires on Faversham's Almshouses Chapel were successfully reinstated.

ACKNOWLEDGMENTS

Client: The Trustees of the Faversham United
                       Municipal Charities
                       The Almshouses
                       South Road
                       Faversham
                       Kent   ME13 7LU

Architects: Purcell Miller Tritton & Partners
                       9 London Road
                       Sevenoaks   Kent   TN13 1AH

Structural
Engineers: Gary Gabriel Associates
                       Bat and Ball Studio
                       168 St Johns Hill
                       Sevenoaks   Kent   TN13 3PF

Contractors: R J Barwick (Building) Limited
                       Coombe Valley Road
                       Dover   Kent   CT17 0UJ

The Restoration of Agia Kiriaki in Grevena, Greece

K. Theologidou

Ministry of Culture, 11th Ephory of Byzantine Monuments, Greece

ABSTRACT

All stages necessary for the restoration of the church of Agia Kiriaki are described, starting from first inspection and observations on site. Next, the research work on site and in the office and the first conclusions for the diagnosis of the problems are presented. Finally, the restoration works are described, which include the pulling back of an outward leaning wall and its consolidation to the vertical, the consolidation of the other walls of the church and the arrangement of the direct environment.

INTRODUCTION

The church of Ag. Kiriaki is located in the village Mavronoros, county of Grevena. Mavronoros is a small village with limited facilities, at a distance of approximately 15km from the capital of the county, Grevena. The church dates from the 16th century. Unfortunately, it has been neglected in the last decades. Therefore, its problems were seriously aggravated. A program of restoration works started in 1989 for its preservation. Ministry of Culture -11th Ephory of Byzantine Monuments was in charge of this project, which was supervised by the author of this paper.

DESCRIPTION OF THE MONUMENT

The church has a rectangular form and small dimensions, namely 8,00m long and 5,00m wide (fig. 1). Its height varies from 2,5m to 4,0m, depending on the inclination of the ground. The church was covered with a timber roof with two slopes and the roofing material was slate . The walls of the church are built of rubble stone and lime mortar. The masonry is strengthened with timber tie beams.

The entrance to the interior is a low opening on the western facade. The old wooden door has been preserved in good condition. The interior was initially lighted up with one window on the south wall and two small ones, like slots, on the east wall. Later, in the first half of this century, a second window was opened on the south wall. The floor of the church is at a lower level than the ground around the monument. It was covered with stone slabs which have been preserved in good condition.

fig. 1 The church of Ag. Kiriaki in 1989 before the restoration works. Western facade.

All the walls of the interior and the western facade were covered with mural paintings. Those on the east and the west wall have been preserved in good condition, the ones on the south wall in a fairly good condition, while the mural paintings on the north wall have been destroyed almost completely. The other three facades of the monument are simple. Traces on the south wall show that once they were plastered.

THE CONDITION OF THE MONUMENT BEFORE THE RESTORATION WORKS

In 1989 an inspection was made during which the following defects were recorded:

- The east part of the south wall had collapsed at a length of approximately 4m (fig. 2). This part of the wall had collapsed once again in the past and had been rebuilt of stone and mud mortar.

- The rest of the south wall had strongly leaned outwards (fig. 3). This inclination measured 43cm, while the height of the wall was 400cm and the depth 75cm.

fig .2   South east corner.

fig. 3   The outward leaning south wall

- The upper part of the north wall had leaned inwards in the middle by 15cm. It should be noted that both faces of this part were above the ground level.

- The internal face of the north wall formed a bulge in the middle of its lower part. The corresponding external face of this part was partly under the ground level.

- Serious cracks appeared on the three corners of the monument (the southeast corner had collapsed). Among them, those on the north and south wall were assessed as being in a critical condition (fig. 4).

fig. 4 Northern facade. Destroyed tie beams, moisture and cracks are some of the problems.

- Timber tie beams were partly destroyed, especially at their joints.

- The mortar was in fair condition.

- Excessive moisture appeared on the lower parts of the north and east wall.

In addition to the above, the inspection of the direct environment also showed that:

- There were a number of trees at a small distance from the monument recently cut.

- There was strong inclination of the ground level.

- One of the villages roads passed by, at a distance of about 4m
from the north wall.

- Finally, a telecommunication pole was located at a distance of 1m
from the northeast corner of the monument.

RESULTS FROM THE ARCHIVES RESEARCH

A research was also undertaken into the archives of the 11th
Ephory of Byzantine Monuments, so as the history and the problems
of the monument to be further investigated. From this research, together with photographs dated from the same period (fig. 5), a fairly
complete picture of the condition of the monument in the last two
decades was obtained.

fig. 5   The south wall in 1981. The rebuild part of the east end can
be distinguished, as well as the trees very close to the
monument.

In 1968 the east part of the roof had already collapsed, while
the east part of the south wall was ready to collapse (Tsioumi [1]).
Indeed, ten years later the above part of the wall was found collapsed and at the same time the west part of the roof was about to.

The rest of the south wall had strongly inclined, while the other walls were in a better condition, although cracked and weathered (Vasilas [2]). In a report written in 1981, it was observed that the east and west wall were still in a sound condition. The inclination of the north and the south wall measured 15cm and 40cm respectively. These inclinations are attributed by the writer to the collapse of the roof, which pushed the two walls while it was falling. On the other hand, the collapsed part of the wall was attributed to the rainwaters which moistened it after the roof had collapsed. Among the proposals included in this report for the conservation of the monument, a reconstruction of the south wall as well as the inclined part of the north wall was proposed (Lembidas [3]).

In 1984, according to photographic records, some measures were taken aiming at slowing down the evolution of the defects, such as shoring and temporary roofing. During those works the remains of the roof were destroyed. No report was kept about the form and structure of the roof trusses and their traces and position on the top of the walls; therefore a future reconstruction of the roof may entail a number of imprecisions.

The above research showed that there was a very fast destruction of the monument in the last two decades and especially in the 1970s. Thus, among other reasons, abandonment and neglect were critical for its problems at that time. The measures taken in 1984 were proved to be very helpful because they stabilised to some extent the condition of the monument.

SITE INVESTIGATIONS

Both the information gathered from the archives and the site inspection showed that previous attempts to diagnose the problems were inadequate. Furthermore, no report had taken into account the fact that the collapsed part of the south wall had already collapsed in the past, at least once. Therefore, a program of further site investigations was set off concerning the form and the conditions of the foundations. Two sections were made on the ground, one on the south east corner and the other in the middle of the north wall (fig. 6). The position of these two sections was chosen, taking into account on the one hand the form, the position, the direction and the width of the cracks, the deformations and the destructions and on the other hand the characteristics of the direct environment (such as inclination of the ground level, high trees, etc.).

These sections revealed a number of useful features relevant to the problems of the monument. More specifically:

- The foundations were in a very short depth, namely 40cm lower than the floor of the church and as thick as the wall upon it. Moreover, at a distance of 1m onwards from the south wall, the level of the ground was lower than that where the foundation lay.

- The foundation of the collapsed part of the south wall lay partly on the ground and partly on a grave. Between the foundation and the grave there was a layer of soil, 30cm thick.

- At a distance of 1,5m from the south wall, the foundation of the south wall of an older building was found. The east wall of this building continued just under the east wall of the church. The above grave lay within the perimeter of this building. Further excavation showed that the surrounding àrea used to be a cemetery. Therefore, though the excavations have not yet been completed it is presumed that the older building was a church as well.

fig. 6   South east corner. The grave and the foundations of an older building.

Together with the research work on site and in the office, these inspections proved that the main reason for the collapse of the east part of the south wall was its foundation partly on the soil and partly on the grave. A further reason was the fact that the rest of this wall was founded on the ground, while the east wall on the foundation of an older building. This conclusion is supported by the fact that the collapsed part of the wall was the only one which had created serious problems in the past.

Therefore, the destruction process can be described as follows. The east part of the south wall had again collapsed in the past and was roughly rebuilt of stone and mud mortar. Consequently, the south part of the roof was seated on a wall which was partly built of lime mortar and partly of mud mortar. Furthermore, the poor construction was founded in a different way than the other walls. These problems, together with the weathering of the timber elements of the roof, caused the collapse of its eastern part. It is possible that the movements of the roof up to its collapse pushed the north wall inwards and the south outwards. The whole condition was aggravated by the stong inclination of the ground and the trees around the monument. It should be noted that the two sections also revealed the roots of the trees under the foundations.

Furthermore, the bulging on the lower part of the north wall was mainly due to the ground damp, because the external face of this wall was partly buried and therefore absorbed a large amount of humidity. The whole condition of the monument was further aggravated by the aging of its materials and especially the timber tie beams, as well as its abandonment and neglect in the last decades.

RESTORATION WORKS

The restoration works dealt with the inclination of the north and south wall and the bulging of the north wall. In addition, they dealt with the destruction of the tie beams, the cracks, the weathered mortars and the arrangement of the direct environment of the monument.

The north wall had no stability problems and so it was restrained in the inclined position. On the contrary, the south wall was pulled back to vertical position and was held there, because of its serious stability problems, the form and history of its defects. The mural paintings were retained on this wall and were temporary stabilized, so that no damage would be caused to them during the whole operation.

The pulling back (Macgregor [4]) concerned the full height of the wall, because its foundation was shallow and its leaning started from there to the top. In order to proceed to this work, its west end was disconnected from the west wall. The east end was already free because of its collapsed part, as described above. The window was temporarily blocked up with masonry of stones without mortar, while a hole was left so that the wire cable could pass through it.

The slabs of the floor were taken away across the internal face of the wall and a concrete foundation was inserted in short lengths under the existing foundation. At this stage this foundation reached half the width of the wall. A slot was left between the stone foundation and the concrete one, so that there was space for the wall to move towards its new position.

Both faces of the wall were fully covered with planks, which were connected together with timber beams. The two timber faces were also connected together, so as to form a non flexible structure, with the wall in it. Internally, a layer of spongy material

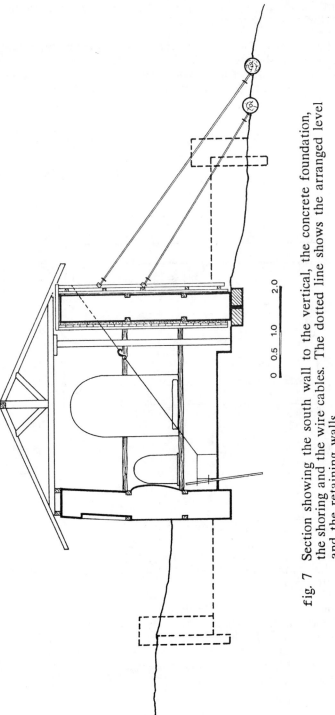

fig. 7   Section showing the south wall to the vertical, the concrete foundation, the shoring and the wire cables. The dotted line shows the arranged level and the retaining walls.

0   0.5   1.0   2.0

was put between the face of the wall and the planks in order to protect the mural paintings.

The external face of the wall was supported by raking shoring tightened up with screw jacks. These screw jacks could be expanded approximately 35cm each. Two screw jacks were fixed on the two ends of each shoring bar; therefore, each could expand up to 70cm.

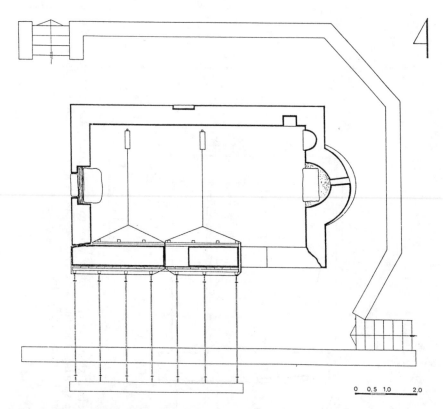

fig. 8   Horizontal plan, showing the position of the wire cables and the raking shoring and also the arrangement of the direct environment.

The wall was hauled back with the help of two pulleys, which were fixed on metal bars driven into the ground, after the floor slabs were removed. The wire cables, fixed on the pulleys, were embracing the wall. Each time the wall was pulled a few centimeters, the shoring was stressed by screwing the jacks, thus minimizing the possibilities for collapse due to unexpected factors (fig. 7,8).

After the wall was pulled back (fig. 9), a series of works followed to retain it in a vertical position. Firstly, the other half of the concrete foundation was inserted in short lengths along the external facade of the wall. The rebuilding of the collapsed east part and the disconnected west end followed. The two corners were strengthened with stainless steel bars. The timber tie beams, at the top of the wall, were reconstructed to connect it to the east and west wall, as well as the tie beam at the lower part of its external face.

fig. 9 The south wall to vertical position.

The cracks and the weathered mortar were pointed and grouted. This work proceeded gradually, starting from the lower parts of the wall. The planks and the raking shoring were also gradually removed, corresponding with the parts of the wall to be repaired. This was a precautionary measure to prevent any collapse or damage in the case of their direct total removal. Grouting was made by hand as there were no facilities on site. Moreover, by this method it was secured that no pressure would be applied to the wall, which might cause problems. The grout composition was based on lime and pozzolonic material, to which a small quantity of cement was added (Penelis [5]).

A note was taken of the quantity of grout each point absorbed and the positions where the liquid flowed out from. Taking as specific weight for this type of masonry 1800kg/m3, the weight of the pulled back part of the wall was calculated approximately 22t. This part absorbed 1.7t of grout, which is proportionate to the 7.8% of its weight.

The ground was lowered to the north in order to be kept approximately at the same level around the monument. A retaining wall was constructed by concrete around the three facades of the monument to support the soil. The top of these walls and their visible face were built of stone masonry (fig. 8).

Pointing, limited rebuilding where necessary and grouting were also applied to the other walls. In all four walls, the destroyed timber tie beams were replaced where this was possible. However, replacement was not possible everywhere, firstly because of the mural paintings and secondly because of their inaccessibility in the inner parts of the walls, where some of them were embedded. Therefore, the four corners of the walls were strengthened with stainless steel bars, positioned horizontally, at different heights. The above repairing works were applied to the north wall as well, and were assessed adequate for its consolidation (fig. 10,11).

The works have not yet been fully completed. It is planned to be continued and completed in summer 1991.

fig. 10   South east corner after the restoration works. A comparison to figure 3 shows the position of the south wall before and after the works.

fig. 11   The church after the restoration works.

REFERENCES

1. Tsioumi Mavropoulou, C. Inspection Report, Archives of the 11th Ephory of Byzantine Monuments, Veria, 1968.
2. Vasilas, V. Inspection Report, Archives of the 11th Ephory of Byzantine Monuments, Veria, 1978.
3. Lembidas, D. Inspection Report, Archives of the 11th Ephory of Byzantine Monuments, Veria, 1981.
4. Macgregor, J. E. M. Outward leaning walls, Society for the Protection of Ancient Buildings, Technical pamphlet 1, London, 1971.
5.   Penelis, G. Karaveziroglou, M. Leondaridis, D. Stylianidis, K. Structural Study of Rotonda, Vol. 1, Aristotelian University of Thessaloniki, Thessaloniki, 1980 (unpublished).

The Huelva Pier of the Riotinto Railway: Description and Present Situation

R. Picón, J. Cañas, F. París

Department of Continuum Mechanics, Engineering School (University of Seville), Av. Reina Mercedes s/n. 41012 Seville, Spain

ABSTRACT

In this work, a complete description of the Pier of the Rio Tinto Railway is presented, including an analysis of structural material properties. The present situation of the Pier is then described. Future steps to be taken for the repairing of the Pier will be detailed in a subsequent paper.

INTRODUCTION

The Huelva Pier of the Rio Tinto Railway is a peculiar vestige of the early iron industry in the middle of the 19th century. It rendered service in discharging iron minerals for almost a century, from 1876 till 1975. The discharge system, using rising and falling gradients, allowed 1000 Tons/hour to be discharged. The bearing structure, consisting of cast-iron columns and wrought-iron girders, was designed to take advantage of the mechanical properties of both materials. The Pier was abandoned in 1975, the structure having suffered considerable deterioration since then. In this work, after brief historical notes, a complete description of the Pier is presented. Then, an analysis of the properties of the structural materials is reported. Finally, the present situation of the Pier is described. Future steps to be taken for the repairing of the Pier will be detailed in a subsequent paper.

HISTORICAL NOTES

The historical notes presented in this section are taken from the book "El Muelle de Rio Tinto" ("The Rio Tinto Pier") by the architect Gonzalez Vilchez [1]. This work is an extract from the same author's Doctoral Thesis (Gonzalez Vilchez, [2]) on the History of

English Architecture in Huelva.

The pyrite mines of Rio Tinto, in Huelva, are probably among the oldest in the world. As early as the times of the Tartessians, Phoenicians and Greeks, primary working of the mines was taking place, as is testified by the huge slag heaps found in the course of archaeological digs in the area. This activity reached the height of its splendour in Roman times, only to cease for a long period in the Middle Ages, including the Visigothic and Moorish periods.

The modern history of mining in Huelva has been marked from the outset by a lack of interest on the part of the State in the systematic working of the mines. In 1828, for example, the Crown leased the Rio Tinto mines to the Marquis of Remisa, who exploited them for two decades, proving the profitability of the activity, although at the ecological cost of killing off the already scarce vegetation of the area, due to the emission of sulphurous anhydride and the inevitable need for timber.

In spite of this precedent, and the reports in favour of working the mines presented by engineers from Spain and abroad, the exploitation of Rio Tinto on the part of the State continued its long decline, scarcely covering the costs involved, until the mines were finally sold, in 1872, to the Rio Tinto Company Limited (RTCL) for three and a half million pounds.

Once in English hands, the Rio Tinto mines proved a clear and indubitable success, RTCL becoming the largest company in Spain in terms of manpower employed, and mining the most important economic activity in Huelva.

The English company immediately saw the need to construct a railway linking Rio Tinto and Huelva, and to have at its disposal a Pier which would allow the minerals to be loaded efficiently. Up until then, the minerals were transported to the port of Huelva in carts, and the ships loaded using shallow-draughtbarges. Work on the railway and the Pier began at the same time, and the project was placed in the hands of George Bruce, a British engineer of great prestige and experience in the matter of railways and bridges. The project for the Pier which concerns us in this article was presented to the Company by Bruce in February 1874, and then passed on to the Harbour Board and the Ministry of Public Works, being presented under the supervision of M. Ridley, chief engineer of RTCL in Huelva. The official bodies apparently presented technical objections concerning the depth of pile work necessary to ensure the stability of the structure, and the author had to defend his proposals personally. RTCL's decision to have a lower level for ordinary goods traffic forced Bruce to introduce modifications and finally to draw up a revised project, which was presented by Ridley [3], to the Harbour Board in May 1874.

Construction of the Pier began in September 1874, with the contraction of Thomas Gibson as site-engineer. A basic tool for our knowledge of the Pier is the Report presented by Gibson [4] to the Institution of Civil Engineers in 1878, offering an account of the technology and construction methods used, as well as of the various incidents of note which occurred during the work. The report is supplemented by some plans which are of the greatest interest, being those which were actually used in the course of construction.

As regards the metal structure itself, Gibson's plans differ from those of Bruce in some structural and constructional details. There are also differences concerning the auxiliary loading mechanisms and the stucture of the jetty, which was built independently of the Pier to avoid damage to the latter in the course of mooring.

The main difference between Gibson's plans and the originals lies in the foundations. After test-drilling carried out in August 1874 it was established that the subsoil was even softer than expected, and unable to support more than 700 pound/foot^2 at the depth envisaged for the piles (36 feet). Gibson showed, in addition, that even at 80 feet the load-bearing capacity was much the same. As a result, a decision was made to lay down timber platforms, linked to the piles at the level of the sea-bed and resting on the latter, in order to attain a sufficiently large are to support the loads. The platforms were sunk prior to being joined to the pillars, and loaded with ingots and rails until reaching a load roughly equal to 4/3 that of the project itself. Once the platforms were in position (some going down to a depth of up to 5.4 feet) they were joined to the pillars using collars.

The Pier came into operation in March 1876. 1834 Tn. of cast iron, 1582 Tn. of wrought iron and 215 cubic feet of timber were used in its contruction. The final cost came to 145166 pounds. Almost 130 million tons of minerals were loaded from it during the almost one hundred years it was in service, until it was closed in May 1975.

The main problem affecting the functioning of the Pier stemmed from the impossibility of dredging around it, in order to avoid weakening the foundations, which has led to a reduction in draught. Difficulties in this regard were first observed in 1912, and by the last few decades of operation it was a regular occurrence for large boats to run aground at low tide. Today, in the area of the jetty, the sediment can be seen above the level of the water when the tide is low.

With the closure of the Pier in 1975, and the termination of maintenance-work, rapid deterioration ensued. Its appearance has even undergone a drastic change, with the dismantling of a section of about 170 feet in order to build the Huelva estuary promenade, thus breaking the continuity of the land and sea stretches of the structure. Only in 1989 was a clear awareness evident of the need to save the Pier, given both its social connotations as a construction typifying the city of Huelva and the historical interest it holds as a structure representative of the late 19th century iron industry.

DESCRIPTION OF THE PIER

The approach from the station-yard to the pier is over an embankment followed by a set of timber trestle frames, along a total length of 1500 feet. From this point on the railway lines rest on the iron structure, which consists of three lengths, of 600, 775 and 525 feet respectively, of which the first and third portions are straight and the second is curved, with a radius of 600 feet (Fig. 1). At the time of building of the pier, the shore was at the beginning of the first of these portions, but nowadays it is at the beginning of the second one. Moreover, a length of about 170 feet has been eliminated to make way for a road.

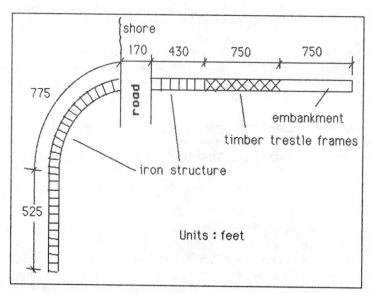

Fig. 1 General Plan

The rail-lines are laid on three levels. On the first (ground) level there are, starting from the pier head, three lines that are combined later into one single line. This level was used only for ordinary traffic. The other two levels originate from a single line coming from the embankment, that divides into three; one of these, the central one, continues with rising gradient, divides itself into two lines and, with falling gradient, ends at the pier head; this is the third level. The other two lines go sideways, with falling, null, and rising gradients, as far as the pier head, where they meet with the two upper lines; this is the second level.

The wagons with ore were pushed by an engine up to the highest point of the third level, then descended by gravitation to the pier end, returned along side lines of the second level, discharged their loads into ships, and returned by gravitation as far as the original single line . Figure 2 is a drawing of the two upper lines, showing the number of lines of rails and their gradients.

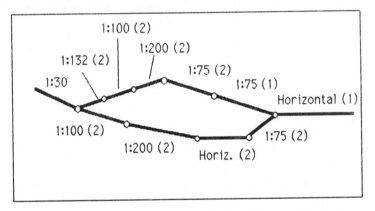

Fig. 2 Gradients (rail lines) of upper levels

The main subject of this paper is the iron structure and, from now on, we will deal exclusively with this. The total length of the iron structure (1900 feet) was made up of 29 spans of 50 feet each, and 30 groups of 8 columns, in two rows of 4 columns each, these being 15 feet from centre to centre. Columns are 15 inches in diameter.

Two drawn views, transversal and longitudinal, of a basic bay of the pier are shown in Figs. 3 and 4. The former corresponds to the deep water portion of the pier, and shows one row of columns, these ending in screw piles and resting, at an intermediate height, on the timber platform, which transmits to the sea bed the greater part of the loads. The screw piles and the columns were made up in lengths, with external flanges that were bolted together. Several bracing elements can be seen in Fig. 3: diagonal tie rods between columns (a), lattice girders between columns and second level main lattice girders (b), lattice girders betwen third level main lattice girders (c), rolled I and U beams (d), angle stays (e) between columns, and beams of variable depth between columns (f). Morever, at the centres of the 50-feet girder there is, at first level, an I bracing beam with T iron knees riveted to the top booms of the main girders; at second level, this bracing function is achieved by a lattice box, made up of angle irons and flat bars. At third level along the 50 feet span, there are three bracing lattice girders like the one labelled "c" in Fig. 3, which bind together the two main lattice girders on third level. Finally, crossed flat bars are riveted to the under-side of the bottom booms of first and third level main girders throughout the entire length of the pier. Joins are made by riveting, if possible, by hoops to columns, or by flanges small cast in the columns, in some cases. At some points, tie rods join columns by passing through the latter, the former being fixed at the back by a bolt pressing on a cast bubble.

The rail-lines are centred on main lattice girders at second and third levels and on the middle of the three spans at first level.

In the longitudinal view of Fig. 4 can again be seen the screw piles, columns, and some longitudinal bracing elements between columns. Apart from the columns, the most important resisting elements of the pier are the main lattice girders, which are also shown in Fig. 4. The first level main lattice girder is 4 feet deep. Top and bottom booms are plates with riveted angles. Vertical members are made up of three angle irons, two of them vertical, 11 inches apart, and the third horizontal, 18 inches above the bottom boom of the girder, riveted to the other two; this latter angle forms the support of the transversal beams of iron or timber, which carried the roadway. Diagonal members are plates, riveted at their centres. Six hinged bars (three at each side of the main lattice girder), not appearing in the original project, embrace the external 50-feet lattice girder, thus making it stiffer. The ends of the bottom booms of the three and ten opening lattice girders are fixed on the flanges of the column by two bolts. The end vertical plates of these lattice girders are bolted to the end plates of the cross girder of variable depth through oval holes, which allow expansions and contractions. Two short rectangular cast flanges join together these end plates and the column (Fig. 5).

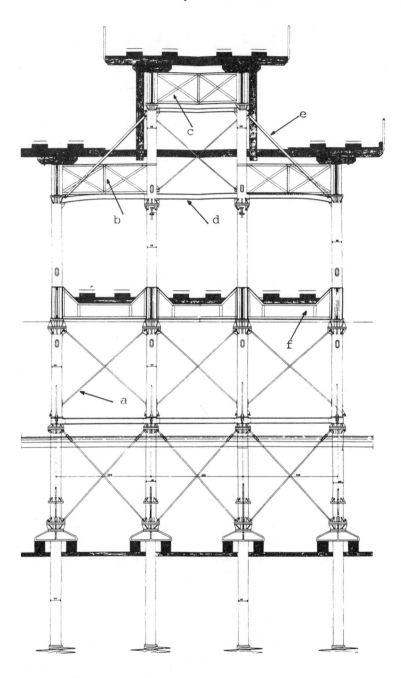

Fig. 3 Transversal view of the pier

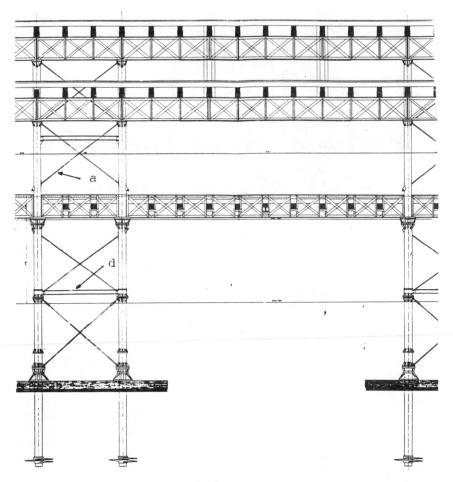

Fig. 4. Longitudinal view of the pier.

The top and bottom booms, and diagonal elements of the second level lattice girder are similar to those of first level lattice girder. Vertical members are made up, in some cases, of two T profiles with opposite flanges, and in others, of four angles and two plates. Again, the ends of the bottom booms are bolted to the column flanges, but now the column ends there, the end vertical plates being in contact and joined with bolts.

Third level lattice girders are equal to the second level one while there is a single line of rails; when there are two lines, lattice girders are bigger, with lengths of distinct depth, and more resistant profiles. Junction to columns is equal to that of the second level.

Fig. 5. Open junction box at first level.

A general view of a bay is shown in Fig. 6.

Fig. 6. General view of a bay.

MATERIAL PROPERTIES

There are two kinds of materials in the pier. Columns are made of cast iron and the rest of the structure is wrought iron. Average chemical properties of 5 samples of cast and wrought iron are shown in Table 1. From this table it can be concluded that cast iron

Table 1. Chemical Properties of materials.

Material	%C	%Mn	%Si	%S	%P
Cast Iron	3.3	.50	2.0	.11	1.41
Wrought Iron	.006	.24	.64	.03	.35

composition is typical of a grey cast iron, but with a higher percentage of phosphorus, presumably for bettering castability. Wrought iron composition is typical of irons made directly from iron ore, its carbon percentage being much lower than in present-day nowadays steels.

Compression tests on 5 samples of cast iron gave an average proportionality limit of 48.10^3 psi and an average compression strength of 97.10^3 psi . Tension tests on 4 samples of wrought iron gave an average elastic limit of 33.10^3 psi and an average tension strength of 43.10^3 psi . Figures of ultimate percentage elongation were extremely varied, ranging from 2.5% to 15.5%. Tie rods yielded similar strength properties, but average ultimate percentage elongation was about 22%.

PRESENT SITUATION

Elements under first level

Columns. Between the heights of high and low water line, columns have a very good outward appearance, because sea sediments have protected the cast iron. The columns' union flanges at this zone present corrosion of the triangular stiffeners and this also occurs at edges of the flanges; loss of material can be appreciated though the great bulk of the material seems to be in a good state. Bolts are in a very bad state, being destroyed at a slight knock from a hammer.

At the top of the box that joins columns with transversal variable depth beams and longitudinal lattice girders there is, in about 10% of the columns, a very strong hoop. The opening of one of these hoops has revealed a near full circumferential crack (Fig. 5), and it is therefore likely that all the hoops hide this kind of damage.

Near the holes for the tie rods, there is clear exfoliation, it being possible to extract the slices of material by hand. A set of ultrasonic thickness measurements makes it clear that, in general, the actual thickness is greater than 80% of the nominal. At certain points, this ratio drops to 50%, presumably as a result of manufacturing defects, but this damage never spreads in any direction. These comments are also applicable to the holes in the columns between first and second level.

There is an evident loss of parallelism between some columns, perhaps due to settling.

Wrought iron elements. All the   lattice girders and bracing elements at this zone are in an extremely bad state, with generalized corrosion, great losses of material, and even absence of complete elements. (Fig. 7)

Fig. 7. Bad state of first level.

Elements between first and second levels

Columns. About 90% of these elements have a very satisfactory appearance, with only minor pitting. The remaining 10% present a worse aspect and some of them have a long longitudinal crack. Again, loss of parallelism is observed. A small number of columns have a great longitudinal crack.

A few columns have hoops half-way up, these being in a defective condition.

Column-column union presents a satisfactory aspect, with only minor pitting in flanges.

Unions of columns with bracing elements (**I** and **U** beams, tie rods, transversal lattice girders, etc...) are very bad, with exfoliations, and about 40% of these unions are broken (Fig. 8).

Fig. 8. Broken tie rod-column union.

<u>Main lattice girders.</u> The ten and three opening longitudinal lattice

girders present some pitting, with slight losses of thickness at top and bottom booms. At the latter, made up of a plate and two angle irons, these angles are extremely deformed and exfoliated, with a great separation of their vertical webs (Fig. 9); this has been caused, apparently, by expansion of an unknown substance which was used to fill the space between vertical webs. Moreover, the bottom plate is often deformed, with loss of straightness.

The junction between ten and three opening girders appears very irregular, with separations between end vertical plates; this separation is sometimes at the upper side, sometimes at the lower side.

Corrosion is more extended at the zones of timber supports, with exfoliations and, in specific cases, breaking of top boom.

Fig. 9. Bottom boom of second level lattice girder.

Bracing elements. Bracing transversal lattice girders present pitting with loss of material in upper side elements. Some junctions (about 10%) between constitutive bars of these girders are broken. Hoops for union with columns have greater corrosion than other elements around them.

Tie rods have a high degree of corrosion, with severe pitting and loss of thickness, this being more pronounced near columns' holes. A few of them are broken.

There is also pitting and loss of thickness in bracing I and U beams between columns, and in crossed flat bars, especially on their upper side. Unions of **I** and **U** beams with columns are broken in many cases (Fig. 10), some of these unions having been repaired.

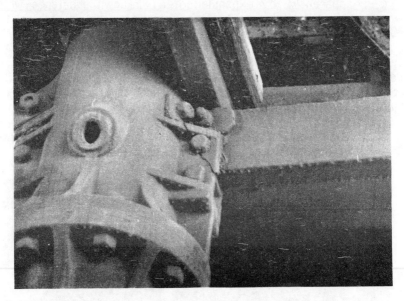

Fig. 10. Broken channel-column union.

Lattice boxes between main longitudinal lattice girders have greater corrosion near their unions with the latter, with losses of material and exfoliations.

Elements between second and third level

Columns. In general, these present a satisfactory appearance, with minor pitting and lack of protection. A minor degree of corrosion appears at the zones where there are hoops, these themselves, on the contrary, having a high degree of corrosion. The rest of the unions are in a good state.

Lattice girders. Again, in general, their appearance is good, though there are exfoliations at the unions to other elements and some pitting on the top boom, with minor loss of thickness.

Junctions to columns present a generally good state, though in some cases there are losses of material and exfoliation.

Bracing elements. Transversal   lattice girders between columns have a good appearance. There is isolated pitting and loss of thickness, mainly on the upper side of the elements. Transversal lattice girders between main girders are in a similar state, the greater corrosion being at the union with the latter.

Bracing **I** beams also have minor pitting and loss of thickness, mainly in their upper side. Cross flat bars present pitting on the upper side and at the edges.

Tie rods are fine, with only very superficial corrosion, the worst part of them being the union to columns.

Apart from the iron structure, there is a great deal of timber in the pier, with bracing or flooring functions. All this timber is in a very bad state.

CONCLUSIONS

Abandonment of the Huelva Pier of the Rio Tinto Railway has accelerated its natural deterioration under environmental action, and today there are several instances of serious damage in the structure.The most serious cases are the following:

a) The wrought iron structure under first level is completely unusable

b) A number of columns present vertical and horizonal cracks of very great size.

c) Many unions of bracing elements to columns are broken.

d) Bottom boom of first level lattice girders is extremely deformed, with great losses of material.

Future steps to be taken for the repairing of the pier are described in a subsequent paper.

ACKNOWLEDGEMENTS

The remarkable work of A. Cañas and J.L. Puntas in the visual inspection of the pier is gratefully acknowledged. The authors also acknowledge, with thanks, the colaboration of E.M.A.H.S.A. and specially to L. Manzano and I. Tomico.

REFERENCES

1. Gonzalez Vilchez, M. The Rio Tinto Pier (in Spanish), Excma. Diputación Provincial de Huelva, Huelva, 1978.

2. Gonzalez Vilchez, M. History of English Architecture in Huelva (in Spanish), Servicio de Publicaciones de la Universidad de Sevilla/Excma. Diputación Provincial de Huelva, Seville, 1981.

3. Ridley, M. The Pier of The Rio Tinto Railway: Report of the projected variation (in Spanish), Archivos del Puerto autónomo de Huelva, Huelva, 1874.

4. Gibson, T. The Huelva Pier of the Rio Tinto Railway, Excerpt Minutes of Proceedings of The Institution of Civil Engineers, Vol. LIII, Session 1877–88, Part. III, London, 1878.

The Huelva Pier of the Riotinto Railway: Analysis and Repair

J. Cañas, F. París, R. Picón, J.L. Puntas

Department of Continuum Mechanics, Engineering School (University of Seville), Av. Reine Mercedes s/n. 41012 Seville, Spain

ABSTRACT

The description of this structure as well as its present situation of maintenance are included in a previous paper also presented to this Conference. In this paper, bearing in mind the main problems of the structure previously stated, a proposal for repairing it is given. An analysis of the structure is made first of all in order to evaluate, with the tools usually employed today in the structural analysis , its load capacity. This analysis will allow a quite realistic impression of the stress state at the different elements of the structure, which in turn might give an explanation of some general defects observed in the structure.

The repairs that need to be done are carefully described including the corresponding structural analysis. This analysis does not usually need to be performed on the whole structure, a partial analysis of a substructure being possible, due to its original conception.

The repair implies in some cases just the substitution of the original element or its elimination. Structural reasons are in these cases adduced to support such decisions.

INTRODUCTION

The topology and the present situation of the Huelva Pier of the Riotinto railway has been described in a previous paper, Picón, Cañas and París [1], in order to consider the possibility of its reutilization for recreational purposes. The situation of the pier was deduced through a visual inspection together with the realization of different tests, both destructive and non destructive using ultrasounds. It was concluded, after the inspection, that

306   Dynamics, Stabilisation and Restoration

several zones of the pier are not currently operational, their substitution being absolutely necessary. Other main parts of the structure are, fortunately, in good condition, their load bearing capacity just requiring checking with the new loads that are to act on the pier according to its new use.

In this paper, the repairs, together with the calculations which justify them, that the pier needs in order to guarantee its structural integrity, are described. With this objective in mind, a global model of the structure (obviously with some simplifications), has been made and it is described in the next section. This model using the modern tools of structural analysis, offers an impression of the original design, evaluating the present state of stress in the different elements of the pier, assuming it to be in good condition.

Bearing in mind the conclusions obtained from such an analysis and considering the probable origin of the generalized damage found along the pier, its repair is described in section 3.

It must be observed that the aim of this paper is to analyze the decisions taken in the original design of the pier which could be at the root of part of the present defects, independently of the damage created under the effect of natural agents acting synergetically with the lack of maintenance of the pier over the last fifteen years. The new design has been conceived to palliate such defects, trying to ensure that the esthetic image of the pier remains unaffected by the necessary modifications.

GLOBAL MODEL OF THE PIER. ANALYSIS.

The pier can be viewed horizontally as a set of units which, with some small differences between them, are repeated along its length. Three levels can be distinguished in vertical direction, starting at the level defined by low water.

Each of these units is composed of eight columns of cast iron, which transmit the load to the foundation, and lattice girders with a length of 15.3 m. and 4.6 m., which directly receive the load derived from the use of the pier.

The foundation is composed of screw piles and a timber platform which lies directly on the bed of the river. The soil-structure interaction has been considered following some studies performed on the bottom of the river, Justo, Manzano and Gonzalez [2]. The soil has been modelled using ballast coefficients in vertical and horizontal directions, both varying linearly with the depth.

Due to the, at least apparent, hyperstaticity of the structure of the pier, it seemed to be clearly necessary to have a three dimensional model of the structure, in order to have a proper knowledge of the distribution of loads between its different elements. A finite element model, Przemieniecki [3], has been developed requiring the following hypotheses, remarks and considerations:

– Due to the impossibility of modelling the whole structure (about 30000 elements), only one of the units previously referred to has been modelled. This implies that in fact a pier of infinite length and without curvature is being analyzed, assuming that the load does not change from one units to another, two planes of symmetry having been applied to delimit the unit studied. Several analyses, with a simplified model, were carried out to estimate the real transmission of loads between neighbouring units, confirming the validity of the assumption made.

– Beam elements have been used for the structure and plate elements for the foundation. A general view of the model is represented in Figure 1.The original properties of the elements of the structure, both geometrical and mechanical, have been considered independently of their present situation. The original plans and several measures carried out on the structure have constituted the bases for defining the model.

– Pedestrian load, wind and thermal effects have been considered as actions on the structure. A combination of them has been followed in accordance with MV 103.

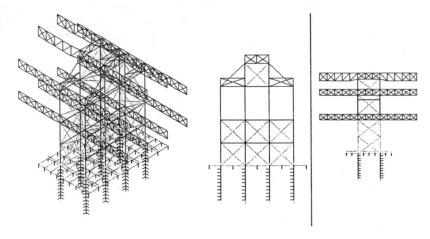

Fig.1 Finite element model: a) general view b) transversal section
     c) lateral view.

- A post-processor to evaluate the equivalent stress has been developed. Although some conservative assumptions have been employed in it, the analysis confirms the impression that the structure is overdimensioned, at least under static load, which will be the kind of load in the future use of the pier. The following table resumes the highest level of stress for each of the different elements:

Element	Maximun Stress (Kg/cm^2)	$(\sigma_{max}/\sigma_E) \times 100$
Columns	344	12%
Tie Rods	544	24%
Lattice Girders	1300	55%
Beams of Variable Inertia	357	16%

Table 1 Level of stress in different elements of the structure.

As regards the stress level of the elements of the original design, the only thing clearly appreciable is the inefficient distribution of the transversal section of the diagonal of the lattice girder, giving rise to poor resistance to compressions.

The remaining comments on the original design will be given in the next section, studying each element independently from the rest of the structure , which is quite adequate due to the reasonable static uncoupling between the different elements (cast iron columns , lattice girders that have to be redesigned, etc.). As will be explained later, only some transversal beams require information from the global model for their calculations. A final checking of the design with the global model was performed, in any case.

REPAIRING OF THE RESISTANT ELEMENTS.

Tie Rods.

These elements have a clear esthetic but also an important resistant function, which can be clearly observed by eliminating them in the global model. For both reasons they are to be maintained, some of them (practically all under the level of the water) being in bad condition. One of the more extensive types of damage suffered by this element is the connection to the column. For such cases the piece shown in Figure 2 has been designed. This piece will be screwed to the columns making use of the old orifices.

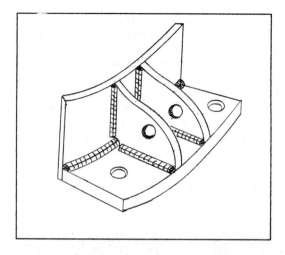

Fig. 2 Union element of the tie rod to the column.

Column flanges.

Their present situation is generally good, although some of them present damage in the triangular stiffners. In such cases, the part of the triangular stiffner that remains can be eliminated , an element similar to the one described in Figure 2 being used for it, substituting the elements with the orifice of union to the tie rod by new triangular stiffners.

Columns.

The majority of the columns are in extremely good conditions of maintenance. The only generalized damage observed is associated to a loss of thickness near the longitudinal orifice which permits the tie rod to pass through it. To avoid progressive deterioration of this zone and assuming that it has been produced by splashing, a 3 mm. thick plate has been designed to be screwed to the column. This plate will cover the original orifice permitting, although conveniently sealed, the passage of the tie rod.

The great value of the original transversal section of the columns, which results in a low level of stresses, allows them to absorb the load with the present thickness.

Some longitudinal cracks, fortunately in a small number of

columns, have been detected. Different devices, in the form of hoops were used in the past to repair them, with varying fortune. More dangerous and more extended are the horizontal cracks localized near the connection of the columns to the transversal elements of union at first level. The origin of these cracks, the majority of them localized at first level, could lie in lateral actions (shocks produced by ships) and in the tremendous flexural rigidity of the column in the transversal plane motivated by the two short rectangular flanges that connect the column to the transversal variable inertia beam. Very heavy hoops, Figure 3, were designed and used in the past to solve this problem and have proved their efficiency in palliating the damage, it being necessary, for this reason, to maintain them.

Fig. 3 Hoops designed to embrace the cracked part of the column.

Bracing between columns.

There are two different kinds of these bracings : One corresponds to laminate steel beams in I or U, which are connected to the columns through flexible screwed joints. There are a great number of broken elements connecting the beams to the columns. The reason for this generalized damage does not seem to be structural. In the zone of the pier where these elements are broken they are not placed in their original position, but some centimetres higher. It is believed that some time in the past, it was necessary to avail of a greater height, the damage being produced either by the dismantling or by the incorrect functioning of the connection in the displaced position. There is no problem in returning these beams to their original position, lying on a small cast flange on the column.

The other kind includes the lattice girder that connect transversally the top of the external columns with the central ones at second level. The present situation of these elements does not require any repair.

Elements at first level.

This section includes all the elements positioned approximately at the horizontal plane corresponding to pedestrians. After the visual inspection, it was concluded that the resistant elements of this level should be replaced, due to their precarious situation. Figure 4 gives a scheme of the new design.

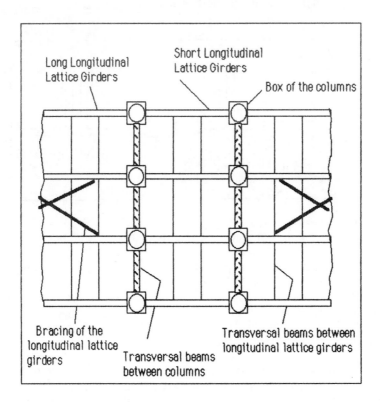

Fig. 4 Resistant elements at first level.

An attempt has been made, as a general rule, to maintain the present topology although the following changes have been considered suitable.

a) Lattice girder.

In the new design, in accordance with the main use of the pier which is to be pedestrian, the vertical position of the platform at first level will coincide with the top of the lattice girder. For this reason and to ensure that a lorry of 8 Tn. will be able to operate along the pier, the plate of the top boom of the lattice girder has been designed narrower than the original, in order to avoid local effects.

The bottom boom of the plate has been designed without a plate, Figure 5, in an attempt to avoid the accumulation of water and corrosive materials along the boom.

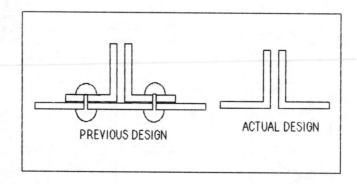

Fig. 5 Old and new design of the bottom boom.

The diagonals of the lattice girder have been designed using L sections. The original design had plates with a high degree of slenderness, beyond the values recommended by present practical rules. In fact, some of them have undergone buckling, although this could also be due to the present level of degradation of the diagonals in the bottom part.

A neoprene block has been designed to be placed at the zone of the column flanges where the lattice girder lies. This kind of support has several advantages. It permits the absorption of the dilatations originated by the temperature without transmitting load to the column. The contact stresses are also regularized (non - hertzian contact) and the neoprene also prevents the accumulation of humidity on the contact surface (due to its natural roughness), preventing some local corrosion.

b) Transversal beams between longitudinal lattice girders.

These beams were originally made of wood except the one at the center of the span where it was a laminated steel. The new design, shown in Figure 6, includes a laminated steel with double T section, connected by screws to the vertical element of the longitudinal lattice girder.

This design aims to avoid the transmission of torsional effects to the longitudinal lattice girder , the bracing function of the transversal beams being maintained.

c) Transversal beams between columns.

These were designed, originally, as beams of variable inertia. In the new design a laminated steel with an H section has been employed. Trying to avoid bending connections with the columns, the support of these beams has been designed to be flexible, as is indicated in Figure 7. A seal must be prepared to prevent material or water deposits along the non-welded edges.

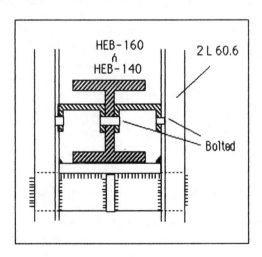

Fig.6 Scheme of the connection of the transversal beams
    to the longitudinal lattice girder.

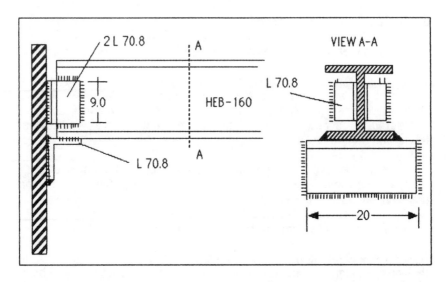

Fig. 7 Scheme of the connection of the transversal beams to the box
      of the columns .

Some considerations regarding the design of the longitudinal lattice
girders. The appearance of this lattice girder has been maintained
in the new design, although some of the diagonals do not have
structural functions. The material employed is A 42b, all the joints
being welded. The basic loads are represented in table 2, giving
rise to 34 different loads.

Load	Value
DEAD LOAD	200 Kg/m^2
PEDESTRIAN	750 Kg/m^2
LORRY	8000 Kg.
FRICTION	5320 Kg.

Table 2 Loads acting on the longitudinal lattice girder.

The friction load corresponds to the maximum horizontal
estimated value that can appear at the neoprene support.

A matrix structural analysis has been performed, the structure
necessarily being modelled as a frame instead of a truss. Table 3
recovers some values showing the different values of the analysis
in both cases (for simplicity of the loads, the results presented
correspond to the second level). The reason for the high values of
the so-called secondary bending moments lies in the high values of
the stiffnesses of the different elements of the lattice girder.

ELEMENT	σ^F	σ^{LG}	σ^F / σ^{LG}
BOOM	625	482	1.3
DIAGONALS	687	617	1.2
VERTICAL MEMBER	421	119	2.8

Table 3 Different stresses in the elements of the longitudinal lattice girder second level analyzed as a truss and as a frame.

Due to the fact that the transversal beams do not brace the top boom of the longitudinal lattice girder, a checking of its lateral buckling is necessary. A finite element 3D model was again performed, although in this case an analytical approach following Timoshenko and Gere (4), was also developed. The buckling lateral load, in a second order analysis, was in both approaches very close to the design load. A system of bracing in the horizontal plane, at the level of the transversal beams, has accordingly been designed as is indicated in Figure 8. With this device a double value of the lateral buckling load is reached.

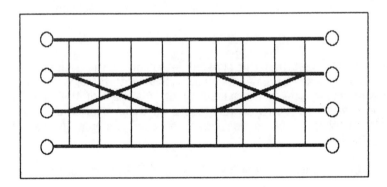

Fig. 8 Bracing of the longitudinal lattice girders to avoid lateral buckling.

It is interesting to note that although the study of lateral buckling of lattice girders was not absolutely developed at the time of building the pier, the problem was known to the engineers, a device being included for this case, which is described in the original project by Gibson [5]: "At the centre of the 50-feet spans, a cross stay-plate girder with T-iron knees is riveted to the top booms of the main girders, thereby binding them together transversely at their centres ".

Some considerations regarding the design of the transversal beams
between longitudinal lattice girders. These beams have two
different numbers of supports (two or four), depending on the
longitudinal position along the pier. Hypotheses for stress and
displacement limits have to be considered separately.

Some considerations regarding the design of the transversal beams
between columns. Due to the fact that these beams brace the
columns in the transversal direction, an axial effort can appear due
mainly to lateral actions. This effort is transmitted through the
bottom boom of the cross section, producing bending along the
beam. The value of this axial force (5.8 Tns.), has to be taken from
the results obtained from the three dimensional analysis with the
global model.

With the modification of the connection between the column and
this beam (clamped to simple supported), an average reduction of
about 20 % in the bending moments in the column near the joint is
attained. As was previously mentioned, the transversal cracks in
the columns could have been due in part to the high bending
stiffness of this joint. Thus, the liberalization of the bending degree
of freedom at the extremes of this beam can collaborate, since the
structure is more flexible, to carry out lateral actions.

Elements at second and third level.

Due to the fact that the present situation of the elements of these
levels is, as a general rule, quite satisfactory, it was only
necessary to check the adequacy of this part of the structure for
the new loads, which are analogous to those applied at first level ,
the differences being described for each element in the following
paragraphs.

a) Long longitudinal lattice girders (ten openings).

The matrix analysis performed on this lattice girder showed
that the stress level in its elements was acceptable, except for the
diagonals, which could undergo buckling due to their slight inertia in
transversal direction. The substitution of these elements would
make the repair of the pier very expensive, more expensive, in
fact, than complete replacement of the structure. For this reason
and for the historical value of the original structure, an alternative
redistribution of the stresses has been investigated assuming the
elements susceptible of buckling to have failed. Fortunately, the
remaining part of the structure can carry the load, so the original
lattice girder can be maintained.

The lateral buckling of the longitudinal lattice girders of this level is controlled by three-dimensional substructures placed in transversal direction, at the center of the spans. These substructures are generally in good condition, only light repairs at the joints being necessary.

The only serious problem to be solved in these lattice girders is the bottom boom. It presents along a considerable part of the length of the pier an extremely bad state of maintenance, with generalized exfoliation. The origin of this problem seems to be two-fold in time. The presence of a plate (as in the lattice girder of first level), probably led to accumulation of corrosive material. It seems than in a second phase, the groove was filled with a tarry substance which has led to the present situation. The substitution of the bottom boom would lead to the same considerations as for the diagonals. In this case, the solution schematized in Figure 9 has been found appropiate, welding a new element, in the form of inverted channel, after the original boom had been conveniently cleaned.

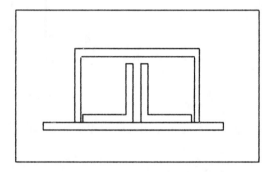

Fig. 9 Repair of the bottom boom at second and third level.

b) Short longitudinal lattice girders (three openings).

This lattice girder, although shorter than the previous one, has to be considered, due to the smaller value of the transversal section of its elements and to its different connection to the columns , being horizontally connected to them at both extremes. Temperature plays an important role with this kind of support. To analyze this effect, the model shown in Figure 9 has been considered. Some diagonals are again susceptible of buckling, but an alternative resistant system can again be found. It has to be clarified that these lattice girders did not require any comment at first level because with the new design they present a lower level of stress than the long lattice girders.

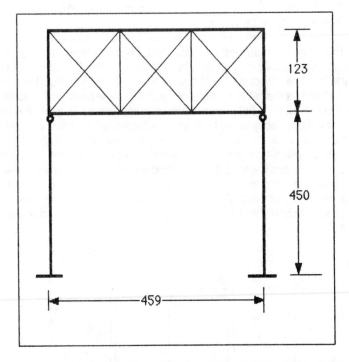

Fig. 10 Model for the analysis of the short longitudinal
lattice girders.

c) Lattice girders of the third level .

These lattice girders do not require any additional
consideration because the geometrical properties (area, inertia,
etc.) of their elements are greater than those of the lattice girder
of second level (probably because in the original function of the
pier the train ran with minerals along third level), while the load
will be the same, in their future use, for both levels. Additionally,
the bottom boom is in better condition in these lattice girders,
previous repair being required only locally.

GLOBAL ANALYSIS OF THE NEW DESIGN.

An analysis with the new design was finally performed in order to
check the validity of the hypotheses considered for the analysis of
each substructure, a maximum difference of 12 % in stresses
having been found.

CONCLUSIONS

A project for the repair of the Huelva pier of the Rio Tinto railway, with a view to its rehabilitation for recreational purposes, has been presented. The main characteristics of this project are:

- All the elements considered recuperables have been maintained, for historical reasons.

- When a substitution has been absolutely necessary, it has been made trying to preserve the original esthetic of the pier.

- The modifications presented have tried to satisfy a double purpose. To carry the loads originated by the new use of the pier and to solve certain problems associated with the original design, which have been explained in this paper.

As a general and concluding remark it can be established, after 116 years of existence that the original design and construction of the structure of the pier were very good, it being clear that several phenomena, properly analyzed only later, were known to the engineers who designed and built the pier.

ACKNOWLEDGEMENTS

The authors acknowledge, with thanks, the collaboration of E.M.A.H.S.A. and specially to L. Manzano and I. Tomico.

REFERENCES

1. Picón R., Cañas J. and París F., The Huelva Pier of the Rio Tinto Railway: Description and Present Situation, STREMA, 1991.

2. Justo J. L., Manzano L., Gonzalez M., The Restoration of Rio Tinto Pier: functional and foundation aspects. STREMA, 1991.

3. Przemieniecki, J. S., Theory of matrix structural analysis, McGraw-Hill, 1968.

4. Timoshenko S. P. and Gere J. M., Theory of elastic stability. McGraw-Hill, 1961.

5. Gibson, T. The Huelva Pier of the Rio Tinto Railway, Excerpt Minutes of Proceedings of the Institution of Civil Engineers, Vol. LIII, Session 1877-88, Part. III, London, 1878.

Reconstruction and Restoration of Petrovski Passage

S. Ince, H. Yiğin

ENKA Construction and Industry Inc., 80780 Balmumcu, Istanbul, Turkey

ABSTRACT

Main aspects of the reconstruction, restoration and repair works performed for the re-utilization of Petrovski Passage in Moscow USSR are presented. The structure, built in 1906, is characterised by gallery-like shop floors surrounding two large parallel central atriums which provide covered crossings between two main streets. Significant damage and deterioration of the building parts occurred after years of continuous use. The Passage was shut down in 1985, to be reconstructed and restored as a modern department store, incorporating new functional and technical requirements while preserving the historical features. The skylight lanterns were dismantled and completely renewed in close conformance to the original appearance, the floors were totally replaced by reinforced concrete slabs, lift shafts were added, foundations were strengthened by the High Pressure Injection method to withstand increased loads, the basement drainage system was renewed and an underground annex was constructed adjacent to the Passage. The facades and interior were restored in accordance with the original drawings and carefully recovered patterns and motifs. All works were completed within only twenty three months, seven months ahead of the 30-month contract period.

HISTORICAL BACKGROUND

Records in the Architectural and Historical Archives Department of Moscow City show that the earliest piece of information concerning the ownership of the property on which Petrovski Passage is located dates back to September 1832. The property was initially owned by the mayor of Moscow. In 1844 it was sold to Captain Voeikov, to be followed by several other owners until 1891 when it was finally purchased by Mrs. Firsanova Vera Ivanovna. At the time the property contained 27 housing units of various sizes and types, all rented out. In March 1903 Mrs.

Ivanovna petitioned to Moscow Municipality for permission to tear down all the houses for construction of a four-storey mansion. In May 1903 a revised petition was submitted by the same owner, this time for the construction of a three-storey shopping center. The design documents for both projects carried the signature of architect S.M. Kalugin. The second petition (Petrovski Passage Project) was approved by the Municipality and construction began in the spring of 1904, to be completed in November 1906. Original drawings existing in the archives indicate that some deviations from the original design occurred during construction.

In 1911 some major modifications were proposed and implemented by architect M.G. Geisler. Several staircases were re-located and the basement floor was re-arranged to accomodate a restaurant. Framed openings with wired glass were inserted into the first floor slab to provide natural illumination to the basement. Construction work was finished in 1912, thus providing Moscow with the most luxurious restaurant of the time, "Rish". In 1913 architect Barkov made a few minor changes on the Neglinnaya street side of the building, namely, wooden doors were converted to iron doors and a new staircase was added. The building became State-owned after the October 1917 Revolution and in 1920-21 a replica of the "Worker" relief carving, by sculptor M.G. Maniser, was engraved on the Petrovka facade. In 1928 the Passage was taken over by Mostorg and, after some modifications by engineer V.M. Vladimirov, was converted into a supermarket for consumer goods.

Petrovski Passage remained operative for 79 years. In 1985 it was shut down by the authorities due to its dilapidated condition and a restoration project incorporating new functional and technical requirements was prepared by Mosproject 2. The construction contract was awarded to ENKA Construction and Industry Inc. in 1988. All detailed design drawings (architectural, structural , mechanical, electrical) were prepared by ENKA taking into consideration the specific requirements of the contract and the architectural characteristics of the building. Except for the facades and main load-bearing members, the Passage was totally reconstructed and returned to service in November 1990.

DESCRIPTION OF BUILDING

Petrovski Passage is located in a densely-populated district of central Moscow, between Neglinnaya and Petrovka streets, as seen in the location plan, Fig. 1. The Passage is a valuable architectural and historical monument exemplifying a specific type of shopping mall common at the turn of the century. The design provides two covered parallel crossings, each lined with shops on both sides, between two main streets. Entrance from the streets is achieved through two high and vaulted galleries, each

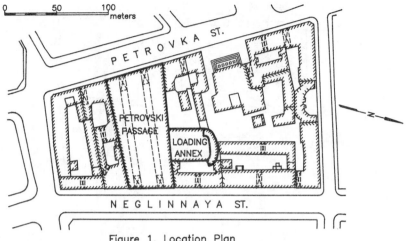

Figure 1. Location Plan

leading to a long atrium lined with shops on both sides. The
street facades are ornamented in baroque style. Flower motifs
seen in the original facade drawings have later been changed to
lion, eagle, maiden-head, etc. motifs during construction.
Interior ornamentation of the Passage, however, is rich in
elegant flower motifs.

   The building is about 110m long with the width increasing
from 42m on the Neglinnaya St. end to 57m on the Petrovka St.
end. It consists of three storeys with a combined height of 14m
above the entrance level plus a basement reaching 4m below that
level. The end parts contain the entrance galleries, all 5.5m
wide and 9m high, with respective lengths of 12.5m and 14.5m for
the Neglinnaya and Petrovka ends. The central part contains the
two parallel atriums, 77m and 82m long, respectively, spaced 8m
apart, and located 7m to 9m away from the longitudinal edge
walls of the building. Each atrium is 8m wide at the entrance
level and contains four crossover pedestrian bridges on the
second floor to facilitate access between the floor strips.

   As a representative plan for the general arrangement of the
building, the layout plan for restoration of the first floor is
given in Fig.2. Also, two versions of a typical transverse
cross-section between axes 80 - 90 are given in Fig.3, along
with two versions of a typical partial longitudinal section at
the Petrovka St. end given in Fig. 4, for a better understanding
of the original building and of the extent of the reconstruction
and restoration work that has been undertaken.

   In general, the floor structural system of the original
building consisted of secondary steel I-beams, mostly 1.0 - 1.5m
apart, supported by girders and/or load bearing walls. Girders

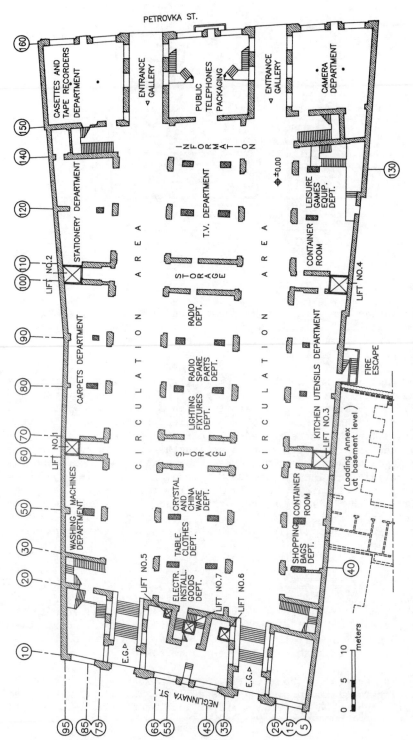

Figure 2. Layout plan for restoration of the first floor

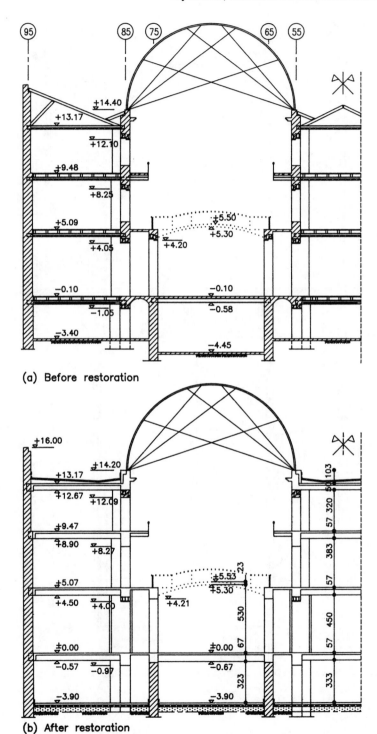

(a) Before restoration

(b) After restoration

Figure 3. Typical transverse cross-sections

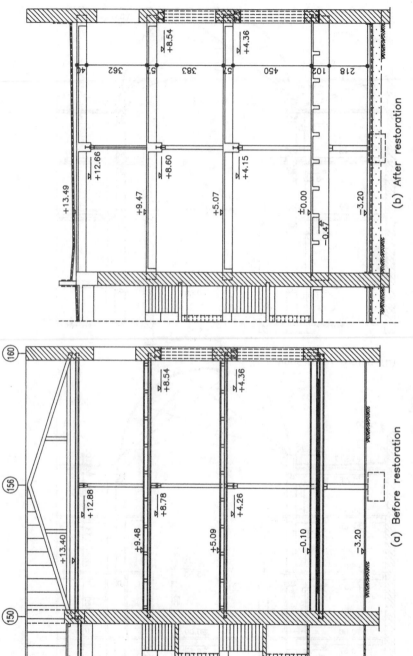

(b) After restoration

(a) Before restoration

Figure 4. Partial longitudinal sections at Petrovka St. end

at the central part were all composed of three parallel I-beams bearing on massive piers located along the longitudinal axes 15 to 85 (Fig.3a). At the Petrovka St. end, floor girders were supported by round cast-iron hollow columns placed midway between axes 150-160 (Fig.4a). At the Neglinnaya St. end, however, girders and cast-iron columns were used for the roof floor only, between axes 10-20. The floor and ceiling assembly was constructed in a variety of ways, some of which are

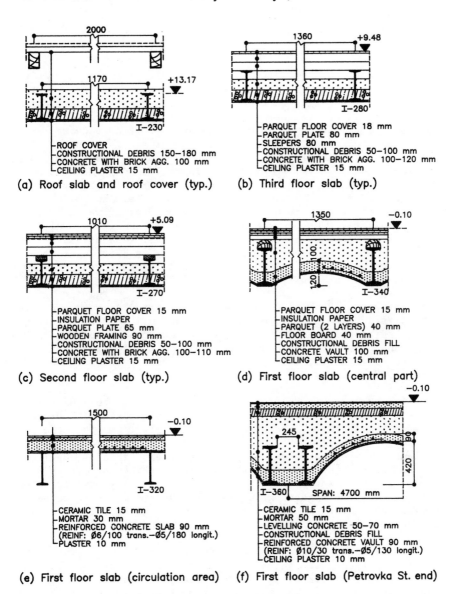

(a) Roof slab and roof cover (typ.)

(b) Third floor slab (typ.)

(c) Second floor slab (typ.)

(d) First floor slab (central part)

(e) First floor slab (circulation area)

(f) First floor slab (Petrovka St. end)

Figure 5. Typical floor and ceiling assemblies (before restoration)

illustrated in Fig.5. It is interesting to note that at all floors and roof, thermal insulation was provided by earth and constructional debris, of varying thickness, placed directly above the ceiling structure.

At roof level, the atriums are covered with semicircular skylights, 13.5m in span (Fig.3). In the original design the remaining parts of the roof deck were protected against atmospheric effects by metal sheet construction on wooden rafters.

RESULTS OF INVESTIGATIONS BEFORE RESTORATION

Years of continuous use and lack of adequate maintenance led to significant damage and deterioration of the building parts. Before the restoration work began, the appearance of the facades and of the interior clearly reflected the dilapidated state of the building. Many of the ornaments on the facades were weathered and broken. The ornamental columns in front of the entrance galleries had been torn down to provide space for glass display cases. A wire net was installed on the facades, supported by steel brackets along the third floor level, to prevent injury to the pedestrians from falling pieces of cornice, plaster, ornaments, etc. The interior was in a much worse condition. Wall ornaments were highly damaged. Wall and ceiling plaster had come off in many places. Balustrades and cornices were broken. Ornamental covers on cantilever steel beams supporting the balconies were totally destroyed and the exposed steel was highly corroded.

Between 1966 and 1980 numerous detailed surveys and investigations were performed by State authorities to determine the condition of the building and the extent of damage at the time and also to evaluate the load-carrying capacities of structural members. The results of these investigations are summarised below:

The building is founded on a sand bank, 0.6 to 3.0m thick, of medium density and containing brick rubble mixed with gravel. Beneath this layer recent alluvial deposits, up to 2.5m in thickness, containing sand, muddy sand and loam, rest upon the ancient alluvial terrace formation in the old bed of Neglinka river. These Quaternary deposits of total thickness 5.6 to 8.0m below the basement level, are based on Jura clays typical for Moscow area. The highest ground-water level is measured to be at -4.70, at a depth of 25cm from the lowest basement floor level before restoration.

Foundations under the walls are of strip type, of widths varying between 120 and 170cm and constructed of bricks and roman cement mortar at the top part and of limestone blockwork near the bottom. The foundations mostly extend down 120 to

350cm below the basement level, to the top of natural soil layers. At some locations wooden piles are encountered beneath or adjacent to the strip foundations. These piles, most probably used for compaction purposes, are found to be partly in a rotten condition. Drainage sumps located on the basement floor are observed to be filled with soil and debris.

The load-bearing walls and massive piers are constructed of solid red brick and roman cement mortar, satisfactory in workmanship and still in good condition, generally 70 to 90cm in thickness. Calculations for first floor walls show that removal of parts of the bearing walls during the use of the building has resulted in considerable overloading of the remaining adjacent parts. A few individual transverse cracks up to 2mm wide are observed in the brickwork of the basement piers under the main steel beams. A horizontal layer of asphalt is placed between the walls and strip foundations to prevent capillary water rise in the basement walls. Test results on numerous samples indicate that compressive crushing strengths of red brick and mortar (corrected for standard 70mm cube) are around 8 MPa and 3 MPa respectively.

The circular hollow cast-iron internal columns at both end parts of the building are all in satisfactory condition. The accepted design strength for these columns is 150MPa.

In the first floor (elevation -0.10) the steel beams supporting the concrete and reinforced concrete vaults (Fig.5,d,f) are seriously affected by corrosion with flaking up to 3mm in thickness. Longitudinal and transversal cracks are observed in the vaults. In several places the parquet flooring and wooden framing underneath are rotten and destroyed. Similar conditions exist at circulation areas; rainwater and snow penetrating through the broken glass of the skylights and ponding on the atrium floors have caused destructive corrosion of the slab reinforcement and steel beams (Fig.5,e). Most parts of the floor vibrate during normal walking.

In the second and third floors many cracks are observed in the monolithic concrete slabs supported by the lower flanges of secondary beams (Fig.5,b,c). These beams appear to be in relatively good condition except for the cantilever parts supporting the balconies. New statical calculations indicate that some of the larger span beams carrying 12-16cm thick debris fills would have been overstressed under a presumed live load of 4 kN/m2. Corrosion effects on the girders are negligible.

Corrosion and flaking of 1-2mm are observed in the steel beams of the roof deck, together with highly cracked regions in the concrete slab. Constructional debris fill thickness on the slabs varies between 12cm and 60cm, resulting in overloading of several beams. The damage is mainly caused by water penetration through many deteriorated parts of the roof cover. Several joints on the rafters are found to be decayed and distorted.

The typical load-carrying member of the Shukhov-type skylight lantern is constructed from a single angle 75x50x10 mm bent into a semicircular arch and braced with 6 digonal symmetrical ties, diameter 12mm . The arches are located at 1500mm uniform spacing. Base plates of the arch are 180 x 255 x 26 mm, anchored to the brickwork by two bolts, each 18mm in diameter. Purlins constructed of angles 45 x 45 x 6 mm at 750mm spacing support the metal frames encasing the glass panels. Partial corrosion is observed in several arches, base plates and purlins. The metal frames, however, are found to be mostly destroyed by corrosion. Glass cracks and occasionally drops down, the reason attributed to dried putty and large thermal deformations of the metal encasements.

REQUIREMENTS FOR RECONSTRUCTION AND RESTORATION

The objective is defined by the Client as, " Reconstruction and Restoration of the Department Store Petrovski Passage and Erection of a Loading Annex ". The main principle during reconstruction is to preserve the historical features of the interior, while equipping the building with all the technical requirements for a modern department store. The Neglinnaya St. and Petrovka St. facades are to be restored in accordance with original documents from the archives and subject to approval by authorities for historical and cultural monuments.

Architectural and functional requirements
The Passage is to be designed for the sale of recreational commodities, household commodities and goods for sewing and needlework. Some additional services for customers and personnel (restaurant, cafeteria, first-aid centre, beauty parlour, etc.) are also to be provided.

A loading annex (1060 m2) for delivery of cargo via Neglinnaya St. is to be constructed adjacent to the north wall of the Passage (Fig.1) and is to be connected to the basement. Central part of the basement (4000 m2) is to be rearranged for storage. Transport of goods between the loading annex and storage area is to be provided by forklifts. Staircases between axes 60 and 70, and between axes 100-110 are to be replaced by lift shafts (lifts 1 to 4) for delivery of goods to the upper floors. The two end parts of the basement are to be used for technical services (1400 m2).

Central part of the first floor is to be rearranged as a totally open shopping hall (Fig. 2). The space between the two entrance galleries at the Petrovka St. end is to be modified for entry of personnel and to accomodate two new staircases leading to the offices on the upper floors. Total reconstruction area on the first floor is 5400 m2.

The second floor (elevation +5.07) is also to be arranged as an open shopping area. A cafeteria serving 360 customers and a beauty parlour are to be located on the Neglinnaya St. end. Total reconstruction area on the second floor is 4060 m2.

The third floor (elevation +9.47) is to be totally rearranged to contain all the offices, computer room, and technical rooms for ventilation. A 92-seat restaurant for use of personnel   only and a first-aid centre are to be located on the Neglinnaya St. end. Total reconstruction area on the third floor is 3900 m2.

The roof covering over the roof slab (elevation +13.17) is to be converted into flat-type roofing (3200 m2). The skylight lanterns are to be renewed in conformance with the original. A new technical room (300 m2) is to be constructed on the roof slab of Neglinnaya St. end for ventilation of the restaurant and cafeteria.

Technical requirements
To give an idea as to the nature and extent of the technical requirements, the systems and equipment envisaged for the modernization of the Passage may be briefly listed as follows.

Mechanical systems Potable Water System, Waste Water Disposal System,   Heating,   Ventilation,   Smoke   Removal Systems, Refrigeration System, Garbage Compactor and Paper Press System, Loading and Unloading Ramps, Lifts, Underground Water Drainage and Pumping System, Fire Fighting Water System.

Electric power (380/220V) supply Air Handling Units, Air Heaters, Smoke Extract Fans, Exhaust Fans, Pressurizing Fans, Fire-fighting Pumps Sprinkler Pumps, Sump Pumps, Lifts, Kitchen Equipment (cooking, mixers, grinding, hot-plate, cold room, dishwashing), Lighting Systems (working, evacuation, emergency).

Weak current systems Telephone Network (city telephone, local telephone, intercom system, inquiry system), Public address and warning system (music, announcement), Fire Alarm System, Clock, Wire Radio System, TV Reception Network, Security System.

Computer facilities Host Computer (for the entire database management and accounting), 6 minicomputers (interfaced with host computer, each controlling up to 10 electronic cash registers), 18 dummy-terminals, 13 Personal Computers.

Building automation Monitoring and control of all engineering and technical equipment.

Structural requirements
All floors are to be reconstructed in reinforced concrete, to be designed for the factored live loads specified according to the use of the floor area. Steel girders are to be individually

checked and be removed or strengthened as may be deemed necessary. All vertical load-bearing members are to be checked, overloaded piers are to be strengthened with a reinforced concrete outer shell. Similarly, foundations of walls, piers and cast-iron columns are to be checked and, whenever necessary, strengthened to withstand the increased loads.

DESIGN AND IMPLEMENTATION

Detailed design work started immediately after the signing of the contract, and continued for nearly twelve months, with close coordination of all the disciplines involved. On-the-spot measurements and checks for levels and dimensions, together with investigations and evaluations for existing material, members and joints, were conducted throughout the design work for appropriate structural, architectural and technical detailing. Also, great care was exercised during the demolition of partitions and stripping of wall plastering in order not to overlook any hidden motifs, details and patterns of historical and architectural value.

The time schedule for construction is shown in Fig.6. Floors were demolished in segments and concreted in such a sequence as not to cause short-term stress changes of large magnitude in the vertical load-bearing members. Dismantling and erection of the skylights had to be completed before winter in

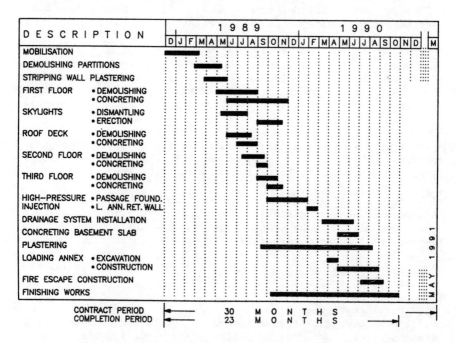

Figure 6. Petrovski Passage – time schedule

order to be able to heat the inside space for the extensive labour required during the cold months. Strengthening of the foundations was started at the construction stage where the new foundation loads roughly corresponded to those under the former dead loads. The principles followed in the design and detailing of the main structural units are described below along with some points of special interest related to the construction aspects the project.

Skylight lanterns

Statical calculations performed for the original main arch showed that the strict loading requirements set forth in SNIP (Construction Standards and Rules) 2.01.07-85 "Loads and Forces" resulted in stresses far above the yield stress specified for the particular steel grade (St37/ Fe E 235) used.In redesigning the structure,it became necessary to use a higher grade (Fe E 355) steel while maintaining member dimensions and spacings so

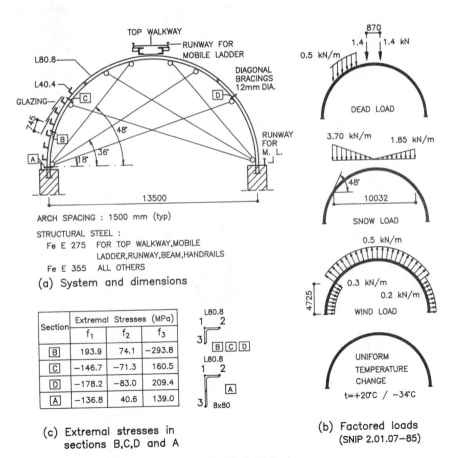

(a) System and dimensions

ARCH SPACING : 1500 mm (typ)

STRUCTURAL STEEL :
  Fe E 275 FOR TOP WALKWAY,MOBILE LADDER,RUNWAY,BEAM,HANDRAILS
  Fe E 355 ALL OTHERS

Section	Extremal Stresses (MPa)		
	f_1	f_2	f_3
B	193.9	74.1	-293.8
C	-146.7	-71.3	160.5
D	-178.2	-83.0	209.4
A	-136.8	40.6	139.0

(c) Extremal stresses in sections B,C,D and A

(b) Factored loads (SNIP 2.01.07-85)

Figure 7. Skylight lantern

that the original appearance of the structure could be preserved. In all the design calculations for the improved structure shown in Fig.7a, geometric non-linearity was accounted for and only those diagonal braces under tension were included. Each load combination, specified in SNIP 2.01.07-85, had to be analysed individually due to the non-linear character of the mathematical formulation. Calculated extremal stresses (Fig.7c) showed that the improved structure safely met all relevant loading requirements.

Each arch was manufactured in 3 sections for ease of transport, and the sections were assembled together at site on a horizontal template. Diagonal braces were connected and turnbuckles were slightly tightened to take up the slack. A temporary tie-rod was installed between the supports to prevent relative displacements during erection. The semicircular arch was lifted and positioned with the aid of a mobile portal frame on the roof deck. The tie-rod was removed, downbolts were installed at the supports but left loose until final aligning, and the arch was tied to the previously erected parts with temporary members (except that the first two arches were permanently joined together before being lifted and the anchor bolts were tightened after positioning, to provide the initial support). When three arches were thus placed, the temporary members were replaced by purlins, 4500mm in length, connecting these foremost arches to the rest of the system. After all the arches and purlins were installed, final levelling and aligning were completed, followed by total rechecking of the joints and tightening of all the bolts.

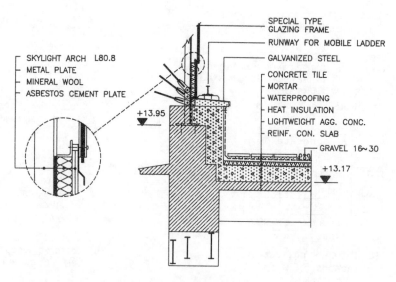

Figure 8. Skylight lantern support detail and roofing

Specially designed glazing frames, of 500mm x 775mm
external dimensions and open along the bottom edge, were used to
form the transparent cover of the skylight lanterns. The frames
were delivered with the glass installed and projecting 40mm from
the open end. Each frame was secured to the purlins with self
tapping screws and was placed so that the glass projecting from
the open end overlapped the top edge of the previously placed
frame by 40mm,leaving a permanent 8mm x 400mm ventilation gap at
each overlap. This type of construction had been used previously
in similar other structures and was found to be quite effective
against icing and snow accumulation on the skylight. The support
regions were detailed as indicated in Fig.8 to minimize thermal
bridging effects.

Floor slabs
An important consideration in the redesign of floor slabs in
reinforced concrete was to keep the relative load distribution
among the load-bearing walls, piers and cast-iron columns as
close to that in the original structure as possible. This was
achieved by essentially retaining the original floor structural
system which consisted of secondary rib-beams (joists), 1.20m to
1.50m apart, supported by main beams and/or vertical load
bearing members. The joists were embedded in walls   and
diaphragms were constructed at the supports (except at regions
containing vertical ducts) to provide a uniform load-transfer
from joists to walls (Fig. 9).

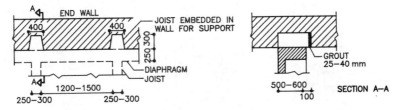

Figure 9. Concrete joists—typical support detail at end walls

Statical calculations showed that all steel girders would
have to be strengthened to safely carry the new increased loads.
For uniformity in the floor structural system and ease of
construction it was decided to replace all steel girders by
reinforced concrete main beams, except those the removal of
which would be detrimental to the rest of the structure. Steel
girders left in place were strengthened by encasement in
concrete, with sufficient stirrups installed around the girders.
In design calculations, 50% of the total bottom flange area of
the steel girders was included as tension reinforcement for the
mixed steel/concrete beam. Bearing checks were made and,whenever
found necessary, support regions were strengthened by inserting
reinforced concrete seats under the girder ends to spread the
support loads.

The second floor formwork plan is shown in Fig.10 to

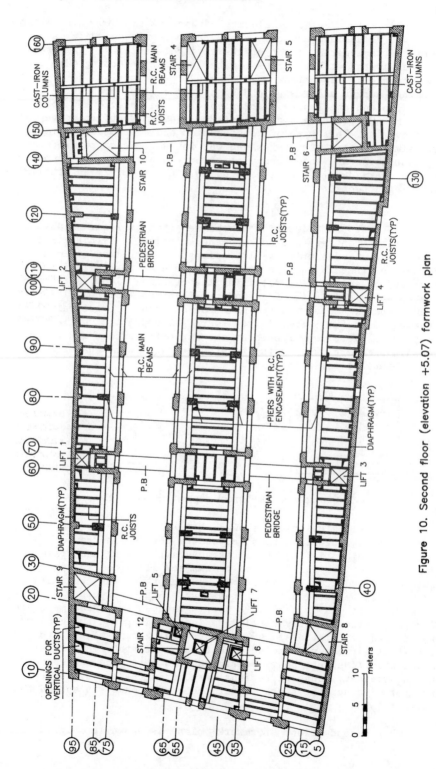

Figure 10. Second floor (elevation +5.07) formwork plan

provide a general picture of the floor reconstruction in reinforced concrete. This type of construction facilitates the casting of concrete in segments to minimize shrinkage effects.

A typical section of the pedestrian bridges on the second floor is given in Fig.11 to indicate the particular support strengthening used during reconstruction, as well as to illustrate the characteristic features of such a pedestrian bridge constructed around the turn of the century.

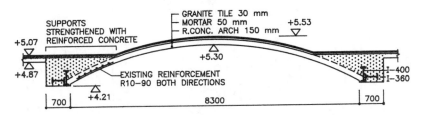

Figure 11. Pedestrian bridges — typical section

Vertical load-bearing members

Based upon evaluation of numerous tests in light of provisions of SNIP II.B.2-62, the design compressive strength of existing walls was determined to be 1.2 MPa. Strengthening of the continuous walls was not found necessary as the calculated maximum stresses were in the range of 0.5MPa - 0.6MPa for the new increased loads. Isolated piers located between the first and second floors (Fig.10), however, were all found to be highly overstressed, the calculated compressive stresses being between 1.9MPa and 3.4MPa. These piers, of varying cross-sectional dimensions, were all strengthened by 120mm thick reinforced concrete encasement.

All cast-iron columns supporting the main beams at the Petrovka and Neglinnaya St. end were checked and were found to have adequate strength.

Lift shafts added to the building were formed with reinforced concrete walls, 200mm in thickness and connected to floor slabs. All shaft walls extended down to a mat foundation on HPI-piles. Walls at the basement and the mat foundations were carefully tanked with waterproof membrane to prevent seepage of water into the shafts.

Foundations and drainage

The design strengths of the soil base (R-values) under the foundations of walls, piers and cast-iron columns were calculated according to SNIP 2.02.01-83, taking into account soil layer thicknesses and the parameters related thereto. The necessity and required extent of strengthening were determined

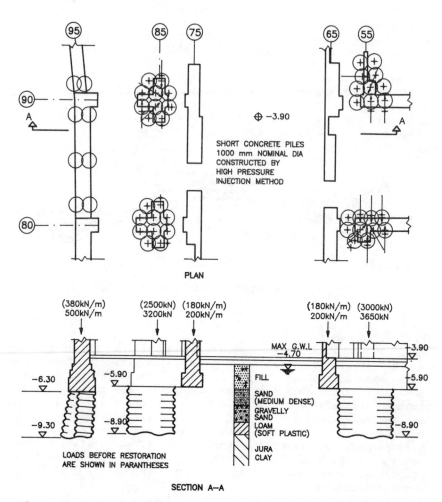

Figure 12. Wall and pier foundations strengthening with HPI method (typ)

by considering the old and new foundation loads, the R-values and the requested architectural changes in basement floor levels. No strengthening was deemed necessary for foundations on sand layers if anticipated load increases were less than 15% and, in addition, the adjacent new floor level was not lower than the old one.

Among the various strengthening methods considered, short concrete piles of 1000mm nominal diameter constructed by the High Pressure Injection method proved to be the fastest and most economical. The piles were designed to extend 2.5m to 5.5m below the foundation level, ending in sand or glacial moraine, partly in Jura clay (Fig.12). Foundations subject to localised loads from massive piers and cast-iron columns were all strengthened so as to safely carry the new total loads. For such foundations different HPI-pile lengths and patterns were worked out in order to stay below the soil R-value calculated at the pile bottom. The direction and inclination of the drillings were specified such that the piles overlapped each other by at least 1.5m below the foundation bottom. The wall foundations, however, were strengthened only if the new soil stress at the particular location under consideration was found to be above the R-value of the soil. In such cases, HPI-piles were added to support the load in excess of that corresponding to the R-value. The piles used for foundation strengthening totalled altogether 2100m in length.

During construction of each pile a hole was bored through the foundation with a 127mm drill bit, extending to a depth equal to the design length of the pile below the bottom of the foundation. The injection lance was placed and cement slurry was injected through 2-3 mm nozzles at 500 bars pressure while the lance was slowly withdrawn under rotation. The diameter and strength of the pile were controlled by the speed of rotation, the speed of withdrawal and the composition of the slurry. Withdrawal time and rotation speed were around 4 min/m and 14 rpm, respectively. All piles were required to reach up tightly to the foundation bottom. Extreme care was required during the process to prevent uplift caused by the high pressure under foundations. An adjacent pile was manufactured only after the strength of the previous pile reached the strength of the surrounding soil, which meant a time lapse of minimum 24 hours.

After completion of the HPI-piles a drainage system, consisting of a network of perforated PVC-pipes connected to sump pits, was installed below the basement floor (Fig.13) for collection and discharge of water caused by rises in the under-ground water table and infiltration from outside surfaces. The network was designed such that the distance from any point to the nearest pipe would not exceed 5m, minimum pipe slope would be 0.8% and the invert level at sump pitswould not be more than 1.0m below the finished floor level. Vertical inspection pipes were inserted at most joints to facilitate operation and maintenance. Sump pumps automatically operated with level switches were installed for discharge of the collected water. A similar system was also constructed below the floor slab of the loading annex.

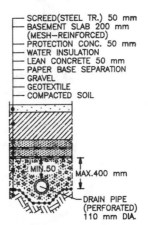

— SCREED(STEEL TR.) 50 mm
— BASEMENT SLAB 200 mm
  (MESH—REINFORCED)
— PROTECTION CONC. 50 mm
— WATER INSULATION
— LEAN CONCRETE 50 mm
— PAPER BASE SEPARATION
— GRAVEL
— GEOTEXTILE
— COMPACTED SOIL

MIN.50
MAX.400 mm

DRAIN PIPE
(PERFORATED)
110 mm DIA.

Figure 13. Drain pipe
system section

A new horizontal water barrier was installed in the basement walls. Inclined holes spaced 300mm apart, each 22mm in diameter and 400mm in length, were drilled 40-50cm above the basement level and filled with a two-component silicone-based compound. The filling was repeated until saturation of the wall. Average consumption of compound was about 6 litres per meter of wall length.

Loading annex
The loading annex shown in Fig.14 was constructed for the unloading of cargo from trucks onto a platform 1.20m above the floor slab (elevation -5.10) and to contain some of the technical rooms needed for operation of the department store. An unobstructed manoeuvering area of dimensions 19m by 23m and clear height 4.25m was required in front of the platform. In addition, the roof deck of the annex was to be used as parking area for fire-trucks. These requirements led to a heavy roof construction consisting of a composite deck formed by a reinforced concrete slab 200mm in thichness and IPE 500 steel beams at 2350mm spacing, supported by built-up steel girders 20m in span. The girders were designed to be transported in three sections and joined at site with high-strength bolts. Each completed girder weighed about 170 kN. and was 1800mm in height.

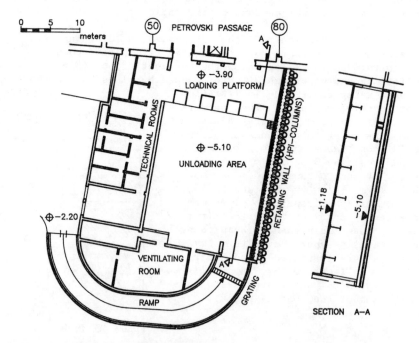

Figure 14. Loading Annex

The west wall of the loading annex was to act both as a support for the main girders and as a retaining wall for the the soil outside the building. Since adequate work space was not available at this location due to relatively close city central-heating mains and foundations of transformer buildings, the wall was designed as a gravity-type retaining wall formed by overlapping rows of HPI-piles to be constructed before excavation for the loading annex.

CLOSING REMARKS

8,800 m3 of structural concrete (C25/30) and 970 metric tons of reinforcing steel (S 420) was used, together with 170 metric tons of high-strength (Fe E 355) and 55 tons of mild (Fe E 235) structural steel for the skylight lanterns and the loading annex roof deck. The number of workers at peak reached up to 550. The 23 month completion period targeted by ENKA Construction and Industry Inc. was achieved by a proficient project management, through the use of highly skilled work and continuous monitoring. The monumental Petrovski Passage was completely reconstructed and restored, including the addition of a loading annex, seven months ahead of contract schedule, preserving all its historical features while equipping it with all the amenities of the modern day science and technology.